D1071679

THE AMERICAN ART POTTERY PRICE GUIDE

A COMPREHENSIVE COLLECTION OF AUCTION RESULTS 1990-2000

A PRESENTATION BY TREADWAY GALLERY, INC. OF CINCINNATI, OHIO
IN ASSOCIATION WITH THE JOHN TOOMEY GALLERY OF OAK PARK, ILLINOIS

**This Weller Pelican lawn ornament
sold for $5,000
in July of 1997**

First edition published in 1999 by Treadway Gallery Inc.
Under the direction of Don Treadway

Text and photographs Copyright © Treadway Gallery Inc., 2000

Printed in Paducah, Kentucky, United States of America.

Layout/Design: Stephen Large, Dave Warren
Cover Design: Teresa Dorsey

First published in the United States in 2000 by
Treadway Gallery Inc.
2029 Madison Road
Cincinnati, Ohio 45208
Phone: (513) 321-6742
Fax: (513) 871-7722
E-mail: Treadway 2029@Earthlink.net
Web Site: www.treadwaygallery.com

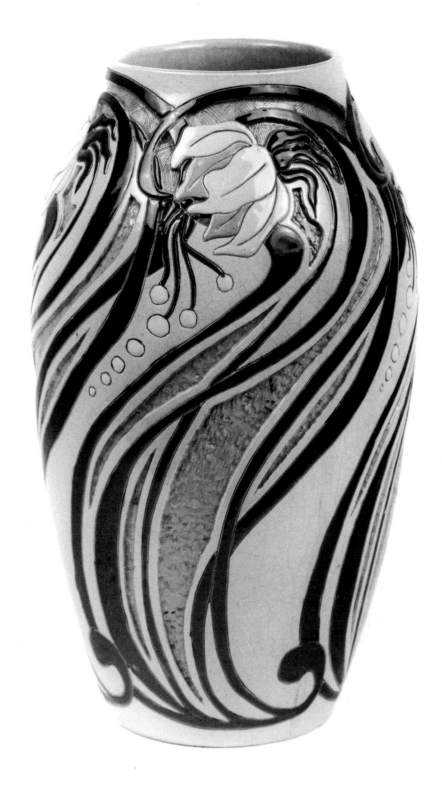

**This Roseville Rozane Della Robbia vase
sold for $16,000
in October of 1994**

**In May of 1993,
this Roseville Rozane Della Robbia vase
sold for $26,000**

**In July of 1999,
this Weller Eocean vase
sold for $9500**

**This set of six Weller tiles
sold for $20,000
in July of 1996**

1. **RV Rozane Della Robbia** vase, deeply carved and cut-back floral design, whiplash stems and leaves in a multi-toned green glaze, signed with wafer mark, artist signed, 14"h, two minor flakes   6500-8500
July 11, 2000   Sold for $7000

Not Pictured:

2. **RV Rozane Della Robbia** vase, stylized fish design in light green hi-glaze against textured ground of medium green, geometric band design at base, a rare form we have never seen, initialed by artist D.B., wafer mark, 10.5"h, two repaired chips   2000-3000   July 17, 1996
Sold for $2000

3. **RV Rozane Della Robbia** vase, carved decoration of stylized trees and rocks in shades of green, wafer mark, 9.5"h, minor flakes   2500-3500   June 2, 1996
Sold for $1900

4. **RV Rozane Della Robbia** vase, carved decoration of warriors with helmets, spears, shields and armor flanked by a chariot pulled by two horses all in tan, white and brown against a dark brown textured ground, stylized floral and geometric carving in tan, olive and white surrounds base and wide flat rim, 17"h, base of pottery uneven, mint   2500-3500   June 12, 1995
Sold for $4750

For more details please call:
(513) 321-6742

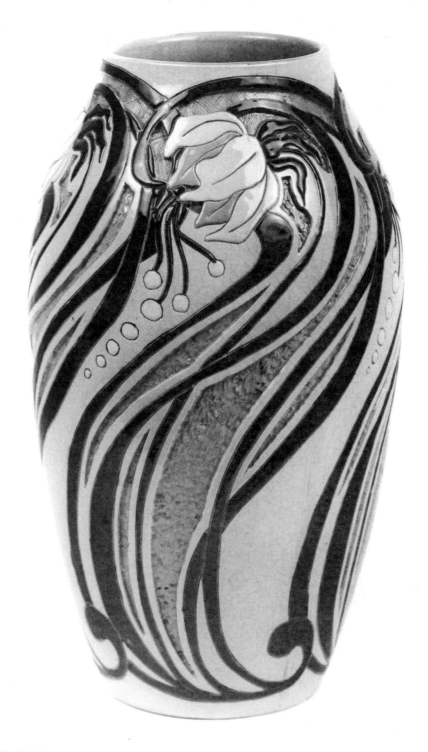

5.   **RV Rozane Della Robbia** vase, carved and painted flowers in peach tones on green stems and leaves, incised and painted foliage in a whiplash style, between the flowing stems and leaves are deeply cutback panels in an aqua tone against the light green background, stamens with cream balls flow from the centers of the flowers, six colors, initialed R.B., 9"dia. x 15"h, mint   15,000-20,000   October 23, 1994   Sold for $16,000

6.   **RV Rozane Della Robbia** vase, carved panels with poppies on long, well detailed stems and leaves in emerald green top to bottom, flowers painted in white revealing the underneath side below their light tan exterior, center of poppies in darker tan, all set in the deeply carved and recessed panels with chocolate brown ground revealing minute carving strokes, the six panels below a reticulated top collar, this waisted broad shouldered form works well to display the artwork, 15.5"h, mint
10,000-15,000   May 2, 1993   Sold for $26,000

For more details please call:
(513) 321-6742

7.	**RV Rozane Della Robbia** vase, reticulated pattern surrounding rim, decorated with eight carved and painted daffodils in two-tone yellow with brown centers on olive green vertical stems among olive green leaves, blue cutback horizontal band at shoulder behind daffodils, against a light green background, six colors, artist initials, Rozane Ware seal, 12"h, two minor base chips
10,000-15,000   May 19, 1996 Sold for $10,000

8.	**RV Rozane Della Robbia** vase, reticulated geometric pattern around rim, five vertical panels with tan, dark brown and white poppies with olive and gray/green centers, buds atop narrow twisting green stems with small heart-shaped leaves against a cut away blue/gray background, narrow carved line surrounds panels and reticulated work, all on a blue background, artist's initials E.C., 17"h, restoration to top 9000-12,000
May 21, 1995   Sold for $7000

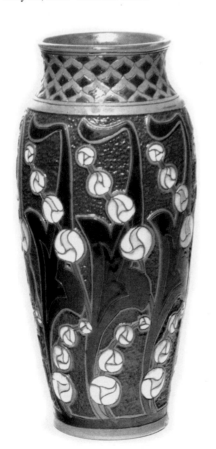

9.	**RV Rozane Della Robbia** vase, carved and painted stylized roses in cream and yellow, background of chocolate brown is carved back, the entire surface is etched, whiplash leaves of olive and navy extend top to bottom and are outlined in caramel, flared top collar is a series of painted and incised overlapping leaves in caramel and green, unmarked, artist initialed H.L., 11"h, small chips at base
12,000-17,000   December 3, 1995 Sold for $15,000

10. **RV Rozane Della Robbia** vase, carved and incised stylized flowers in three shades of green combined with yellow, brown and cream, signed with Rozane Ware seal and artist signed, 11"h, mint   3500-5000 September 30, 1990   Sold for $3750

11. **RV Rozane Della Robbia** vase, carved floral design in Art Nouveau whiplash style from top to bottom, the green carved stems holding white flower and green leaves, a cut-out band of dark tan in between light tan background, Rozane Ware seal, 9"h, flaw to top edge in making   3000-5000   March 24, 1991   Sold for $3250

12. **RV Rozane Egypto** vase, double overlapping leaves at bottom beneath iris buds and flowers extending to shoulder, covered with a green matt suspended glaze, signed with Rozane Ware seal, 13"h, mint   3500-4500   May 15, 1994   Sold for $4500

13

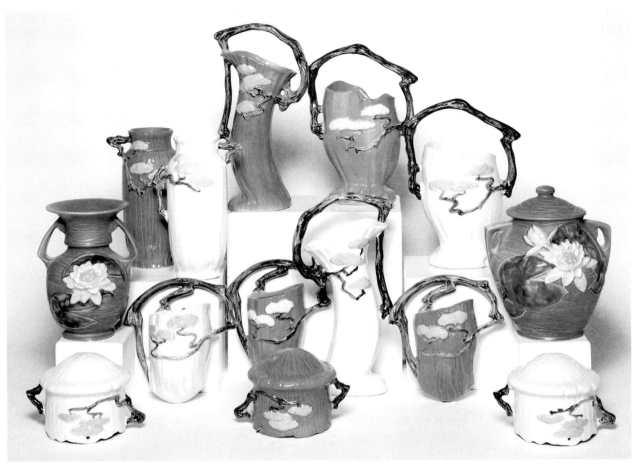

13. **RV Ming Tree** basket, white, 4.5"h, mint   150-250
July 11, 2000   Sold for $100

14. **RV Water lily** vase, blue, 9.5"h, mint   200-250
July 11, 2000   Sold for $130

15. **RV Ming Tree** wall pocket, white, 8"h, mint
200-250   July 11, 2000   Sold for $150

16. **RV Ming Tree** vase, green, 10"h, mint with factory
chip   200-250   July 11, 2000   Sold for $110

17. **RV Ming Tree** vase, white, 10"h, minute chips to base
150-200   July 11, 2000   Sold for $110

18. **RV Ming Tree** vase, green, 14"h, mint   200-250
July 11, 2000   Sold for $160

19. **RV Ming Tree** wall pocket, blue, 8"h, mint
150-250   July 11, 2000   Sold for $190

20. **RV Ming Tree** basket, green, 4.5"h, mint   150-250
July 11, 2000   Sold for $120

21. **RV Ming Tree** vase, white, 14"h, mint   200-300
July 11, 2000   Sold for $150

22. **RV Ming Tree** vase, blue, 12"h, mint   200-250
July 11, 2000   Sold for $150

23. **RV Ming Tree** wall pocket, green, 8"h, mint
150-250   July 11, 2000   Sold for $190

24. **RV Ming Tree** vase, white, 12"h, mint   200-300
July 11, 2000   Sold for $150

25. **RV Water lily** cookie jar, blue, 8"h, minor glaze skip,
mint   250-350   July 11, 2000   Sold for $240

26. **RV Ming Tree** basket, white, 4.5"h, mint   150-250
July 11, 2000   Sold for $130

27. **RV Windsor** vase, double handled
form, 9"w x 8"h, mint   500-700
July 11, 2000   Sold for $1100

28. **RV Windsor** vase, double handled
form, 9"h, minute flake to handle
500-700   July 11, 2000
Sold for $650

29. **RV Fuschia** vase, double handled form, green, foil label, 6.5"h, mint 150-200 July 11, 2000 Sold for $300

30. **RV Bushberry** vase, double handled form, blue, 8.5"h, mint 200-250 July 11, 2000 Sold for $190

31. **RV Fuschia** bowl, double handled form, green, 10.5"dia., mint 200-250 July 11, 2000 Sold for $130

32. **RV Fuschia** handled basket with flower frog, green, 9"h, mint 250-350 July 11, 2000 Sold for $400

33. **RV Fuschia** vase, flattened double handled form, green, 8"h, mint 200-250 July 11, 2000 Sold for $200

34. **RV Fuschia** vase, double handled form, green, foil label, 6"h, minute chip to rim 100-200 July 11, 2000 Sold for $100

35. **RV Fuschia** hanging basket, three handles, green, mint 200-300 July 11, 2000 Sold for $400

36. **RV Fuschia** vase, double handled form, green, 7"h, mint 150-250 July 11, 2000 Sold for $160

37. **RV Fuschia** vase, double handled form, green, impressed mark, 8"h, mint 150-250 July 11, 2000 Sold for $190

38. **RV Fuschia** jardinere, double handled form, green, 3"h, mint 100-150 July 11, 2000 Sold for $110

39. **RV Fuschia** ewer, green, 10"h, mint 200-300 July 11, 2000 Sold for $220

40. **RV Fuschia** wallpocket, double handled form, green, 8"h, mint 200-300 July 11, 2000 Sold for $375

41. **RV Fuschia** bowl, double handled form, green, 9.5"dia., mint 150-250 July 11, 2000 Sold for $160

42. **RV Bushberry** vase, double handled form, blue, 6"h, mint 200-250 July 11, 2000 Sold for $190

43. **RV Fuschia** vase, double handled form, green, 6"h, mint 150-250 July 11, 2000 Sold for $150

44. **RV Falline** vase, double handled form, excellent color, 6.5"h, mint 600-800 July 11, 2000 Sold for $1100

45. **RV Wisteria** vase, double handled form, foil label, 8.5"h, mint 600-800 July 11, 2000 Sold for $750

46. **RV Water lily** bowl, two handles, 13"dia., mint 150-250   July 11, 2000   Sold for $140

47. **RV Water lily** vase, double handled form, 12"h, mint 300-400   July 11, 2000   Sold for $180

48. **RV Water lily** basket, 10"h, mint   250-350 July 11, 2000   Sold for $150

49. **RV Water lily** vase, double handled form, 7"h, with a **RV Water lily** vase, double handled form, 6.5"h, both with base repair, or minor chip   100-200   July 11, 2000 Sold for $100

50. **RV Water lily** vase, double handled form, 10.5"h, minor roughness to handle   200-300   July 11, 2000 Sold for $110

51. **RV Water lily** vase, double handled form, 14"h, mint 400-500   July 11, 2000   Sold for $280

52. **RV Water lily** hanging basket, 9"dia., minor glaze skip, mint   150-250   July 11, 2000   Sold for $230

53. **RV Water lily** ewer, 16"h, mint   350-450 July 11, 2000   Sold for $325

54. **RV Water lily** vase, double handled form, 8.5"h, mint 150-250   July 11, 2000   Sold for $110

55. **RV Water lily** bowl, double handled form, 8.5"l, mint 150-250   July 11, 2000   Sold for $70

56. **RV Water lily** vase, double handled form, 6.5"h, mint 150-250   July 11, 2000   Sold for $100

57. **RV Water lily** vase, double handled form, 8.5"h, factory glaze skip to rim, chip to side; with a **RV Water lily** basket, 12"h, repaired   250-350   July 11, 2000 Sold for $170

58. **RV Water lily** bowl, two handles, 11"dia., mint 150-250   July 11, 2000   Sold for $90

59. **RV Futura** vase, 8"w x 6"h, mint   350-450 July 11, 2000   Sold for $425

60. **RV Futura** vase, 10"h, mint   700-900   July 11, 2000 Sold for $1900

61. **RV Fuschia** candlesticks, pair, 5.5"h, mint   150-250
July 11, 2000   Sold for $190

62. **RV Fuschia** jardinere, label, 4.5"h, mint   100-150
July 11, 2000   Sold for $150

63. **RV Fuschia** vase, two handled, 8.5"h, mint   150-200
July 11, 2000   Sold for $190

64. **RV Fuschia** vase, two handled, 7.5"h, mint   150-200
July 11, 2000   Sold for $180

65. **RV Fuschia** vase, double handled form, 12.5"h, mint
250-350   July 11, 2000   Sold for $375

66. **RV Fuschia** handled basket, 10"h, mint   250-350
July 11, 2000   Sold for $375

67. **RV Fuschia** vase, double handled, 6.5"h, mint   100-200
July 11, 2000   Sold for $160

68. **RV Fuschia** vase, two handled, 16"h, mint   300-400
July 11, 2000   Sold for $650

69. **RV Fuschia** bowl, two handled, 8.5"dia., mint   100-200
July 11, 2000   Sold for $110

70. **RV Fuschia** candlesticks, pair, two handles, mint
100-150   July 11, 2000   Sold for $130

71. **RV Fuschia** vase, two handled, 10"h, mint   250-350
July 11, 2000   Sold for $260

72. **RV Fuschia** vase, two handles, 8.5"h, mint   150-250
July 11, 2000   Sold for $190

73. **RV Fuschia** vase, double handled form, 4"h, minute
burst bubble to handle, mint   100-150   July 11, 2000
Sold for $120

74. **RV Fuschia** cornucopia, 6"h, mint   100-150
July 11, 2000   Sold for $110

75. **RV Dogwood** vase, possibly experimental, 9"h, chip to
foot and side   200-300   July 11, 2000   Sold for $2600

76. **RV Clemana** vase, double handled form, blue, 6.5"h,
mint   200-300   July 11, 2000   Sold for $210

For more details please call:
(513) 321-6742

77. **RV White Rose** teapot, blue, 3.75"h, mint, with cream and sugar, mint   150-250   July 11, 2000   Sold for $375

78. **RV White Rose** candlesticks, pair, 2"h, insignificant flake to rim of one   50-100   July 11, 2000   Sold for $40

79. **RV White Rose** vase, double handled flattened form, 8.75"h, mint   150-250   July 11, 2000   Sold for $270

80. **RV White Rose** cornucopia, 6.25"h, mint   50-100   July 11, 2000   Sold for $60

81. **RV White Rose** vase with flower frog, 4.75"h, chip to base   50-100   July 11, 2000   Sold for $60

82. **RV White Rose** bowl, blue, 11.5"dia., mint with an **RV White Rose** flower frog, 3"h, minute flake   100-150   July 11, 2000   Sold for $140

83. **RV White Rose** basket, handled form, blue, 10.5"h, mint   250-350   July 11, 2000   Sold for $230

84. **RV White Rose** vase, blue, 3.25"h, mint   50-100   July 11, 2000   Sold for $40

85. **RV White Rose** candlesticks, pair, 4.5"h, one with repair   100-150   July 11, 2000   Sold for $110

86. **RV White Rose** wallpocket, blue, 8.75"h, mint   150-250   July 11, 2000   Sold for $475

87. **RV White Rose** hanging basket, 7"dia., bubble to side   200-300   July 11, 2000   Sold for $150

88. **RV White Rose** candlesticks, pair, minor chip to flower and repair to one   100-150   July 11, 2000   Sold for $60

89. **RV Windsor** vase, double handled form, 12"dia. x 3"h, mint   350-450   July 11, 2000   Sold for $475

90. **RV Windsor** vase, double handled form, foil label, 7.5"h, mint   400-600   July 11, 2000   Sold for $1300

Not Pictured:

91. **RV Windsor** bowl, double blue, 10"dia., minute flake, with a **RV Windsor** candlesticks, blue, large foil label, 4.5"h, repaired   200-300   July 11, 2000   Sold for $475

92. **RV Fuschia** vase, 6.5"h, mint   150-250   July 11, 2000
Sold for $200

93. **RV Fuschia** bowl, 9"dia., mint   150-250   July 11, 2000
Sold for $170

94. **RV Fuschia** jardinere, 7"h, mint   200-250
July 11, 2000   Sold for $400

95. **RV Fuschia** jardinere, 4.5"h, mint   100-200
July 11, 2000   Sold for $200

96. **RV Fuschia** wallpocket, 8"h, minor factory chip to back
200-300   July 11, 2000   Sold for $900

97. **RV Fuschia** console bowl with flower frog, 15"l,
minor glaze imperfections, mint   200-300
July 11, 2000   Sold for $425

98. **RV Fuschia** handled basket with flower frog, 8"h,
mint   250-350   July 11, 2000   Sold for $450

99. **RV Fuschia** vase, 9"h, mint   200-300
July 11, 2000   Sold for $500

100. **RV Fuschia** vase, 8"h, mint   200-300   July 11, 2000
Sold for $300

101. **RV Fuschia** planter, two handles, 7"h, minor hidden
flake to base with factory drill hole   150-200
July 11, 2000   Sold for $110

102. **RV Fuschia** vase, 7"h, mint   150-200   July 11, 2000
Sold for $300

103. **RV Fuschia** vase, 6.5"h, mint   150-200   July 11, 2000
Sold for $230

104. **RV Fuschia** bowl, 10.5"dia., mint   150-200
July 11, 2000   Sold for $190

105. **RV Fuschia** bowl, 8.5"dia., mint   150-200
July 11, 2000   Sold for $150

106. **RV Fuschia** vase, 8"h, mint   100-200   July 11, 2000
Sold for $250

107. **RV Rozane Olympic** vase, double handled pedestal
form, painted mark, "Euryclea discovers Ulysses", 11"h,
minor glaze scratches, restored   2500-3500
July 11, 2000   Sold for $2000

108. **RV Rozane Pauleo** vase, wonderful painted decoration
of grapes, leaves, and vines, 10.5"h, chip repair
900-1200   July 11, 2000   Sold for $1700

For more details please call:
(513) 321-6742

109. **RV Ming Tree** basket, white, 4.5"h, mint   150-250
July 11, 2000   Sold for $100

110. **RV Waterlily** vase, blue, 9.5"h, mint   200-250
July 11, 2000   Sold for $130

111. **RV Ming Tree** wall pocket, white, 8"h, mint   200-250
July 11, 2000   Sold for $150

112. **RV Ming Tree** vase, green, 10"h, mint with factory
chip   200-250   July 11, 2000   Sold for $110

113. **RV Ming Tree** vase, white, 10"h, minute chips to base
150-200   July 11, 2000   Sold for $110

114. **RV Ming Tree** vase, green, 14"h, mint   200-250
July 11, 2000   Sold for $160

115. **RV Ming Tree** wall pocket, blue, 8"h, mint   150-250
July 11, 2000   Sold for $190

116. **RV Ming Tree** basket, green, 4.5"h, mint   150-250
July 11, 2000   Sold for $120

117. **RV Ming Tree** vase, white, 14"h, mint   200-300
July 11, 2000   Sold for $150

118. **RV Ming Tree** vase, blue, 12"h, mint   200-250
July 11, 2000   Sold for $150

119. **RV Ming Tree** wall pocket, green, 8"h, mint   150-250
July 11, 2000   Sold for $190

120. **RV Ming Tree** vase, white, 12"h, mint   200-300
July 11, 2000   Sold for $150

121. **RV Waterlily** cookie jar, blue, 8"h, minor glaze skip,
mint   250-350   July 11, 2000   Sold for $240

122. **RV Ming Tree** basket, white, 4.5"h, mint   150-250
July 11, 2000   Sold for $130

123. **RV Windsor** vase, blue, 7.5"h, chips to
handle repaired   150-250   July 11, 2000
Sold for $500

124. **RV Windsor** vase, blue, 5.25"h, factory flaw
to rim   200-300   July 11, 2000
Sold for $500

125. **RV Fuschia** candlesticks, pair, 5.75"h, mint   150-250
July 11, 2000   Sold for $140

126. **RV Fuschia** vase, 4"h, mint   100-200   July 11, 2000
Sold for $120

127. **RV Fuschia** vase, 10.5"h, mint   250-350
July 11, 2000   Sold for $230

128. **RV Fuschia** vase, 6.5"h, mint   100-200   July 11, 2000
Sold for $120

129. **RV Fuschia** console bowl with frog, 15"l, mint
150-250   July 11, 2000   Sold for $270

130. **RV Fuschia** vase, 6.5"h, mint   100-200   July 11, 2000
Sold for $150

131. **RV Fuschia** basket, flower frog, 8.5"dia., mint
250-350   July 11, 2000   Sold for $210

132. **RV Fuschia** bowl, 8.5"h, mint   100-200   July 11, 2000
Sold for $100

133. **RV Fuschia** vase, 16"h, mint   350-550   July 11, 2000
Sold for $550

134. **RV Fuschia** vase, 7"h, mint   100-200   July 11, 2000
Sold for $140

135. **RV Fuschia** vase, 12.5"h, mint   250-350
July 11, 2000   Sold for $300

136. **RV Fuschia** candlesticks, pair, 2"h, mint   100-150
July 11, 2000   Sold for $90

137. **RV Fuschia** cornucopia vase, 6"h, mint   100-150
July 11, 2000   Sold for $90

138. **RV Rozane** vase, brown glaze, painted portrait of a bull,
impressed mark, artist signed, 14"h, mint   1500-2500
July 11, 2000   Sold for $2300

139. **Owens Utopian** vase, brown glaze with portrait of a
kitten portrait, impressed mark, artist signed, 6"w, minor
scratches, mint   1000-1500   July 11, 2000
Sold for $1500

21

140. **RV Bushberry** vase, two, one shown on right, 4"h, both mint   150-250   July 11, 2000   Sold for $220

141. **RV Bushberry** jardinere, 7.5"h, mint   100-200 July 11, 2000 Sold for $150

142. **RV Bushberry** candlesticks, pair, 2.25"h, with a **RV Bushberry** bowl, 14"l, both mint   150-250 July 11, 2000   Sold for $250

143. **RV Bushberry** vase, 9.5"h, mint   150-250 July 11, 2000   Sold for $280

144. **RV Bushberry** wallpocket, 7.5"h, minute flake to handle   150-250   July 11, 2000   Sold for $375

145. **RV Bushberry** vase, 12.5"h, mint   250-350 July 11, 2000   Sold for $475

146. **RV Bushberry** ewer, 6"h, mint   150-250 July 11, 2000   Sold for $150

147. **RV Bushberry** basket, 12"h, mint   250-350 July 11, 2000   Sold for $375

148. **RV Bushberry** vase, 8.5"h, mint   150-250 July 11, 2000   Sold for $160

149. **RV Bushberry** jardinere, 3"h, mint   100-150 July 11, 2000   Sold for $80

150. **RV Bushberry** vase, double handled form, 12.5"l, mint 100-200   July 11, 2000   Sold for $275

151. **RV Bushberry** vase, 10"h, mint   150-250 July 11, 2000   Sold for $250

152. **RV Bushberry** jardinere, 6"h, minute flake to side, burst bubble   100-150   July 11, 2000 Sold for $90

153. **RV Rozane** vase, elk portrait, 21"h, minor surface scratches and repair to top   1200-1700   July 11, 2000 Sold for $800

154. **Weller Aurelian** vase, multi-colored floral decoration, artist signed, impressed mark, 17.5"h, burst bubbles and minor flakes   1000-1500   July 11, 2000 Sold for $1700

155. **RV Fuschia** candlesticks, pair, 5.75"h, mint 150-250 July 11, 2000 Sold for $210

156. **RV Fuschia** hanging basket, 5.5"h, minute flakes to edge 150-250 July 11, 2000 Sold for $220

157. **RV Fuschia** ewer, 10"h, minor glaze skip to spout, mint 250-350 July 11, 2000 Sold for $270

158. **RV Fuschia** vase, two handles, 6"h, mint 100-200 July 11, 2000 Sold for $240

159. **RV Fuschia** bowl with flower frog, foil label, 15"l, mint 150-250 July 11, 2000 Sold for $425

160. **RV Fuschia** vase, 15.5"h, mint 450-650 July 11, 2000 Sold for $1700

161. **RV Fuschia** vase, 7.5"h, mint 100-200 July 11, 2000 Sold for $160

162. **RV Fuschia** planter, 6"h, mint factory drill hole 100-200 July 11, 2000 Sold for $110

163. **RV Fuschia** basket, 10"dia., mint 250-350 July 11, 2000 Sold for $230

164. **RV Fuschia** jardinere, two handles, 3"h, minute glaze flake to side 50-100 July 11, 2000 Sold for $100

165. **RV Fuschia** vase, 9"h, mint 250-350 July 11, 2000 Sold for $300

166. **RV Fuschia** vase, 8.5"h, mint 250-350 July 11, 2000 Sold for $280

167. **RV Fuschia** candlesticks, pair, 2.25"h, mint 100-200 July 11, 2000 Sold for $140

168. **RV Fuschia** vase, foil label, 4.5"h, mint 100-200 July 11, 2000 Sold for $180

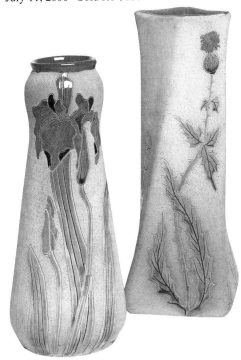

169. **RV Rozane Woodland** vase, incised and painted design of irises, wafer mark, 9"h, minor wear, mint 900-1200 July 11, 2000 Sold for $850

170. **RV Rozane Woodland** vase, incised and painted thistles on all four sides, wafer mark, 10"h, mint 1000-1500 July 11, 2000 Sold for $1200

171. **RV Thornapple** vase, green, 4.25"h, mint   100-150
July 11, 2000   Sold for $80

172. **RV White Rose** bowl, 8.75"dia. x 2.5"h, mint   100-150
July 11, 2000   Sold for $80

173. **RV White Rose** handled basket, blue, 12"h, chip to
handle, with a **RV White Rose** vase, 4.5"h, chip to base
150-200   July 11, 2000   Sold for $150

174. **RV Thornapple** vase, green, 6.5"h, mint   200-300
July 11, 2000   Sold for $300

175. **RV White Rose** jardinere, 7.75"dia. x 4"h, chip to base
100-150   July 11, 2000   Sold for $40

176. **RV White Rose** vase, 12.5"h, chip to base and flower
200-300   July 11, 2000   Sold for $160

177. **RV White Rose** basket, blue, 8.5"h, minor chip to base
150-200   July 11, 2000   Sold for $100

178. **RV White Rose** jardinere, 9"dia. x 6"h, chip to handle,
bruise to side   150-200   July 11, 2000   Sold for $70

179. **RV White Rose** vase, 6.5", mint, with a **RV White
Rose** planter, 5.5"h, repair to base   150-200
July 11, 2000   Sold for $70

180. **RV Iris** bud vase, 7.5"h, repair, with a **RV Thorn
Apple** vase, green, 8.5"h, hairline   200-300
July 11, 2000   Sold for $110

181. **RV White Rose** jardinere, 4"h, mint, with a **RV White
Rose** jardinere, not shown, 4.5"h, minor flake to interior
200-250   July 11, 2000   Sold for $110

182. **RV White Rose** ewer, 6"h, mint, with a **RV White
Rose** handled vessel, 7.5"h, minor chips to base
150-200   July 11, 2000   Sold for $180

183. **RV Olympic** vase, transfer decoration of Minerva,
Hector & Mercury, marked in full, 12"h, repaired
1500-2000   July 11, 2000   Sold for $2000

184. **RV Rozane Azurine** vase, floral decoration, impressed
mark, 8"h, minor glaze imperfection to flower, deteriorating repair to top   400-600   July 11, 2000
Sold for $260

185. **RV Water lily** bowl, two handles, 13"dia., mint 150-250   July 11, 2000   Sold for $140

186. **RV Water lily** vase, double handled form, 12"h, mint 300-400   July 11, 2000   Sold for $180

187. **RV Water lily** basket, 10"h, mint   250-350 July 11, 2000   Sold for $150

188. **RV Water lily** vase, double handled form, 7"h, with a **RV Water lily** vase, double handled form, 6.5"h, both with base repair, or minor chip   100-200   July 11, 2000 Sold for $100

189. **RV Water lily** vase, double handled form, 10.5"h, minor roughness to handle   200-300   July 11, 2000 Sold for $110

190. **RV Water lily** vase, double handled form, 14"h, mint 400-500   July 11, 2000   Sold for $280

191. **RV Water lily** hanging basket, 9"dia., minor glaze skip, mint   150-250   July 11, 2000   Sold for $230

192. **RV Water lily** ewer, 16"h, mint   350-450 July 11, 2000   Sold for $325

193. **RV Water lily** vase, double handled form, 8.5"h, mint 150-250   July 11, 2000   Sold for $110

194. **RV Water lily** bowl, double handled form, 8.5"l, mint 150-250   July 11, 2000   Sold for $70

195. **RV Water lily** vase, double handled form, 6.5"h, mint 150-250   July 11, 2000   Sold for $100

196. **RV Water lily** vase, double handled form, 8.5"h, factory glaze skip to rim, chip to side; with a **RV Water lily** basket, 12"h, repaired   250-350   July 11, 2000 Sold for $170

197. **RV Water lily** bowl, two handles, 11"dia., mint 150-250   July 11, 2000   Sold for $90

198. **RV Rozane** vase, painted portrait of Rembrant, executed and signed by Arthur Williams, impressed mark, 14.5"h, minute flake under base   2500-3500 July 15, 1998 Sold for $1700

199. **Weller Velva** vase w/lid, marked, 7.5"h, mint 200-300 July 13, 1999 Sold for $450

200. **Weller Baldin** vase, marked, 7"h, mint 200-300 July 13, 1999 Sold for $260

201. **RV Foxglove** double bud vase, marked, 7"w x 5"h, mint 150-250 July 13, 1999 Sold for $150

202. **Weller Burntwood** jardinere, scene with sheep, marked, 10"dia. x 8"h, mint 250-350 July 13, 1999 Sold for $350

203. **RV Futura** wallpocket with chains, 7"dia. x 5"h, mint 250-350 July 13, 1999 Sold for $300

204. **RV Zephyr Lily** vase, marked, 12.5"h, repaired top edge; with a **RV Foxglove** vase, marked, 8.5"h, repaired top edge 200-300 July 13, 1999 Sold for $290

205. **RV Magnolia** double bud vase, marked, 8.5"w x 4.5"h, mint; with an **RV Magnolia** flower frog, marked, 4"h, mint 250-350 July 13, 1999 Sold for $150

206. **RV Cherry Blossom** vase, not marked, 8"h, mint 400-600 July 13, 1999 Sold for $600

207. **RV Topeo** bowl, not marked, 8"dia. x 2.5"h, mint 200-300 July 13, 1999 Sold for $150

208. **Weller Velva** vase, marked, 9"h, mint 200-300 July 13, 1999 Sold for $375

209. **RV Forest** jardinere, marked, 6" x 5"h, mint 200-250 July 13, 1999 Sold for $180

210. **RV Dahlrose** wallpocket, not marked, 8"h, mint 200-300 July 13, 1999 Sold for $300

211. **RV Bleeding Heart** vase, marked, 9"h, mint 200-300 July 13, 1999 Sold for $290

212. **RV Clematis** bowl and candlesticks, three pieces, marked, bowl 8.5"dia., candlesticks, 4.5"h, chip to bowl 200-300 July 13, 1999 Sold for $110

213. **RV Rozane Della Robbia** vase, painted and carved cherry decoration in seven colors, with a deeply cut-back ground below reticulated top, artist signed H. Smith, with the Rozane ware seal, 12.5"h, restoration to top and a few minor flakes 5500-7500 July 13, 1999 Sold for $4250

214. **RV Blackberry** vase, 6"h, mint   400-600
June 6, 1999   Sold for $350

215. **RV Tourmaline** vase, mottled blue and cream with
cream gloss glaze, 7"h, mint   300-400   June 6, 1999
Sold for $350

216. **RV Wisteria** vase, nice color and mold, paper label,
8"h, mint   700-900   June 6, 1999   Sold for $650

217. **RV Carnelian II** vase, handles, 7"h, mint   300-400
June 6, 1999   Sold for $300

218. **RV Futura** vase, two handles, 7.5"h, chip to body
250-350   June 6, 1999   Sold for $250

219. **RV Dahlrose** vase, double handled form, 8"h, mint
350-450   June 6, 1999   Sold for $180

220. **RV Futura** vase, 2.75"h, mint   900-1200
June 6, 1999   Sold for $1500

221. **RV Bushberry** bowl, brown and orange, marked, 15"l,
repaired   100-200   June 6, 1999   Sold for $50

222. **RV Clemana** vase, sharp mold, impressed mark, 9.5"h,
mint   600-800   June 6, 1999   Sold for $750

223. **RV Blackberry** vase, 4"h, mint   250-350
June 6, 1999   Sold for $600

224. **RV Baneda** vase, green, small handles at top, 6.5"h,
flake to top in making   250-350   June 6, 1999
Sold for $280

225. **RV Blackberry** jardinere, 4"h, chip to base   250-350
June 6, 1999   Sold for $260

226. **RV Wisteria** vase, double handled form, label, 9.5"h,
mint   900-1200   June 6, 1999   Sold for $900

227. **RV Imperial II** vase, purple and yellow hi-glaze, 6.25"h,
mint   300-500   June 6, 1999   Sold for $325

228. **RV Tourmaline** vase, turquoise, 5.5"h, chip to bottom
100-150   June 6, 1999   Sold for $60

229. **RV Rozane Della Robbia** vase, large form with cut-
back and incised floral design in shades of blue, aqua
and olive green, brown and yellow, 10.5"h, restoration
to top and bottom   5000-7000   June 7, 1998
Sold for $8000

230. **RV Blackberry** vase, 4"h, mint   250-350
June 6, 1999   Sold for $425

231. **RV Magnolia** creamer, marked, 2.5"h, mint; with a **RV Tuscany** vase, 5"h, chip to base   100-200   June 6, 1999 Sold for $40

232. **RV Wisteria** vase, 5"h, mint   300-400   June 6, 1999
Sold for $325

233. **RV Bushberry** bud vase, marked, 7"h, mint   100-200
June 6, 1999   Sold for $130

234. **RV Snowberry** bud vase, marked, 7.5"h, mint   100-200
June 6, 1999   Sold for $110

235. **RV Bushberry** vase, marked, 3"h, mint   50-100
June 6, 1999   Sold for $80

236. **RV Donatello** wallpocket, stamped mark, 10"h, mint
150-250   June 6, 1999   Sold for $120

237. **RV Carnelian I** vase, 9"h, restored bottom   150-250
June 6, 1999   Sold for $90

238. **RV Corinthian** vase, 10"h, chip to top   100-200
June 6, 1999   Sold for $160

239. **RV Apple Blossom** bud vase, marked, 7.25"h, mint
100-200   June 6, 1999   Sold for $120

240. **RV Futura** footed vase, 9.5"h, mint   700-900
June 6, 1999   Sold for $1000

241. **RV Sunflower** vase, 5"h, mint   650-850   June 6, 1999
Sold for $750

242. **RV Snowberry** vase, marked, 7"h, mint   150-250
June 6, 1999   Sold for $110

243. **RV Fuschia** bowl, marked, 7"dia. x 2.5"h, water stains,
mint   100-200   June 6, 1999   Sold for $120

244. **RV Donatello** vase, not marked, 4"h, mint   50-100
June 6, 1999   Sold for $80

Not Pictured:

245. **RV Ferella** vase, brown, 6"h, mint   400-600
June 6, 1999   Sold for $375

246. **RV Ferella** lamp, brown, pottery 8"h, mint   700-900
June 6, 1999   Sold for $700

247. **RV Sunflower** vase, 8.5"dia. x 6", minute flake to rim
600-800   July 15, 1998   Sold for $850

248. **RV Bushberry** basket, marked, 12"w x 12"h, mint
250-350   June 6, 1999   Sold for $475

249. **RV Florentine** sand jar, marked, 21.5"h, mint   400-600
July 13, 1999   Sold for $425

250. **RV Juvenile** creamer, rabbit design, 3.5"h, mint
150-250   July 15, 1998   Sold for $375

251. **RV Falline** bowl, low form with two handles, 10.5"l,
mint   400-500   July 15, 1998   Sold for $375

252. **RV Cherry Blossom** vase, two handles, 8.5"h, mint
300-400   June 7, 1998   Sold for $425

253. **RV Imperial** basket, purple flowers and green leaves,
12.5"h, no marks, mint   250-350   June 7, 1998
Sold for $450

254. **RV Tourmaline** vase, mottled blue matt glaze, six
sides, 8"h, mint   200-300   June 7, 1998   Sold for $350

255. **RV Falline** vase, 6.5"h, mint   350-450   June 7, 1998
Sold for $850

256. **RV Sunflower** vase, two-handled form, 5"h, mint
450-650   June 7, 1998   Sold for $550

257. **RV Pinecone** vase, paper label, 11"h, flake to body 250-350   June 6, 1999   Sold for $260

258. **RV Water lily** vase, 6"h, mint   100-200   June 6, 1999 Sold for $90

259. **RV Pinecone** vase, 9"h, minor flaws at base   200-300 June 6, 1999   Sold for $190

260. **RV Futura** wallpocket, 8.5"l, paper label, minor flake 200-300   June 6, 1999   Sold for $210

261. **RV Sunflower** vase, 5.5"w, mint   450-650 June 6, 1999   Sold for $450

262. **RV Dahlrose** vase, 12.5"h, mint   400-600 June 6, 1999   Sold for $325

263. **RV Cherry Blossom** vase, 5.5"h, mint   300-400 June 6, 1999   Sold for $240

264. **RV Foxglove** bookends, pair, 6"h, mint   350-450 June 6, 1999   Sold for $450

265. **RV Jonquil** vase, 7.5"h, mint   350-450   June 6, 1999 Sold for $220

266. **RV Sunflower** vase, 6.5"h, mint   450-650 June 6, 1999   Sold for $650

267. **RV Blackberry** vase, 5.5"h, mint   300-400 June 6, 1999   Sold for $350

268. **RV Blackberry** wallpocket, 8.5"h, mint   700-900 June 6, 1999   Sold for $1300

269. **RV Pinecone** double bud vase or candlestick, 5"h, mint 150-250   June 6, 1999   Sold for $300

270. **RV Morning Glory** vase, 9.5"h, mint   800-1100 June 6, 1999   Sold for $900

271. **RV Clematis** cookie jar, 10"h, mint   500-700 June 6, 1999   Sold for $300

272. **RV Dahlrose** vase, 6.5"h, mint   200-300   June 6, 1999 Sold for $100

Not Pictured:

273. **RV Cherry Blossom** vase, green, 10.5"h, tiny flake to top edge, repair to base   250-350   June 6, 1999 Sold for $280

274. **RV Florentine** vase, stamp mark, 6"dia. x 5"h, chip to top edge   100-150   June 6, 1999   Sold for $240

275. **RV Pinecone** basket, brown, marked 11.5"l x 7"h, broken handle   100-200   June 6, 1999   Sold for $120

276. **RV Pinecone** window basket, brown, marked, 13.5"w, chips   200-250   June 6, 1999   Sold for $160

277. **RV Rozane** vase, brown glaze with pansies, wafer mark, artist Myers, 7.5"h, scratches to body   100-200 June 6, 1999   Sold for $200

278. **RV Normandy** jardinere, 10"dia. x 9"h, chips to exterior and drill hole   200-250   June 6, 1999 Sold for $200

279. **RV Tourmaline** vase, brown, gold label, 8.5"h, mint 150-250   June 6, 1999   Sold for $190

280. **RV** pottery jardinere, molded Egyptian figures, nice matt glaze, 9"dia. x 9"h, mint   200-300   June 6, 1999 Sold for $250

281. RV Apple Blossom cornucopia vases, pair, marked, 6"h, one damaged 150-200 June 6, 1999 Sold for $100

282. RV Clematis triple bud vase, marked, 5"h, mint 50-100 June 6, 1999 Sold for $80

283. RV Lotus candlesticks, pair, 2.5"h, mint 50-100 June 6, 1999 Sold for $50

284. RV Freesia bowl, marked, 12"l x 2.5"h, chips 100-200 June 6, 1999 Sold for $90

285. RV Freesia candlesticks, pair, marked, 4.5"h, one with chips 50-100 June 6, 1999 Sold for $30

286. RV Peony mug, marked, 3.5"h, mint 100-150 June 6, 1999 Sold for $30

287. RV Iris vase, marked, 4"h, filled chip 50-100 June 6, 1999 Sold for $30

288. RV Wincraft vase, marked, 12.5"h, mint 200-300 June 6, 1999 Sold for $230

289. RV Water lily cornucopia vase, marked, 6"h, mint 100-150 June 6, 1999 Sold for $60

290. RV Teasel vase, marked, 6"h, mint 150-250 June 6, 1999 Sold for $110

291. RV Water lily vase, marked, 4"h, mint 100-150 June 6, 1999 Sold for $60

292. RV Clematis bud vase, marked, 7.5"h, mint 100-200 June 6, 1999 Sold for $210

293. RV Peony cornucopia vase, marked, 6"h, mint 100-150 June 6, 1999 Sold for $50

294. RV White Rose vase, marked, 4"h, mint 50-100 June 6, 1999 Sold for $40

295. RV Poppy vase, marked, 3.5"h, chip to base 50-100 June 6, 1999 Sold for $30

296. RV Snowberry vase, marked, 4"h, chip 50-100 June 6, 1999 Sold for $20

297. RV Florentine bowl, stamp mark, 8"dia., chip to lip; with an **RV Florentine** pedestal vase, stamp mark, 4"h, mint 150-200 June 6, 1999 Sold for $90

298. RV White Rose cornucopia vase, marked, 6"h, mint 100-150 June 6, 1999 Sold for $60

Not Pictured:

299. RV Cosmos window box, tan with floral decoration, 10.5"l, mint 150-250 July 15, 1998 Sold for $220

300. RV Rozane Aztec vase, squeezebag decoration, artist signed, 9"h, minor flakes 350-450 July 14, 1999 Sold for $220

301. RV Rozane Pauleo vase, flowers and strawberries, numbered, 16.5"h, mint 1000-2000 July 14, 1999 Sold for $1200

302. RV Juvenile pitcher, cream with green band and yellow chick, 3.5"h, mint 150-250 July 15, 1998 Sold for $260

303. RV Peony hanging planter, green, 7"dia.; **RV Peony** mug, not shown, green, 4"h, both mint 250-350 July 15, 1998 Sold for $210

304. RV Jonquil bowl, flower frog, brown, 10"dia., mint; with a **RV Corinthian** bowl, green and white, 7"dia., minor flaw 250-350 July 15, 1998 Sold for $650

305. **RV Peony** hanging basket, 7"dia., mint   150-250
June 6, 1999   Sold for $80

306. **RV Water lily** bookends, 5", mint   250-350
June 6, 1999   Sold for $350

307. **RV Columbine** vase, 6", minute flake   150-250
June 6, 1999   Sold for $90

308. **RV Tuscany** vase, 7"dia., mint   150-250
June 6, 1999   Sold for $160

309. **RV Ming Tree** vase, 8"h, mint   150-250   June 6, 1999
Sold for $120

310. **RV Bushberry** bowl, 14"dia., mint   250-350
June 6, 1999   Sold for $100

311. **RV Tuscany** vase, 6"dia., mint   100-200   June 6, 1999
Sold for $70

312. **RV Ivory Florentine** vase, 10"h, minor chip   100-200
June 6, 1999   Sold for $120

313. **RV Apple Blossom** ewer, 8", mint   150-250
June 6, 1999   Sold for $170

314. **RV Wincraft** ewer, 8", mint   150-250   June 6, 1999
Sold for $100

315. **RV Clematis** vase, 10"h, mint   200-300
June 6, 1999   Sold for $140

316. **RV Water lily** vase, 5"dia., minor flakes   50-100
June 6, 1999   Sold for $50

317. **RV Pinecone** vase, 7"dia., mint   150-250
June 6, 1999   Sold for $270

318. **RV** bookends, pair, 6"h, mint   250-350   June 6, 1999
Sold for $240

319. **RV Magnolia** ewer, 10"h, mint   200-300
June 6, 1999   Sold for $150

320. **RV Gardenia** vase, 7"dia., mint   100-200
June 6, 1999   Sold for $110

Not Pictured:

321. **RV Donatello** compote, 6"h; with a **RV Donatello**
jardinere, not shown ink mark, 7"h, both mint   200-300
July 15, 1998 Sold for $260

322. **RV Clematis** cookie jar, orange to green, yellow flower,
10"h, mint   300-400   July 15, 1998   Sold for $375

323. **RV Zephyr Lily** vase, blue, 19"h, restored base
200-300   July 15, 1998   Sold for $400

324. **RV Apple Blossom** hanging basket, green, 8"h, mint
200-300   July 15, 1998   Sold for $200

325. **RV Fuschia** bowl, brown, 14"w, with a flower frog,
3"h, bowl mint and frog with flake; with a **RV Ixia**
planter, yellow, 6"h, minor roughness at edge   250-350
July 15, 1998   Sold for $260

326. **RV Rozane Crocus** vases, pair, squeezebag decoration
in Arts & Crafts style, one with wafer seal, both with
artist initials, 9.5"h, both with restored chips   400-600
July 14, 1999   Sold for $650

327. **RV Rozane** vase, large pillow form shape, cherries with
branch and leaves, wafer mark, 10"h, flake to foot and
chipping to wafer mark   250-350   July 14, 1999
Sold for $400

328. **RV Futura** jardinere, orange to green, 8"h, repaired
chips   350-550   July 14, 1998   Sold for $220

329. **RV Cosmos** vase, script mark, 5"h, mint 100-150
July 13, 1999   Sold for $120

330. **RV Poppy** vase, script mark, 5"dia x 4.5"h, mint
150-250 July 13, 1999 Sold for $130

331. **RV Magnolia** vase, script mark, 3"h, mint 50-100
July 13, 1999 Sold for $60

332. **RV Apple Blossom** hanging basket, 7.5"dia., mint
200-250 July 13, 1999 Sold for $190

333. **RV Peony** planter, script mark, 6.5"l x 3"h, mint
100-200 July 13, 1999 Sold for $80

334. **RV Clematis** bowl, script mark, 9"dia. x 3"h, chip to
top 100-200 July 13, 1999 Sold for $60

335. **RV White Rose** vase, script mark, 4"h, mint 100-200
July 13, 1999   Sold for $90

336. **RV White Rose** vase, script mark, 6.5"h, mint 100-200
July 13, 1999   Sold for $160

337. **RV Rozane pattern** vase, script mark, 6"h, mint
100-200 July 13, 1999 Sold for $120

338. **RV Bushberry** vase, marked, 4"h, mint 100-200
July 13, 1999   Sold for $150

339. **RV Clematis** vase, triple opening, marked, 6"w x 5"h,
mint 100-200 July 13, 1999 Sold for $70

340. **RV Magnolia** vase, marked, 6"h, mint 100-200
July 13, 1999 Sold for $60

341. **RV Columbine** vase, marked, 3"h, chip to top 50-100
July 13, 1999 Sold for $40

342. **RV Snowberry** hanging basket, 7"dia. x 6"h, mint
200-300 July 13, 1999 Sold for $180

343. **RV White Rose** vase, marked, 4"h, mint 100-200
July 13, 1999 Sold for $100

344. **RV Mock Orange** vase, marked, 6.5"w x 3"h, mint
100-200 July 13, 1999 Sold for $70

Not Pictured:

345. **RV Silhouette** double planter, white with floral panels,
9"; with a **RV Silhouette** bowl, white and green, 6"dia.,
both mint 250-350 July 15, 1998 Sold for $250

346. **RV Silhouette** pitchers, pair, white with floral panel,
green, 10"h; with a **RV Silhouette** miniature creamer,
6"h, all mint 350-550 July 15, 1998 Sold for $250

347. **RV Florane** wallpockets, pair, brown and orange, 9"l,
both mint 250-350 July 15, 1998 Sold for $325

348. **RV Mostique** spittoon, 5.5"h; with a **RV Mostique**
vase, 8"h; with a **RV Mostique** bowl, 7"dia., all mint
350-450 July 15, 1998 Sold for $450

349. **RV Zephyr Lily** vase, blue, marked, 7"h, mint; with a
RV Magnolia basket, green to brown, arched handle,
marked, 12"w x 12.5"h, chip to bottom 150-250
July 15, 1998 Sold for $210

350. **RV Peony** hanging basket, yellow and green, 6"w; with
a **RV Dogwood I** vase, green, 5"h, both minor flaws;
with a **Weller Forest** vase, 4"h; and a **Weller Knifewood**
vase, multicolored hi-glaze, impressed mark, 4"h,
both with hairlines 250-350 July 15, 1998
Sold for $240

351. **RV Wisteria** vase, brown to green with bright purple
wisteria and green leaves, unmarked, 7"h, mint
300-400 July 14, 1998 Sold for $500

352. **RV Columbine** vase, two handles, pink with green, pink
flowers and green leaves, marked, 10"h, mint 200-300
July 14, 1998 Sold for $260

353. **RV Pinecone** pitcher and mug set, four pieces, brown,
7"h, mugs are 4"h, all marked and mint 400-600
July 14, 1998 Sold for $700

354. **RV Fuschia** pitcher, yellow to orange/brown ground,
marked, 8"h, mint 200-300 July 14, 1998
Sold for $325

355. **RV Savonna** vase, unmarked, 6.5"dia. x 4"h, small chip to handle 150-250 July 13, 1999 Sold for $90

356. **RV Jonquil** vase, paper label, 4"h, mint 200-300 July 13, 1999 Sold for $200

357. **RV Morning Glory** vase, paper label, 6.5"w x 7.5"h, mint 600-800 July 13, 1999 Sold for $450

358. **RV Dahlrose** vase, 6"h, mint 200-250 July 13, 1999 Sold for $120

359. **RV Sunflower** vase, 7.25"h, mint 800-1100 July 13, 1999 Sold for $850

360. **RV Burmese** bookends, script mark, 8", mint 350-550 July 13, 1999 Sold for $220

361. **RV Russco** vase, 8.5"h, mint 200-300 July 13, 1999 Sold for $150

362. **RV Sunflower** vase, 5.25"h, mint 500-700 July 13, 1999 Sold for $550

363. **RV Cherry Blossom** vase, 5"h, mint 300-400 July 13, 1999 Sold for $400

364. **RV Pinecone** vase, paper label, 3"h, mint 100-200 July 13, 1999 Sold for $120

365. **RV Moderne** compote, impressed mark, 6.25"dia. x 6.25"h, mint 200-300 July 13, 1999 Sold for $300

366. **RV Pinecone** double vase, 8.5"h, mint 350-450 July 13, 1999 Sold for $375

367. **RV Pinecone** vase, nice mold, 7.5"h, mint 250-350 July 13, 1999 Sold for $210

368. **RV Pinecone** vase, good color, 5"h, mint 150-250 July 13, 1999 Sold for $180

369. **RV Baneda** vase, 7.25"h, mint 300-400 July 13, 1999 Sold for $550

370. **RV Jonquil** vase, 4"h, mint 200-300 July 13, 1999 Sold for $160

371. **RV Moderne** bowl, marked, 11"l x 4"h, small chip to top edge 150-250 July 13, 1999 Sold for $250

Not Pictured:

372. **RV Futura** bowl, orange to green/blue ground with molded green leaf and line design, square feet, unmarked, 6"dia. x 5"h, mint 350-550 July 14, 1998 Sold for $750

373. **RV Blackberry** vase, handles, green to brown with black fruit, unmarked, 5"h, mint 250-350 July 14, 1998 Sold for $375

374. **RV Pinecone** pitcher, blue, marked, 8"h, repaired spout 150-250 July 14, 1998 Sold for $230

375. **RV Vista** vase, molded landscape decoration, 8.5"h, minor bruise 350-450 June 7, 1998 Sold for $230

376. **RV Carnelian** pitcher, pink and green matt glaze, ink mark, 12"dia., minor flake to foot 250-350 June 7, 1998 Sold for $200

377. **RV Apple Blossom** basket, handled form in green, 12"h, mint 250-350 June 7, 1998 Sold for $225

378. **RV Thornapple** vase, orange to brown with white floral design, 11"l, mint 200-300 June 7, 1998 Sold for $325

379. **RV Pauleo** vase, lustre glaze in pearl/gray to orange with yellow and red fruit decoration, pale green leaves bordered by green bands around shoulder, impressed mark, 16.5"h, mint 2000-3000 June 7, 1998 Sold for $550

380. **RV Pinecone** triple bud vase, blue, branch handles, 8.5"h, mint 200-300 July 14, 1998 Sold for $450

381. **RV Pinecone** planter with underplate, blue, 6"dia. x 5.25"h, mint 200-300 July 14, 1998 Sold for $290

382. RV Peony vase, marked, 4"h, mint   100-200
July 13, 1999   Sold for $100

383. RV Gardenia vase, marked, 6"h, flaking to top
50-100   July 13, 1999   Sold for $50

384. RV Tuscany vase, not marked, 5"h, filled chip
100-150   July 13, 1999   Sold for $30

385. RV Clemana vase, marked, 7.25"h, mint   250-350
July 13, 1999   Sold for $270

386. RV Iris vase, marked, 6"h, mint   150-250
July 13, 1999   Sold for $100

387. RV Peony vase, marked, 6"h, mint   100-200
July 13, 1999   Sold for $110

388. RV Freesia vase, marked, 8"h, mint   150-250
July 13, 1999   Sold for $110

389. RV Moss vase, marked, 4"h, mint   150-250
July 13, 1999   Sold for $180

390. RV Zephyr Lily vase, marked, 7.5"h, filled chip
100-150   July 13, 1999   Sold for $50

391. RV Morning Glory vase, unmarked, 6", mint   550-750
July 13, 1999   Sold for $375

392. RV Mock Orange vase, marked, 4"h, mint   150-250
July 13, 1999   Sold for $80

393. RV Bushberry vase, marked, 7"h, mint   200-300
July 13, 1999   Sold for $170

394. RV Snowberry vase, marked 8"h, chip to base
150-200   July 13, 1999   Sold for $50

395. RV Thornapple vase, marked, 8"h, mint   150-250
July 13, 1999   Sold for $150

396. RV Peony vase, marked, 7"h, mint   150-250
July 13, 1999   Sold for $100

397. RV Peony basket, marked, 8"h, mint   200-300
July 13, 1999   Sold for $140

398. RV Snowberry basket, marked 7"h, mint   200-300
July 13, 1999   Sold for $160

399. RV Mock Orange vase, marked, 4"h, mint   150-200
July 13, 1999   Sold for $80

Not Pictured:

400. RV Freesia vase, two handles, blue with yellow and
white flowers, marked, 15"h, mint   300-400
July 13, 1998   Sold for $600

401. RV Corinthian wallpocket, green and white, 8.5"l, mint
100-200   July 13, 1998   Sold for $250

402. RV Cosmos wallpocket, blue, paper label, 7", mint
150-250   July 13, 1998   Sold for $400

403. RV Vintage jardinere, brown, 12.5"dia., mint   250-350
July 13, 1998   Sold for $400

404. RV Iris vase, blue, two-handled form, 7.5"h, mint
150-250   July 13, 1998   Sold for $210

405. RV Dahlrose vase, four-sided form, paper label, 10"h,
mint   250-350   July 13, 1998   Sold for $300

406. RV Cosmos basket, blue, 10.5"h, mint   250-350
July 13, 1998   Sold for $300

407. RV White Rose bowl, two handles, blue to green with
white roses, green leaves, 8"dia. x 2.5"h, mint; with a
RV White Rose vase, pedestal form with handles,
green/blue matt, 6"h, both mint   200-250   July 13, 1998
Sold for $200

408. RV Magnolia teapot, green, 8"h, mint   250-350
July 13, 1998   Sold for $300

409. RV Columbine vase, blue, two handles, 9.5"h, mint
150-250   July 13, 1998   Sold for $200

410. **RV Dahlrose** triple bud vase, 7"w x 6.5"h, mint
200-300   July 13, 1999   Sold for $170

411. **RV Magnolia** basket, marked, 7"w x 7"h, mint
200-300   July 13, 1999   Sold for $110

412. **RV Apple Blossom** creamer and sugar, marked, 2.5",
both mint   100-200   July 13, 1999   Sold for $120

413. **RV Pinecone** hanging basket, good color, 7"dia., mint
250-350   July 13, 1999   Sold for $425

414. **RV Pinecone** vase, marked and paper label, 6.5"h, mint
150-250   July 13, 1999   Sold for $140

415. **RV Apple Blossom** console bowl, marked, 15"l, mint
150-250   July 13, 1999   Sold for $230

416. **RV Bleeding Heart** vase, marked, 5"h, mint   100-150
July 13, 1999   Sold for $120

417. **RV Magnolia** vase, marked, 7.5"h, mint   100-150
July 13, 1999   Sold for $70

418. **RV Bleeding Heart** vase, marked, 7.5"h, mint   150-200
July 13, 1999   Sold for $210

419. **RV Jonquil** vase, good color, 5.75"h, mint   200-300
July 13, 1999   Sold for $350

420. **RV Apple Blossom** vase, marked, 4"h, mint   100-150
July 13, 1999   Sold for $70

421. **RV Apple Blossom** candlesticks, pair, marked, 4.5"h,
mint   100-150   July 13, 1999   Sold for $150

422. **RV Columbine** hanging basket with chains, 8"dia, mint
200-300   July 13, 1999   Sold for $230

423. **RV Columbine** vase, marked, 3"h, mint   100-150
July 13, 1999   Sold for $90

424. **RV Dahlrose** vase, 6"h, mint   150-200   July 13, 1999
Sold for $160

425. **RV Freesia** vase, marked, 6.5"h, mint   150-200
July 13, 1999   Sold for $70

Not Pictured:

426. **RV Bushberry** bowl, two green branch handles, blue,
marked, 10.5"dia. x 2.5"h, mint   150-250
July 13, 1998   Sold for $210

427. **RV Rozane** pitcher, squat form with decoration of corn,
impressed number and artist initials, 8.5"w x 5.5"h,
restored; with a **RV Rozane Royal** tankard, brown glaze
with berry design, artist signed Imlay, 14.5"h, heavily
crazed and rim restoration   250-350   July 14, 1998
Sold for $210

428. **RV Bittersweet** hanging basket, orange berries, 5"h,
mint   200-300   July 13, 1998   Sold for $210

429. **RV Silhouette** wallpocket, red, 8"h, mint; with a **RV
Freesia** vase, green, marked, 7.5"h, mint   200-300
July 13, 1998   Sold for $230

430. **RV Bleeding Heart** vase, blue, 12"h, mint   250-350
July 13, 1998   Sold for $600

431. **RV Bushberry** vase, ornate handles, blue with green,
15"h, mint   300-400   July 13, 1998   Sold for $550

432. **RV Pinecone** nut dish, brown, 7", mint; **RV Pinecone**
pedestal, green, 17"h, chips around bottom   200-300
July 13, 1998   Sold for $210

433. **RV Clematis** vase, brown, 10.5"h, mint   150-250
July 13, 1998   Sold for $200

434. **RV Ivory II** vase, two handles, pedestal form, paper
label, 8.5"h; with a **RV Ivory II** vase, two handles,
paper label, 7"h, both mint   200-250   July 13, 1998
Sold for $200

435. **RV Apple Blossom** vase, pink, branch handles, marked,
15.5"h, mint   300-500   July 14, 1998   Sold for $350

35

436. **RV Primrose** vase, 8.5"dia, minor flaw at lip
100-200   July 14, 1999 Sold for $60

437. **RV Peony** vase, 8"h, mint   200-250   July 14, 1999
Sold for $60

438. **RV Artwood** vase, 10"w, mint   150-250   July 14, 1999
Sold for $150

439. **RV Carnelian** vase, 8"h, mint   250-350   July 14, 1999
Sold for $325

440. **RV Bushberry** basket, 11"h, mint   350-450
July 14, 1999 Sold for $500

441. **RV Carnelian** vase, 8"h, mint   250-350   July 14, 1999
Sold for $350

442. **RV Artwood** vase, 6"h, mint   100-200   July 14, 1999
Sold for $60

443. **RV Pinecone** ashtray, 5"w, repaired chip   50-100
July 14, 1999 Sold for $60

444. **RV Clematis** basket, 7"h, repaired chip   100-150
July 14, 1999 Sold for $40

445. **RV Sunflower** vase, 5"h, mint   450-650   July 14, 1999
Sold for $700

446. **RV Bushberry** vase, 7"h, mint   150-250
July 14, 1999 Sold for $210

447. **RV Wincraft** vase, 9"w, mint   100-200   July 14, 1999
Sold for $110

448. **RV Artwood** vase, 6"h, mint   100-150   July 14, 1999
Sold for $80

449. **RV Artwood** vase, 8"h, mint   100-150   July 14, 1999
Sold for $90

450. **RV Gardenia** vase, 6"h, mint   100-200   July 14, 1999
Sold for $60

451. **RV Laurel** vase, 8"h, mint   300-400   July 14, 1999
Sold for $425

452. **RV Freesia** vase, 7"h, mint   100-200   July 14, 1999
Sold for $80

453. **RV Baneda** jardinere and pedestal, jar 9"dia. x 8"h,
pedestal 19.5"h, mint   2500-3500   July 14, 1999
Sold for $1900

454. **RV Artcraft** jardinere and pedestal, jar 9"dia. x 8"h,
pedestal 19.5"h, mint   1200-1700   July 14, 1999
Sold for $1600

455. **RV Pinecone** vase, marked, 4"h, mint 150-250
July 14, 1999 Sold for $170

456. **RV Sunflower** vase, 10"h, line in bottom, repaired chip
and line in top 500-700 July 14, 1999 Sold for $500

457. **RV Pinecone** basket with flower frog, marked, 9"dia,
mint 200-300 July 14, 1999 Sold for $300

458. **RV Peony** shell vase, marked, 9"w x 7"h, mint
200-300 July 14, 1999 Sold for $200

459. **RV Dahlrose** vase, 6"h, chip to top edge 100-200
July 14, 1999 Sold for $160

460. **RV Baneda** vase, 12"h, repaired chips 400-600
July 14, 1999 Sold for $900

461. **RV Pinecone** pitcher, marked, 10"h, mint 300-400
July 14, 1999 Sold for $500

462. **RV Dahlrose** vase, 6"h, flake to foot 100-200
July 14, 1999 Sold for $160

463. **RV Pinecone** basket, marked, 10"h, repair to base
150-250 July 14, 1999 Sold for $260

464. **RV Rosecraft Hexagon** bowl, stamp mark, 2"h, mint
50-100 July 14, 1999 Sold for $260

465. **RV Clemana** vase, marked, 8"h, repaired 100-200
July 14, 1999 Sold for $170

466. **RV Apple Blossom** basket, marked, 12"h, repaired base
150-250 July 14, 1999 Sold for $100

467. **RV Sunflower** vase, 5"h, mint 650-850 July 14, 1999
Sold for $800

468. **RV Dahlrose** triple bud vase, 6"h, mint 200-300
July 14, 1999 Sold for $210

469. **RV Dogwood II** pedestal and jardinere, 33"h, mint
1500-2500 July 14, 1999 Sold for $1700

470. **Weller Dunton** umbrella stand, molded design of birds,
trees and foliage, 22"h, minute chip to top 500-700
July 14, 1999 Sold for $2300

For more details please call:
(513) 321-6742

471. RV Peony hanging basket, pink, two handles, 4.5"h, mint   200-300   July 14, 1999 Sold for $160

472. RV Cosmos vase, white flowers, brown, green, 7"h, mint   200-250   July 14, 1999 Sold for $180

473. RV Peony hanging basket, yellow, two handles, 4.5"h, mint   200-300   July 14, 1999 Sold for $150

474. RV Apple Blossom hanging basket, green, 5"h, mint 200-300   July 14, 1999 Sold for $160

475. RV Pinecone jardinere, green, 14"w, chip repair to base 450-650   July 14, 1999 Sold for $375

476. RV Peony vase, 9"l, mint   100-200   July 14, 1999 Sold for $120

477. RV Donatello wall pocket, 12"h, mint   150-250 July 14, 1999 Sold for $170

478. Weller Fairfield double bud vase, 4"h, mint   100-200 July 14, 1999 Sold for $140

479. RV Water lily vase, yellow, two handles, 8.5"h, repaired base chip   100-200   July 14, 1999 Sold for $70

480. RV Pinecone vase, 8.5"w, minor flake   150-250 July 14, 1999 Sold for $190

481. RV Gardenia hanging basket, gray, 4"h, mint   200-300 July 14, 1999 Sold for $150

482. RV Gardenia hanging basket, brown, 4"h, mint 200-300   July 14, 1999 Sold for $150

483. RV Foxglove vase, two handles, 5.5"h, mint   200-250 July 14, 1999 Sold for $200

484. RV Clematis hanging basket, two handles, 4"h, mint 200-300   July 14, 1999 Sold for $150

Not Pictured:

485. RV Snowberry bowl, two handles, blue, 13"w, small flake on handle; with a **RV Bleeding Heart** vase, green, 8.5"h, mint   200-300   July 13, 1998 Sold for $280

486. RV Foxglove vase, two handles, blue, 9.5"h, mint 200-300   July 13, 1998 Sold for $270

487. RV Peony ewer, pink, 10.5"h; with a **RV Peony** vase, pink, 4"h, both mint   250-350   July 13, 1998 Sold for $240

488. RV Iris vase, blue, two handles, marked, 9.5"h, mint; with a **RV Peony** vase, pink, two handles, marked, 9.5"h, minor chips   250-350   July 13, 1998 Sold for $325

489. RV Dahlrose wallpocket, brown to green, 8"h, mint 200-250   July 13, 1998 Sold for $300

490. RV Ixia bowl, yellow, 11"dia.; with a **RV Apple Blossom** low bowl, green, 17.5"l, both mint 350-450   July 14, 1998 Sold for $210

491. RV Zephyr Lily bowl, brown, 17"l; with a **RV Zephyr Lily** bowl, brown, 16"l, both mint   300-400 July 14, 1998 Sold for $220

492. RV Creamware set, tankard and four mugs, cream with design of elk, pitcher 12"h with repaired lip, mugs 5"h and mint   200-300   July 14, 1998 Sold for $325

493. RV Rozane tankard, grapes, green and blue, signed W. Meyers, 5.25"w x 14"h, repaired chip to top 150-250   July 13, 1998 Sold for $300

494. RV Pinecone vase, brown, 5.5"h, mint   150-250 July 13, 1998 Sold for $210

495. RV Pinecone triple bud vase, blue, 8.5"h, mint 250-350   July 13, 1998 Sold for $280

496. **RV Russco** vase, paper label, 8.5"h, mint 200-300
July 14, 1999 Sold for $140

497. **RV Monticello** vase, 5.5"h, mint 250-350
July 14, 1999 Sold for $180

498. **RV Pinecone** bowl, 11"w, mint 250-350
July 14, 1999 Sold for $210

499. **RV Dogwood** vase, marked, 8"h, minor chips to foot
and body 200-300 July 14, 1999 Sold for $130

500. **RV Pinecone** jardinere, 11.5"w, chips 250-350
July 14, 1999 Sold for $300

501. **RV Wisteria** vase, 6"h, minute flake 350-450
July 14, 1999 Sold for $550

502. **RV Dogwood** wallpocket, 9.5"l, minute bruise
200-300 July 14, 1999 Sold for $230

503. **RV Dogwood** vase, marked, 8"h, minor flake to foot
250-350 July 14, 1999 Sold for $170

504. **RV Cherry Blossom** vase, 7"h, mint 350-450
July 14, 1999 Sold for $425

505. **RV Juvenile** bowl, good image, 6.5"w, mint
150-250 July 14, 1999 Sold for $110

506. **RV Pinecone** wallpocket, 9"l, mint 300-400
July 14, 1999 Sold for $600

507. **RV Pinecone** vase, 9.5"w, bruise to foot 200-300 July
14, 1999 Sold for $200

508. **RV Russco** vase, paper label, 8.5"h, mint 200-300
July 14, 1999 Sold for $150

509. **RV Pinecone** vase, 7"w, mint 200-300
July 14, 1999 Sold for $110

Not Pictured:

510. **RV Baneda** vase, green, two handles, 7"h, mint
450-650 July 13, 1998 Sold for $600

511. **RV Baneda** vase, green, 4"h, mint 200-250
July 13, 1998 Sold for $250

512. **RV Panel** wallpocket, green, ink mark, 9"h, mint
200-300 July 13, 1998 Sold for $270

513. **RV Dogwood** vase, 6"h, mint 250-350 July 13, 1998
Sold for $250

514. **RV Blackberry** vase, two handles, 6.5"h, mint
350-450 July 13, 1998 Sold for $475

515. **RV Panel** wallpocket, green, 9.5"h, mint 250-350
July 13, 1998 Sold for $270

516. **RV Dahlrose** vase, brown, handles, 7.5"h, mint
200-300 July 13, 1998 Sold for $200

517. **RV Panel** vase, green, 10.5"h, mint 250-350
July 13, 1998 Sold for $290

518. **RV Panel** vase with nude, green, ink mark, 6"h, mint
550-750 July 13, 1998 Sold for $550

519. **RV Sunflower** vase, two handles, 4"h, mint 350-450
July 13, 1998 Sold for $400

520. **RV Dogwood II** basket, green, 8"dia., mint 250-350
July 13, 1998 Sold for $220

521. **RV Blackberry** vase, two handles, 6"h, mint 350-450
July 13, 1998 Sold for $425

522. **RV Holland** beer set, tankard and six mugs, cream with
Dutch people, 5"w x 8.75"h, chips 250-450
July 13, 1998 Sold for $550

523. **RV Sunflower** vase, nice 7.5"h, mint 800-1100
June 6, 1999 Sold for $850

For more details please call:
(513) 321-6742

524. **RV Monticello** vase, two handles, original label, 4.5"h, mint   250-350   July 14, 1999   Sold for $350

525. **RV Sunflower** vase, flared shoulder, 5"h, mint 650-850   July 14, 1999   Sold for $700

526. **RV Vista** jardinere, 9.5"h, insignificant chips to base 550-750   July 14, 1999   Sold for $375

527. **RV Baneda** vase, two-handled form, 7"h, mint 500-700   July 14, 1999   Sold for $600

528. **RV Ferella** vase, two-handled form, 10"h, mint 650-850   July 14, 1999   Sold for $700

529. **RV Baneda** vase, two-handled form in red, 15"h, mint 1200-1700   July 14, 1999   Sold for $2800

530. **RV Florane** vase, ribbed decoration in blue matt, 6"h, mint   100-150   July 14, 1999   Sold for $60

531. **RV Baneda** vase, two-handled form in green, 9.5"h, mint   600-800   July 14, 1999   Sold for $800

532. **RV Sunflower** vase, 7"h, firing flaw to side   550-750 July 14, 1999   Sold for $425

533. **RV Morning Glory** vase, two-handled form, 10.5"h, mint   900-1200   July 14, 1999   Sold for $950

534. **RV Vista** vase, molded landscape decoration, 14.5"h, firing flaw to one side   500-700   July 14, 1999 Sold for $375

535. **RV Sunflower** jardinere, 14"dia., flake to one flower 1200-1700   July 14, 1999   Sold for $2100

536. **RV Ferella** vase, 8"h, mint   600-800   July 14, 1999 Sold for $1400

537. **RV Ferella** vase, brown, two handles, 6"h, mint 350-550   July 14, 1999   Sold for $475

538. **RV Sunflower** vase, two-handled form, 4"h, mint 450-650   July 14, 1999   Sold for $500

539. **RV Ferella** vase, brown, two handles, 6"h, mint 350-550   July 14, 1999   Sold for $475

Not Pictured:

540. **RV Vista** bowl, molded landscape design, 8.5"dia., hairline; with a **RV Vista** wallpocket, 9"l, repaired chip 300-400   July 13, 1998   Sold for $450

541. **RV Peony** vase, yellow, two handles, 15"h, mint 350-450   July 14, 1998   Sold for $400

542. **RV Freesia** ewer, green with purple and white flowers, 15.5"h, mint; with a **RV Freesia** ewer, green with purple and white flowers, 15.5"h, both marked, repaired chip to top   300-400   July 14, 1998   Sold for $300

543. **RV Rozane** vase, brown glaze with clover decoration, RPCo. mark, 3.75"w x 8"h, mint   100-200 July 13, 1998   Sold for $230

544. **RV Futura** vase, peach and green matt, 9.5"h; with a **RV Hexagon** bowl, brown with orange, 5.5"dia., both damaged   200-300   July 13, 1998   Sold for $270

545. **RV Baneda** vase, two handles, green, decorated with leaves, stems and blossoms, 7.5"h, repaired handles 200-300 June 7, 1998 Sold for $300

546. **RV Clematis** bowl, orange to green, two handles, marked, 17.5"l, mint 250-350 June 7, 1998 Sold for $120

547. **RV Donatello** powder jar with lid, children playing musical instruments, 5.75"dia., mint 300-400 June 7, 1998 Sold for $350

548. **RV Panel** wallpocket, floral and grape design, brown matt glaze, ink mark, 9"l, mint 200-300 June 7, 1998 Sold for $350

549. **RV Dogwood ll** vase, green glaze with black branches and white flowers, 8"h, mint 250-350 June 7, 1998 Sold for $260

550. **RV Morning Glory** basket, stylized vines and leaves in green, flowers in turquoise and yellow, 10.5"h, restored handle 250-350 June 7, 1998 Sold for $350

551. **RV Water lily** cookie jar, multiple green lily pads with Water lily in full bloom, marked, 10.25"h, restored rim 150-250 June 7, 1998 Sold for $110

552. **RV Peony** ewer, pink shading to green, marked, 6"h, mint 150-200 June 7, 1998 Sold for $90

553. **RV Carnelian ll** vase, rose, gray, green and purple matt glaze, two handles, 10"h, minor bruise to base 250-350 June 7, 1998 Sold for $160

554. **RV Zephyr Lily** bowl, brown, marked, 14"l, mint 150-200 June 7, 1998 Sold for $90

555. **RV Velmoss Schroll** vase, impressed Arts & Crafts design of red flowers with green leaves on brown stems 7.5"h, minor flakes to base 150-250 June 7, 1998 Sold for $350

556. **RV Velmoss** double bud vase, rose ground, paper label, 8.5"h, mint 150-250 June 7, 1998 Sold for $260

557. **RV Futura** vase, design of thistles, 8"h, minor bruise to base 350-450 June 7, 1998 Sold for $325

558. **RV Monticello** basket, arched handle, incised mark, 6.5"h, mint 350-450 June 7, 1998 Sold for $550

Not Pictured:

559. **RV Florentine** bowl, brown, stamp mark, 8"dia., mint; with a **RV Florentine** double bud vase, brown, 8.5"w, mint 200-250 June 7, 1998 Sold for $240

560. **RV Magnolia** ashtray, brown, 6"dia., minor flake; with a pair of **RV Magnolia** handled cups, brown, 3"h, mint 150-250 June 7, 1998 Sold for $230

561. **RV Rosecraft Panel** vase, two handles, orange and brown, stamp mark, 7.5"w x 6"h, mint 100-200 July 14, 1998 Sold for $220

562. **RV Thornapple** vase, blue to green with white flower, handles, nice form, marked, 8.5"h, mint 100-200 July 14, 1998 Sold for $230

563. **RV Zephyr Lily** jardinere and pedestal, orange, jardinere 12.5"dia., 25"h overall, minor chips to handle 550-750 July 14, 1998 Sold for $500

564. **RV Snowberry** bookends, pair, green with white berries, 5.5"h, mint 300-400 June 7, 1998 Sold for $210

565. **RV Dahlrose** vase, brown and cream to green top with floral decoration at top, 6.5"h, mint 150-200 June 7, 1998 Sold for $180

566. **RV Rosecraft Hexagon** vase, green glaze with design in cream, ink mark, 6.5"h, repair 150-250 June 7, 1998 Sold for $110

567. **RV Clemana** vase, orange with floral decoration, 6.5"h, mint 200-300 June 7, 1998 Sold for $210

568. **RV Pinecone** vase, brown with two handles, 8.5"h, mint 250-350 June 7, 1998 Sold for $190

569. **RV Topeo** vase, molded design around neck, deep red top shading to lighter red body, marked, 7.5"h, minor flaws 150-250 June 7, 1998 Sold for $80

570. **RV Mostique** bowl, blue, brown, green and yellow gloss design on gray ground, stamp mark, 7"dia. x 3"h, mint 150-250 June 7, 1998 Sold for $120

571. **RV Pinecone** jardinere, brown with two handles, marked #632, 12" x 16.5", mint 700-900 June 7, 1998 Sold for $1600

572. **RV Bushberry** console bowl, unusual form on pedestal with branch handles from base, orange to green, marked, 12.25"l, mint 250-350 June 7, 1998 Sold for $130

573. **RV Velmoss** vase, blue with leaf and bud design around top, marked, 8.5"h, minor flakes and chip repair 100-150 June 7, 1998 Sold for $90

574. **RV Florentine** bowl, brown with green, stamp mark, 7.5"dia. x 3"h, mint 50-100 June 7, 1998 Sold for $90

575. **RV Carnelian I** vase, blue matt with dark blue drip glaze, stamp mark, 8.25"h, minor chip and chip repair 250-350 June 7, 1998 Sold for $160

576. **RV Panel** vase, brown with panel of orange and green decoration, ink mark, 6"h, minor chip 100-150 June 7, 1998 Sold for $160

577. **RV Savonna** bowl, two handles, blue, 9.5"dia. x 4.5", minor chip 150-250 June 7, 1998 Sold for $90

578. **RV Ferella** vase, two handles, red, 6"w x 4.5"h, mint 350-450 June 7, 1998 Sold for $390

Not Pictured:

579. **RV Dahlrose** wallpocket, 8"l, mint 200-300 June 7, 1998 Sold for $250

580. **RV Bushberry** vase, orange, 7"h, mint; with a **RV LaRose** double bud vase, 8"w, mint 200-250 June 7, 1998 Sold for $200

581. **RV Tuscany** wallpocket, gray, 8.5"l, mint 200-300 June 7, 1998 Sold for $400

582. **RV Morning Glory** vase, handled form, white, 14"h, mint 1300-1600 June 7, 1998 Sold for $1300

583. **RV Dutch** pitcher, two Dutch women and child, 11"h, hairline to handle, chip to spout; with a **RV Dutch** mugs, two, one has Dutch boy, girl and geese, other with boy and girl, 5" x 5", both with hairlines 300-400 June 7, 1998 Sold for $225

584. **RV Pinecone** vase, brown with branch handles, marked, 7.5"h, mint; with a **RV Pinecone** vase, green, 12.5"h, chip to base 300-400 July 14, 1998 Sold for $270

585. **RV Snowberry** ewer, pink, marked, 16"h, mint 300-400 July 14, 1998 Sold for $300

586. **RV Foxglove** vase, rose, 10"h, mint   200-300
July 15, 1998 Sold for $300

587. **RV Imperial II** vase, blue crystalline over cream, 7"h,
mint   250-350   July 15, 1998 Sold for $190

588. **RV Topeo** vase, red, 7"h, mint   200-300   July 15, 1998
Sold for $200

589. **RV Carnelian** vase, two handles, gray drip over blue,
ink mark RV, 8.5"h, chips to foot, minor flake to rim
250-350   July 15, 1998 Sold for $210

590. **RV Primrose** vase, brown, 7"h, minute flake to handle
100-200   July 15, 1998 Sold for $150

591. **RV Silhouette** vase, floral design in panels, red, 12.5"h,
mint   150-250   July 15, 1998   Sold for $230

592. **RV Orian** vase, turquoise with beige interior, original
label, 9.5"h, mint   200-300   July 15, 1998
Sold for $210

593. **RV Moderne** vase, turquoise and gold with handles,
silver label, 6"h, mint; with a **RV Moderne** vase, not
shown, turquoise and gold, 6"h, small flake   200-300
July 15, 1998 Sold for $200

594. **RV Dahlrose** jardinere, 4.5"h, mint   100-150
July 15, 1998 Sold for $90

595. **RV Panel** vase, green, 6"h, mint; with a **RV Panel** vase,
not shown, green, 6"h, bruise to lip   200-300
July 15, 1998 Sold for $260

596. **RV Mock Orange** ewer, pink, 16"h, minor flake to
decoration   200-300   July 15, 1998 Sold for $280

597. **RV Luffa** vase with handles, brown to green, 8"h, minor
flake to body   200-300   July 15, 1998 Sold for $200

598. **RV Monticello** vase, brown, 8"h, mint   300-400
July 15, 1998 Sold for $500

599. **RV Earlam** urn, peach, green and blue matt glaze,
8.5"h, mint   250-350   July 15, 1998 Sold for $400

600. **RV Dahlrose** vase, cylindrical shape with handles, 6"h,
mint   150-250   July 15, 1998 Sold for $150

601. **RV Hexagon** vase, brown, ink stamp RV, 6.5"h, mint
200-300   July 15, 1998 Sold for $350

602. **RV Clemana** vase, brown, 6.5"h, minor chips to foot
200-300   July 15, 1998 Sold for $230

603. **RV Gardenia** vase, gray, 10"h, mint   200-300
July 15, 1998 Sold for $250

Not Pictured:

604. **RV Carnelian** vase, two handles at base, pink and
brown mottled glaze, paper label, 5"h, mint; with a **RV
Columbine** vase, blue, 4"h, mint   200-300
July 14, 1998 Sold for $220

605. **RV Zephyr Lily** jardinere, green with yellow and pink
flowers, 9"dia. x 9"h, mint   250-350   July 14, 1998
Sold for $350

606. **RV Mostique** jardinere, 8"h, tight hairline to top
200-300   July 13, 1999 Sold for $300

607. **RV Mostique** jardinere, green, blue, yellow and brown
geometrics on a gray textured ground, stamp mark, 10"w
x 8"h, mint   300-400   July 15, 1998 Sold for $475

608. **RV Mostique** jardinere, geometric design in yellow,
blue and green on a gray textured ground, 10"h, minor
flakes   350-450   July 15, 1998 Sold for $450

609. **RV Mostique** wallpocket, geometric design in yellow,
blue and green on a gray textured ground, 9"l, minor
flakes   150-250   July 15, 1998 Sold for $300

43

610. **RV Pinecone** vase, green, two handles, 4"h, mint 150-250   June 7, 1998   Sold for $160

611. **RV Wisteria** vase, blue ground, 6"h, mint   400-600 June 7, 1998   Sold for $550

612. **RV Baneda** bowl, 11"l, mint   350-450   June 7, 1998 Sold for $475

613. **RV Wisteria** vase, 7"h, mint   450-650   June 7, 1998 Sold for $500

614. **RV Futura** jardinere, geometric design, 9"dia., mint 350-550   June 7, 1998   Sold for $325

615. **RV Futura** vase, four buttresses at bottom, floral design, 5.5"dia., mint   300-400   June 7, 1998 Sold for $260

616. **RV Luffa** vase, two handles at top, original label, 8"h, mint   350-450   June 7, 1998   Sold for $275

617. **RV Sunflower** vase, 9"h, 500-750   June 7, 1998 Sold for $700

618. **RV Laurel** vase, peach ground, 9.5"h, repaired chips 150-250   June 7, 1998   Sold for $100

619. **RV Baneda** vase, two-handled, 6"h, mint   350-450 June 7, 1998   Sold for $550

620. **RV Coppertone** bowl, frog with flower and lily pads, covered in a green, ivory and brown matt glaze, 11"l, mint   350-550   June 7, 1998   Sold for $700

621. **RV Sunflower** vase, 4"h, mint   400-600   June 7, 1998 Sold for $500

622. **RV Futura** vase, four buttresses at bottom, 4"h, two small chips   200-250   June 7, 1998   Sold for $300

Not Pictured:

623. **RV Baneda** vase, two-handled form in green, paper label, 5"h, mint   300-400   June 7, 1998   Sold for $325

624. **RV Matt Green** jardinere and pedestal, floral design of cream in panels against a matt green ground, one lady profile design in cream, 29.5"h, jar is 11"dia., two minute flakes to jar, chips and hairline to pedestal 900-1200   June 7, 1998   Sold for $600

625. **RV Rozane Aztec** vase, crocus design in squeezebag decoration in yellow, brown and green on a brown ground, impressed number, 9"h, minor flake to bottom 500-750   June 7, 1998   Sold for $375

626. **RV Persian** tea set, three pieces, ivory matte glaze, tapered handles and tops, creamer 3" x 5", teapot 5" x 9", sugar bowl 4" x 6.75", mint   350-550   June 7, 1998 Sold for $550

627. **RV Rozane Chloron** vase, green suspended matt glaze, three legs, 12.25"h, mint   700-900   June 7, 1998 Sold for $900

628. **RV Persian** jardinere, stylized orange colored fruit amid green leaves on a white matt ground, 7"dia., mint 250-350   June 7, 1998   Sold for $400

629. **RV Rozane Woodland** vase, incised floral decoration in various shades of brown on a tan matt ground, wafer mark, 7"h, mint   700-900   June 7, 1998   Sold for $325

630. **RV Monticello** vase, 7.5"w, mint   350-450 July 14, 1999   Sold for $400

631. **RV Moss** vase, marked, 8.5"h, mint   300-400 June 6, 1999   Sold for $425

632. RV Futura vase, peach and green matt glaze, unmarked, 7.25"h, mint   350-450   June 7, 1998 Sold for $425

633. RV Blackberry vase, two-handled form in green to brown, black paper label, 8.25"h, mint   400-600 June 7, 1998 Sold for $800

634. RV Teasel vase, two-handled form in peach with molded thistle design covered in green, marked, 4.25"h, mint   150-250   June 7, 1998 Sold for $150

635. RV Foxglove vase, four buttresses around bottom, flaring top, blue with white floral design, marked, 14.5"h, mint   450-650   June 7, 1998 Sold for $600

636. RV Magnolia vase, blue with white and brown blossoms, marked, 8.5"h, chips   100-200   June 7, 1998 Sold for $80

637. RV Monticello vase, orange with white and black stylized design over incised band at top, two handles, black paper label, 5"h, mint   250-350   June 7, 1998 Sold for $375

638. RV Laurel vase, yellow and black with black interior, design of leaves and berries has a slightly orange glaze, silver paper label, 8.25"h, minor chip repair to base 150-250   June 7, 1998 Sold for $150

639. RV Wisteria vase, two-handled form, paper label, 8.25"h, chip to decoration   400-600   June 7, 1998 Sold for $550

640. RV Rosecraft Hexagon vase, brown to orange matt glaze with incised design, stamp mark, 8.5"h, mint 150-250   June 7, 1998 Sold for $450

641. RV Moss vase, two handles, marked, 12.75"h, couple of minor bruises   350-450   June 7, 1998 Sold for $475

642. RV Carnelian I bowl, light green with dark green drip glaze, stamp mark, 8"dia. x 3"h, mint   150-250 June 7, 1998 Sold for $80

643. RV Rozane vase, white with molded yellow and pink roses and green leaves, stamp mark, 7.25"h, two pin head flakes   100-200   June 7, 1998 Sold for $70

644. RV Panel vase, green matt with panels of floral design in pink, yellow and pale green, stamp mark, 8.25"h, mint 150-250   June 7, 1998 Sold for $375

645. RV Mostique vase, textured gray surface with glossy yellow and green design, stamp mark, 6"h, mint 150-250   June 7, 1998 Sold for $140

646. RV Carnelian II bowl, semi-matt drip glazes in purple and green are intermingled with maroon, two handles, 10.5"l x 3.5"h, mint   150-250   June 7, 1998 Sold for $425

647. RV Pasadena planter, footed form with stylized leaves forming base and flaring top, black with pink drip from top, marked, 5.5"h, mint   150-200   June 7, 1998 Sold for $220

Not Pictured:

648. RV Water lily vase, green, 12"h, mint   200-300 June 7, 1998 Sold for $270

649. RV Vista bowl, low form with landscape decoration, 8.5"w, mint   250-350   June 7, 1998 Sold for $220

650. Weller Glendale vase, bird at nest, 13"h, hairline 400-600   June 7, 1998 Sold for $325

651. RV Vista jardinere, large form with molded landscape decoration, 11"w, hairline to base   450-650 June 7, 1998 Sold for $375

652. RV Florentine sand jar, ivory ground with rust panels and green design, 21"h, minor chips   350-450 June 7, 1998 Sold for $260

653. RV Futura vase, bulbous bottom with stacked neck, 10.5"h, mint   600-800   June 6, 1999 Sold for $900

45

654. RV Apple Blossom vase, pink, good color and mold, 10.5"h, mint   250-350   June 7, 1998   Sold for $400

655. RV Baneda vase, green, 9.5"h, paper label, mint 550-750   June 7, 1998   Sold for $750

656. RV Bushberry vase, brown, 12"h, mint   350-450 June 7, 1998   Sold for $220

657. RV Baneda vase, pink, 8"h, mint   500-700 June 7, 1998   Sold for $800

658. RV Panel vase, nude in ivory on a green ground, stamp mark, 8"h, mint   600-800   June 7, 1998   Sold for $650

659. RV Water lily vase, two handles, 4"h, mint   100-150 June 7, 1998   Sold for $50

660. RV Morning Glory vase, two handled at shoulder, white, original paper label, 6"h, mint   500-700 June 7, 1998   Sold for $500

661. RV Lotus vase, flattened form, 10.5"h, mint   250-350 June 7, 1998   Sold for $230

662. RV Peony hanging basket, yellow, 7"dia., mint 250-350   June 7, 1998   Sold for $170

663. RV Blackberry vase, two handles, 12"h, minor chip to bottom   1200-1700   June 7, 1998   Sold for $1200

664. RV Russco vase, gold and yellow crystalline glaze, partial paper label, 8.5"h, mint   250-350   June 7, 1998 Sold for $170

665. RV Pinecone vase, brown, two handles, 9"h, well repaired chips to base   250-350   June 7, 1998 Sold for $150

666. RV Pinecone vase, green, 9"w, bruise to base 200-300   June 7, 1998   Sold for $150

667. RV Futura jardinere, geometric design, 9"w, mint 350-550   June 7, 1998   Sold for $325

668. RV Apple Blossom vase, green, 10.5"h, mint   250-350 June 7, 1998   Sold for $170

Not Pictured:

669. RV Quaker Tobacco jar, ivory with decoration of two American Colonialists, 6" x 5", restored finial   100-200 June 7, 1998   Sold for $220

670. RV Futura jardinere, leaf design on brown, 9"dia. x 6"h, mint   550-750   July 14, 1999   Sold for $425

671. RV White Rose vase, two-handled form in pink and green, 15.5"h, hairline to top   200-300   July 13, 1998 Sold for $325

672. RV Vista hanging basket, 7"dia., minor glaze chip to top   200-300   July 14, 1999   Sold for $270

673. RV Futura jardinere, leaf design on brown, 9"dia. x 6"h, mint   550-750   July 14, 1999   Sold for $425

674. RV Moderne vase, turquoise and gold, 6.5"h, mint 150-250   July 15, 1998   Sold for $350

675. RV Foxglove jardinere and pedestal, blue, 25"h, minor flakes   600-800   July 15, 1998   Sold for $800

676. RV White Rose vase, two-handled form in pink and green, 15.5"h, chip to base   200-300   July 13, 1998 Sold for $325

677. **RV Savona** vase, blue, 8"h, mint 250-350
June 7, 1998 Sold for $270

678. **RV Baneda** vase, red, 6"h, original label, mint
400-600 June 7, 1998 Sold for $475

679. **RV Bushberry** pitcher, branch handle, marked, 9"h,
mint 250-350 June 7, 1998 Sold for $375

680. **RV Poppy** vase, pink, 5"h, mint 100-200
June 7, 1998 Sold for $100

681. **RV Pinecone** vase, blue, 10.5"h, mint 250-350
June 7, 1998 Sold for $425

682. **RV Zephyr Lily** bookends, pair, brown to green, 5.5"h,
mint 300-400 June 7, 1998 Sold for $210

683. **RV Futura** jardinere, leaf design on orange to green,
14"dia., mint 550-750 June 7, 1998 Sold for $400

684. **RV Morning Glory** vase, white, 7"dia., mint
300-400 June 7, 1998 Sold for $325

685. **RV Silhouette** vase, red glaze with woman in panel,
marked, 7"h, mint 550-750 June 7, 1998
Sold for $350

686. **RV Pinecone** vase, green, 5"h, mint 150-250
June 7, 1998 Sold for $170

687. **RV Pinecone** vase, brown, 14.5"h, mint 250-350
June 7, 1998 Sold for $425

688. **RV Pinecone** vases, pair (one shown), green, 7"h, both
mint 350-450 June 7, 1998 Sold for $150

689. **RV Futura** vase, floral on brown and blue/green, 5"h,
mint 350-550 June 7, 1998 Sold for $600

690. **RV Magnolia** cookie jar, white/pink flowers, marked,
8"h, mint 300-400 June 7, 1998 Sold for $300

Not Pictured:

691. **RV Matt Green** jardinere and pedestal, handles top and
bottom, mottled green matt with stylized Arts & Crafts
rose and leaf design, 29"h, jardinere has impressed mark
and is mint, pedestal is mint 2000-3000 June 7, 1998
Sold for $2000

692. **RV Tourmaline** vase, mottled blue with gold crystalline
glaze, impressed geometric design around top, 4.5"h,
mint 150-250 June 7, 1998 Sold for $230

693. **RV Mostique** vase, gray ground with green, yellow and
blue geometric design, stamped mark, 15"h, mint
450-650 June 7, 1998 Sold for $900

694. **RV Matt Green** vase, triple-legged bud vases circle
center cylindrical vase with incised geometric design,
8.25"h, two minor flakes 300-400 June 7, 1998
Sold for $400

695. **RV Donatello** pedestal, 18"h, mint 250-350
June 7, 1998 Sold for $325

696. **RV Bushberry** pedestal, green, 17"h, minor chips; with
a **RV Foxglove** candlestick, green, 4"dia., mint; with a
RV Moss candlestick, 4"dia., mint; with a **RV Ixia**
candlestick, green, 4", mint; with a **RV Bushberry** frog,
5", glued 300-400 June 7, 1998 Sold for $250

697. **RV Fuschia** wallpocket, 8.5"l, minor roughness to edge
100-200 June 6, 1999 Sold for $400

47

698. **RV Thornapple** vase, pink, 6"h, mint   150-200
June 7, 1998 Sold for $200

699. **RV Apple Blossom** pitcher, pink, 8.5"h, mint   200-250
June 7, 1998 Sold for $130

700. **RV Baneda** vase, green, paper label, 6"h, mint
300-400   June 7, 1998 Sold for $475

701. **RV Luffa** vase, 14.5"h, minor tight line to top   400-600
June 7, 1998 Sold for $375

702. **RV Dogwood** wallpocket, 8.5"l, minor flakes   200-300
June 7, 1998 Sold for $375

703. **RV Vista** vase, molded landscape decoration, 10"h,
mint   400-600 June 7, 1998 Sold for $500

704. **RV Futura** wallpocket, geometric design, 8"l, minor
chip   150-250 June 7, 1998 Sold for $240

705. **RV Ixia** vase, yellow to orange, 10.5"h, chip to bottom
100-150 June 7, 1998 Sold for $100

706. **RV Baneda** vase, green, 12"h, hairline to top
600-800 June 7, 1998 Sold for $600

707. **RV Blackberry** vase, 6"dia., mint   350-450
June 7, 1998 Sold for $425

708. **RV Earlam** strawberry jar, green, blue and peach matt
glaze, 8"h, glaze imperfection to side   200-300
June 7, 1998 Sold for $325

709. **RV Monticello** vase, blue with geometric design, two
handles, 5"h, mint   200-300 June 7, 1998
Sold for $325

710. **RV Sunflower** vase, 7.5"h, hairline   300-400
June 7, 1998 Sold for $325

711. **RV Vista** window box, original liner, molded landscape
decoration, 11.5"l, minute flake to top   350-550
June 7, 1998 Sold for $1200

712. **RV Vista** vase, molded landscape, 17.5"h, mint
800-1100   June 7, 1998 Sold for $950

713. **RV Tuscany** vase, pink, 8"h, mint   200-250
June 7, 1998 Sold for $180

714. **RV White Rose** vase, pink, 6"h, mint   100-200
June 7, 1998 Sold for $90

Not Pictured:

715. **RV Futura** wallpocket, geometric design, 8"l, minor
chip   150-250 June 7, 1998 Sold for $290

716. **RV Futura** vase, blue matt ground with green designs
around shoulder, four green and blue Deco design feet,
8"h, mint   650-850 June 7, 1998 Sold for $850

717. **RV Futura** vase, three sided geometric form, 8.5"h,
mint   450-650 June 6, 1999 Sold for $550

718. **RV Fuschia** vase, two handles, blue, marked, 8"h, mint
150-250 July 14, 1998 Sold for $350

719. **RV Futura** vase, Black Flame, bulbous body with tiered
neck in green hi-glaze with gunmetal at base, 10"h,
repaired chip to lip   600-800 July 14, 1998
Sold for $400

720. **RV Futura** wallpocket, geometric pattern, two handles,
paper label, 8.5"h, minute flake to back   200-300
July 14, 1998 Sold for $325

721. **RV Pinecone** bowl, brown, two handles, 11"l, mint 200-300 June 7, 1998 Sold for $160

722. **RV Lotus** vase, blue and yellow, 10"h, mint 250-350 June 7, 1998 Sold for $250

723. **RV Pinecone** vase, green, 6"h, minor chip to base 200-300 June 7, 1998 Sold for $160

724. **RV Pinecone** vase, green cylindrical form, two handles, 7"h, paper label, mint 250-350 June 7, 1998 Sold for $180

725. **RV Dogwood** wallpocket, stamp mark, 9.5"l, mint 250-350 June 7, 1998 Sold for $325

726. **RV Morning Glory** vase, white, 12.5"h, mint 1000-1500 June 7, 1998 Sold for $800

727. **RV Wincraft** vase, trees and black panther, blue ground, 10.5"h, mint 650-850 June 7, 1998 Sold for $600

728. **RV Jonquil** vase, two handles, molded floral design, 5"h, mint 200-300 June 7, 1998 Sold for $210

729. **RV Juvenile** baby plate with chick decoration, stamp mark, 8"dia., mint 150-250 June 7, 1998 Sold for $110

730. **RV Blackberry** vase, two handles, 6"h, mint 400-600 June 7, 1998 Sold for $550

731. **RV Clemana** vase, two handles, 6.5"h, mint 200-300 June 7, 1998 Sold for $200

732. **RV Dawn** vase, green with two buttresses, white design, 8.5"h, mint 200-300 June 7, 1998 Sold for $170

733. **RV Morning Glory** bowl, two handles, white, original label, 11"l, mint 350-550 June 7, 1998 Sold for $300

734. **RV Thornapple** bookend planters, 5.5"h, mint 300-400 June 7, 1998 Sold for $280

735. **RV Pinecone** vase, blue, handle on side, 7"w, tight line 100-200 June 7, 1998 Sold for $160

Not Pictured:

736. **RV Fuschia** bowl, two handles, deep blue, good mold, marked, 9"dia. x 3.5"h, mint 150-250 July 14, 1998 Sold for $230

737. **RV Magnolia** vase, blue, 7"h; with a **RV Magnolia** vase, brown, 4"h, minor chips; with a **RV Pinecone** vase, blue, 7"h, repaired chip 200-250 July 14, 1998 Sold for $200

738. **RV Water lily** candlestick, brown, 5"h, mint; with a **RV Snowberry** candlestick, green, 2"h, mint; and a **RV Zephyr Lily** ewer, brown, 6", chipped 150-250 July 14, 1998 Sold for $230

739. **RV Ceramic Design** wallpocket, white with green leaf and vine design outlined in gold, 10"l, mint 250-350 June 7, 1998 Sold for $550

740. **RV Dogwood I** vase, ink mark, 9.5"h, mint 250-350 June 7, 1998 Sold for $350

741. **RV Vista** jardinere, molded landscape decoration, 11"w, minor bruise and hairline 450-650 June 7, 1998 Sold for $260

49

742. **RV Bushberry** vase, blue, 5"h, mint   150-200
June 7, 1998   Sold for $80

743. **RV Dogwood** vase, 7"h, mint   300-400   June 7, 1998
Sold for $300

744. **RV Zephyr Lily** pitcher, brown, 6.5"h, mint; with a **RV
Zephyr Lily** cornucopia, not shown brown, 8"h, minor
chip   200-300   June 7, 1998   Sold for $100

745. **RV Rozane** vase, white with roses, 10.5"dia., minor
flakes   250-350   June 7, 1998   Sold for $160

746. **RV Tuscany** vase, pink, 8"h, mint   200-250
June 7, 1998   Sold for $200

747. **RV Morning Glory** vase, green, two handles, blue
around bottom, paper label, 6"h, minor glaze flaws
250-350   June 7, 1998   Sold for $500

748. **RV Dahlrose** vase, three openings, 6"h, mint   200-300
June 7, 1998   Sold for $160

749. **RV Blackberry** vase, 10.5"h, minor damage   400-600
June 7, 1998   Sold for $500

750. **RV Snowberry** vase, green, 8.5"h, mint   150-200
June 7, 1998   Sold for $140

751. **RV Iris** vase, blue, 10.5"h, chip repair to base   250-350
June 7, 1998   Sold for $120

752. **RV Knights of Pythius** tankard and mug set, six mugs,
decal transfers, tankard 11.5"h, mugs 5"h, minor flaws
400-600   June 7, 1998   Sold for $350

753. **RV Sylvan** vase, fox and chickens, matt ground, 9.5"h,
mint   250-350   June 7, 1998   Sold for $475

754. **RV Medallion** jardinere, decorated with transfers in
green and gold, 12.5"dia., minor flaws   300-400
June 7, 1998   Sold for $140

755. **RV Carnelian** candlesticks, brown and green matt,
stamp mark, 5"dia., mint   100-150   June 7, 1998
Sold for $100

756. **RV Zephyr Lily** vase, brown, two handles, 7.5"h, mint
100-150   June 7, 1998   Sold for $90

757. **RV Tourmaline** vase, blue, green and ivory mottled
matt, original label, 5"h, mint   100-200   June 7, 1998
Sold for $110

758. **RV Jonquil** vase, original labels, 4"h, mint   200-300
June 7, 1998   Sold for $140

Not Pictured:

759. **RV Vista** vase, four handles at top, molded landscape
decoration, 18"h, mint   700-900   June 7, 1998
Sold for $850

760. **RV Vista** vase, molded landscape, 17.5"h, minor bruise
to rim   500-700   June 7, 1998   Sold for $750

761. **RV Blackberry** vase, bulbous form, 6"h, heavy pitting
on leaves; with a **RV Cherry Blossom** vase, brown,
4"h, chip to inside edge   300-400   July 14, 1998
Sold for $550

762. **RV Burmese** candleholders, pair, green matt with good
definition, gold highlights, 7.5"h, mint   350-450
July 14, 1998   Sold for $210

763. **RV Lustre** candlestick, light green, 10"h, minor wear,
mint; with a **RV Mayfair** vase, mottled red and black
hi-glaze, 9"h, minor flake; and a **RV** flower arranger,
white with gold and green decoration, 5"w x 3"h, mint
200-250   July 14, 1998   Sold for $210

764. **RV Baneda** vase, green, 4"h, mint 300-400
June 7, 1998 Sold for $350

765. **RV Blackberry** basket, 7"w, minor flake to top
300-400 June 7, 1998 Sold for $650

766. **RV Baneda** vase, green, original label, 6"h, mint
300-400 June 7, 1998 Sold for $425

767. **RV Snowberry** wallpocket, pink, 8"w, mint 200-300
June 7, 1998 Sold for $375

768. **RV Tourmaline** vase, impressed decoration at top,
mottled two-tone blue matt, 6.5"w, mint 150-250
June 7, 1998 Sold for $140

769. **RV Orchid** vase, experimental example with molded
orchids, green to pink, trial numbers on bottom,
"Orchid" incised in back top, 9.5"h, mint 1500-2000
June 7, 1998 Sold for $2300

770. **RV Wisteria** vase, blue ground, 6.5"w, mint 450-650
June 7, 1998 Sold for $600

771. **RV Carnelian** wallpocket, purple, green and blue matt
glaze, ink mark, 8.5"l, mint 250-350 June 7, 1998
Sold for $450

772. **RV Juvenile** bowl, rabbit decoration, 5.5"dia., mint
100-150 June 7, 1998 Sold for $110

773. **RV Zephyr Lily** vase, green, two handles, 7.5"h, mint
100-150 June 7, 1998 Sold for $90

774. **RV Decorated and Gold Trace** candlesticks, gold,
purple and green floral decoration on white, 8.5"h, mint
300-400 June 7, 1998 Sold for $130

775. **RV Baneda** vase, two-handled form in red, 15"h, mint
1000-1500 June 7, 1998 Sold for $2100

776. **RV Futura** vase, green with purple, blue and yellow
balls, four buttresses, 8.5"h, mint 700-900
June 7, 1998 Sold for $1000

777. **RV Monticello** vase, brown with geometric design, two
handles, 4"h, mint 250-350 June 7, 1998
Sold for $300

778. **RV Fuschia** vases, pair, brown to yellow, 6"h, mint
100-150 June 7, 1998 Sold for $250

779. **RV Aztec** vase, geometric design in blue, yellow,
orange and white, 6"h, chips 100-150 June 7, 1998
Sold for $90

780. **RV Vista** hanging basket, molded landscape design with
flower underneath, 7"w, mint 250-350 June 7, 1998
Sold for $210

781. **RV Sunflower** vase, two-handled form, 5"h, mint
400-600 June 7, 1998 Sold for $450

Not Pictured:

782. **RV Blackberry** vase, unmarked, 4"h, mint 250-350
July 14, 1998 Sold for $375

783. **RV Imperial II** vase, mottled red and turquoise glaze
with incised bands around neck, 7"h, mint 350-450
June 7, 1998 Sold for $700

784. **RV Vista** lamp base, molded landscape decoration,
15"h, drill hole in side 350-550 June 7, 1998
Sold for $350

785. **RV Pinecone** ewer, brown, marked, 10"h, mint 200-300 July 13, 1998 Sold for $350

786. **RV Pinecone** bowl, green, marked, 10"l x 4"h, mint 150-250 July 13, 1998 Sold for $230

787. **RV Pinecone** vase, brown with two handles, marked, 6.5"h, mint 100-200 July 13, 1998 Sold for $110

788. **RV Pinecone** pitcher, brown, marked, 9.5"h, mint 250-350 July 13, 1998 Sold for $550

789. **RV Pinecone** vase, pedestal vase, brown, marked, 8.5"h, mint 200-300 July 13, 1998 Sold for $450

790. **RV Pinecone** hanging basket, brown, 6"dia. x 5"h, mint 150-250 July 13, 1998 Sold for $170

791. **RV Pinecone** pitcher, brown, twig handle, marked, 7.5"h, mint 250-350 July 13, 1998 Sold for $475

792. **RV Pinecone** vase, blue, marked, 3.5"h, mint 50-100 July 13, 1998 Sold for $180

793. **RV Pinecone** vase, green, cylindrical shape with two handles, 7"h, mint 100-200 July 13, 1998 Sold for $170

794. **RV Pinecone** jardinere, 10"dia. x 9.5"h, mint 350-550 July 13, 1998 Sold for $800

795. **RV Pinecone** vase, bulbous form in green, two handles, marked, 4.5"dia. x 4.25"h, mint 100-200 July 13, 1998 Sold for $750

796. **RV Pinecone** bowl, brown with green interior, marked and paper label, 12"l x 4"h, mint 150-250 July 13, 1998 Sold for $220

797. **RV Pinecone** vase, brown, two handles, marked, 10"h, mint 300-400 July 13, 1998 Sold for $325

798. **RV Pinecone** vase, brown, marked, 14.5"h, mint 500-700 July 13, 1998 Sold for $650

799. **RV Pinecone** jardinere, brown, marked, 7"d x 6.25"h, some minor pitting in making, mint 150-250 July 13, 1998 Sold for $220

Not Pictured:

800. **RV Pinecone** vase, green, 10.5"h, mint 350-450 July 14, 1999 Sold for $260

801. **RV Pinecone** vase, brown, 8.5"h, mint 250-350 July 14, 1999 Sold for $250

802. **RV Pinecone** vase, green, 9.5"h, mint 400-500 July 14, 1999 Sold for $270

803. **RV Pinecone** vase, green, 2.5"h, mint 300-400 July 14, 1999 Sold for $220

804. **RV Pinecone** basket, green, 11"h, mint 450-650 July 14, 1999 Sold for $400

805. **RV Pinecone** candleholders, pair, brown, paper label and marked, 2"h, one chipped; with an **RV Pinecone** dish, brown, marked, 3"h, chipped; with an **RV Pinecone** vase, blue, marked, 8.5"h, broken handle; with a **RV Pinecone** vase, brown, marked, 5"h, chipped 200-300 July 13, 1998 Sold for $260

806. **RV Pinecone** bowl, brown with green interior, large design with one handle coming over top edge, marked, 11"dia. x 5.5"h, repaired chip to base; with a **RV Pinecone** dish, three feet, brown, marked, 12.5"l x 3.5"h, handle broken 150-250 July 13, 1998 Sold for $325

807. **RV Sunflower** wallpocket, 6"w x 7.25"h, hairline 200-300 July 13, 1998 Sold for $750

808. **RV Dahlrose** vase, flattened form, 8"w x 6"h, mint
200-300   June 7, 1998   Sold for $200

809. **RV Fuschia** vase, yellow to brown, impressed mark,
6.5"h, mint   100-200   June 7, 1998   Sold for $140

810. **RV Water lily** vase, yellow to brown, marked, 16.5"h,
mint   500-700   June 7, 1998   Sold for $500

811. **RV Carnelian** vase, rose matt with mottled yellow to
purple, 7"h, mint   250-350   June 7, 1998
Sold for $240

812. **RV Blackberry** vase, green to brown, paper label, 4"h,
mint   200-300   June 7, 1998   Sold for $325

813. **RV Vista** vase, molded landscape design in blue, green
and purple, 10"h, mint   400-600   June 7, 1998
Sold for $375

814. **RV Fuschia** vase, brown to green, impressed mark, 8"h,
mint   150-250   June 7, 1998   Sold for $180

815. **RV Cherry Blossom** vase, brown with cream banding,
4"h, mint   250-350   June 7, 1998   Sold for $280

816. **RV Clematis** vase, blue/green matt, marked, 10.5"h,
mint   200-300   June 7, 1998   Sold for $150

817. **RV Baneda** vase, red, 9.5"h, water deposit, mint
500-700   June 7, 1998   Sold for $700

818. **RV Jonquil** vase, brown to green, 6"w x 3"h, mint
200-300   June 7, 1998   Sold for $200

819. **RV Futura** vase, triangular form in light to dark blue,
8"h, minor surface scratches   400-500   June 7, 1998
Sold for $300

820. **RV Silhouette** pitcher, rose matt, floral design in
panels, marked, 10.5"h, mint   200-300   June 7, 1998
Sold for $100

821. **RV Rozane Pattern** vase, mottled green glaze, marked,
15.5"h, mint   250-350   June 7, 1998   Sold for $375

822. **RV Vista** wallpocket, molded landscape, 9.5"l, minute
chips around opening for hanging   250-350
June 7, 1998   Sold for $800

823. **RV Baneda** vase, cylindrical form in red, paper label,
7.5"h, mint   300-400   June 7, 1998   Sold for $500

824. **RV Water lily** vase, handles from top to bottom, orange
to brown, marked and #174, 6.5"h, mint   100-200
June 7, 1998   Sold for $100

Not Pictured:

825. **RV Rozane Egypto** vase, green suspended matt glaze,
5.75" x 5.25", mint   400-600   June 7, 1998
Sold for $600

826. **RV Futura** vase, orange stacked neck, unmarked, 7.5"h,
filled chip to bottom; with a **RV Falline** vase, two
handles, mottled orange and brown, 8"h, chip to foot
300-400   July 14, 1998   Sold for $400

827. **RV Zephyr Lily** pitcher, brown, 10"h, mint; with a **RV
Water lily** vase, brown, 6"h, mint   250-350
July 14, 1998   Sold for $220

828. **RV Bleeding Heart** vase, blue, 4"h; with a **RV
Bushberry** vase, blue, 3"h, both with minor flakes; with
a **RV Zephyr Lily** vase, blue, 8" x 9", chips; with a **RV
Zephyr Lily** planter, blue, small chip   300-400
July 14, 1998   Sold for $200

829. **RV Futura** hanging basket, 7.5"w, minor flake
250-350   July 14, 1999   Sold for $200

830. **RV Rozane** vase, floral design on three footed form,
impressed numbers, 10.5"h, minor flake   250-450
July 14, 1999   Sold for $240

831. RV Baneda vase, deep red, 6"h, chip to top edge
150-250 July 13, 1998 Sold for $240

832. RV Snowberry bowl, green to orange with two handles;
with an **RV Snowberry** bowl, (shown at right) pink,
7"dia. x 2"h, mint 150-200 July 13, 1998
Sold for $120

833. RV Juvenile plate, cup and bowl, decoration of duck,
plate 8"dia., cup 3"h, bowl 6"dia. x 2"h, wear on all,
chip to cup and bowl 150-250 July 13, 1998
Sold for $150

834. RV Gardenia vase, brown, 12"h; with a **RV Ming Tree**
basket, blue, 8.5"h, both chipped 200-300
July 13, 1998 Sold for $160

835. RV Pinecone vase, blue, paper label, 11"h, mint
300-400 July 13, 1998 Sold for $550

836. RV Apple Blossom wallpocket, green, branch handle,
marked, 8"h, mint 150-250 July 13, 1998
Sold for $170

837. RV Silhouette planter, blue, 6.5"dia; with a **RV
Clematis** candlesticks, pair, blue, 4.5"h, both mint
200-300 July 13, 1998 Sold for $110

838. RV Snowberry teapot with lid, light to dark pink,
marked, 6.5"h; with a **RV Primrose** vase, orange to
yellow, marked, 6.5"h, both flawed 200-300
July 13, 1998 Sold for $210

839. RV Pinecone vase, blue, marked, 12.5"h, chip to body;
with a **RV Victorian Art Pottery** vase, (shown at right),
gray, 6.5"h, chip and hairline 250-350 July 13, 1998
Sold for $400

840. RV Juvenile plate and cup, cream with brown puppy,
gray band bordered with black, stamp mark, plate 8"dia.,
cup 2"h, both have wear on color 100-150
July 13, 1998 Sold for $150

Not Pictured:

841. RV Blackberry vase, two-handled form, paper label,
6"dia., mint 350-450 July 15, 1998 Sold for $425

842. RV Fuschia vase, blue, 6.5"h; with a **RV Bittersweet**
wallpocket, yellow, 7"; with a **RV Water lily** console
bowl, orange and brown, all marked, 12.5"l x 3"h, all
with minor flaws 100-200 July 13, 1998
Sold for $200

843. RV Clematis wallpocket, blue, marked, 8.5"h, chip to
top; with a **RV Gardenia** wallpocket, 8"h, glaze flake
top front 150-200 July 13, 1998 Sold for $220

844. RV Cherry Blossom vase, two-handled form, caramel
and cream with white blossoms, foil label, 6"dia. x 7"h,
mint 300-400 July 16, 1996 Sold for $375

845. RV Ferella vase, flaring form, red mottled glaze with
ivory and green, 9"h, mint 400-500 July 16, 1996
Sold for $1800

846. RV Jonquil vase, two handles, green, brown, white and
yellow, 7.5"h, mint 250-350 July 17, 1996
Sold for $300

847. RV Jonquil vase, two-handled form, yellow, white and
green floral design, 6"dia. x 6"h, minute flake to
underside of base 250-350 July 15, 1996
Sold for $210

848. RV Luffa vase, two-handled form, caramel and green
with white blossom, foil label, 6"h, mint 250-350
July 15, 1996 Sold for $300

849. RV Clematis candlesticks, pair, brown, 2"h, chip to one
50-100 July 15, 1996 Sold for $60

850. RV Cherry Blossom vase, two-handled form, caramel
and cream with white blossoms, 5"dia. x 5"h, mint
250-350 July 15, 1996 Sold for $240

851. RV Cherry Blossom vase, two-handled form, caramel
and cream with white blossoms, foil label, 8"dia. x 8"h,
mint 250-350 July 15, 1996 Sold for $475

852. **RV Moss** vase, two handles, blue, marked, 6"h, chip to bottom edge 100-150 July 13, 1998 Sold for $150

853. **RV Jonquil** vase, brown to green, paper label, 4"h, mint 150-250 July 13, 1998 Sold for $90

854. **RV Pinecone** condiment dish, blue, marked, 13"w x 6.5"h, mint 200-300 July 13, 1998 Sold for $500

855. **RV Water lily** flower frog, pink to green with five openings, marked, 5"h, mint 50-100 July 13, 1998 Sold for $110

856. **RV Pinecone** vase, brown, marked, 12.5"h, chip to bottom edge 200-300 July 13, 1998 Sold for $375

857. **RV Baneda** vase, two handles at bottom, green to blue, paper label, 7"h, chip to top edge 150-250 July 13, 1998 Sold for $250

858. **RV Dahlrose** vase, handles at top, mint 200-300 July 13, 1998 Sold for $180

859. **RV Bushberry** console bowl, orange to brown, marked, 11.5"l x 3"h, mint 150-250 July 13, 1998 Sold for $130

860. **RV Freesia** wallpocket, green, marked, 8.5"h, mint 150-250 July 13, 1998 Sold for $250

861. **RV Topeo** vase, green to blue ground with design around neck, 6"h, mint 150-250 July 13, 1998 Sold for $280

862. **RV Rosecraft Hexagon** vase, green matt with cream design, 4.5"h, mint 150-250 July 13, 1998 Sold for $290

863. **RV Imperial II** vase, blue and pale green feathered glaze, green wave design around neck, 10"h, mint 350-550 July 13, 1998 Sold for $1000

864. **RV Earlam** planter, green and brown, four small openings on body, opening in bottom, 8"h, mint 250-350 July 13, 1998 Sold for $950

865. **RV Earlam** vase, two small handles, soft green to blue glaze with brown interior, 4"dia. x 4"h, mint 100-200 July 13, 1998 Sold for $160

866. **RV Freesia** creamer and sugar bowl, one shown blue, bowl 2.5"h, creamer 3"h, both mint 150-250 July 13, 1998 Sold for $80

867. **RV Laurel** vase, orange with black and green, 7.5"h, mint 250-350 July 13, 1998 Sold for $250

868. **RV Freesia** vase, two small handles, marked, 4"h, hairline to top; with an **RV Snowberry** vase, light to dark pink, marked, 6.5"w x 6.5"h, mint 150-200 July 13, 1998 Sold for $100

Not Pictured:

869. **RV Zephyr Lily** candlesticks, blue, marked, 2"h, chipped; with a **RV Zephyr Lily** vase, blue, marked, 12.5"h, chipped 100-150 July 13, 1998 Sold for $230

870. **RV Mostique** vases, pair, textured matt gray ground with incised yellow, green and blue gloss decoration, green hi-glaze interior, unmarked, 10"h, one has flaking on exterior, other has minute flake on decoration 250-350 July 14, 1998 Sold for $325

871. **RV Mostique** bowl, gray with incised stylized decoration in blue, yellow, brown and green, 2.75"h; with a **RV Mostique** vase not shown, gray with yellow, green and blue glossy design, blue stamp mark, 6"h, both mint 250-350 July 14, 1998 Sold for $375

872. **RV Mostique** vase, green and brown enamel decoration, 8"h, mint 100-200 July 14, 1998 Sold for $240

873. **RV Ferella** vase, red, 8.5"h; with a **RV Baneda** vase, red, 4"h, both with hairlines 300-400 July 13, 1998 Sold for $900

874. **RV White Rose** vase, two handles, green to brown, marked, 4"h, mint   100-150   July 14, 1998 Sold for $80

875. **RV Vista** hanging basket, blue, gray, green with red and yellow, 7"dia. x 4"h, bruise to top   200-300 July 14, 1998   Sold for $300

876. **RV Vista** basket, blue, gray, green with red and yellow, 5.5"w x 7"h, mint   300-400   July 14, 1998 Sold for $475

877. **RV Peony** basket, cornucopia shape, pink to green with yellow flowers, marked, 7"w x 7.5"h, mint   200-250 July 14, 1998   Sold for $160

878. **RV Futura** vase, twisted shape, green and orange with green floral design and orange stems, paper labels, 6.5"h, mint   250-350   July 14, 1998   Sold for $400

879. **RV Freesia** vase, experimental, brown to green with red flowers and slender green leaves, two handles, incised notation on reverse Freesia white or pink or yellow flowers, 9.5"h, mint   700-900   July 14, 1998 Sold for $2700

880. **RV Futura** vase, ball shape on angular base, pale blue with light blue, blue and green leaf design, paper label, 8.5"h, flake to bottom   300-400   July 14, 1998 Sold for $475

881. **RV Rosecraft Hexagon** vase, green with cream design, 5"h, mint   200-300   July 14, 1998   Sold for $350

882. **RV Falline** vase, two handled, orange with yellow and green design, paper label, 6.5"h, mint   500-700 July 14, 1998   Sold for $900

883. **RV Carnelian I** vase, pedestal form with two flat handles to top, dark blue drip, stamp mark, 7.5"h, mint 150-250   July 14, 1998   Sold for $160

884. **RV Thornapple** vase, brown, orange to yellow, white flower, marked, 6.5"h, mint   100-200 July 14, 1998   Sold for $120

885. **RV Rosecraft Hexagon** vase, brown with orange design and interior, 5"h, stamp mark, mint   150-250 July 14, 1998   Sold for $260

886. **RV Fuschia** basket with built in flower frog, blue, nice mold, marked, 8"w x 8"h, mint   250-350   July 14, 1998 Sold for $425

887. **RV Carnelian II** vase, green and tan glaze, paper label, 8"h, mint   150-250   July 14, 1998   Sold for $300

888. **RV Fuschia** vase, blue to yellow, floral design, two handles, marked, 4.5"h, mint   150-250   July 14, 1998 Sold for $230

889. **RV Falline** vase, two handles, brown to orange, paper label, 7.5"h, mint   400-600   July 14, 1998 Sold for $650

Not Pictured:

890. **RV White Rose** candlesticks with **Dawn** candlesticks, tallest 5"h, both with chips; with a **RV Moss** three arm candlestick; with two unmatched **RV Zephyr Lily** sticks; and a **RV Magnolia** candlestick, largest 7"h, all mint   200-300   July 14, 1998   Sold for $350

891. **RV Sunflower** vase, two handled form, 5.5"h, mint 300-400   June 6, 1999   Sold for $450

892. **RV Teasel** vase, blue semi-gloss glaze, marked, 4"h, mint 150-200 July 14, 1998 Sold for $170

893. **RV Morning Glory** vase, green to blue with purple and yellow flowers, paper label, chip 100-150 July 14, 1998 Sold for $350

894. **RV Teasel** vase, cream to brown, marked, 6"h, mint 200-250 July 14, 1998 Sold for $160

895. **RV Moss** small jardinere, pink to green with green moss and leaves, brown branches, marked, 6.5"dia. x 6"h, mint 250-300 July 14, 1998 Sold for $300

896. **RV Wincraft** vase, mottled lime green to brown hi-glaze, marked, 10"h, mint 250-300 July 14, 1998 Sold for $160

897. **RV Futura** vase, bottom with two handles in brown, unmarked, 14"h, mint 900-1100 July 14, 1998 Sold for $3500

898. **RV Pinecone** vase, green, marked, 12"h, mint 400-500 July 14, 1998 Sold for $400

899. **RV Moss** vase, pink to green with green moss and leaves, two handles, marked, 7"h, slight roughness to bottom 200-250 July 14, 1998 Sold for $230

900. **RV Futura** vase, tiered neck in green hi-glaze with flames on body with gunmetal at base, 10"h, mint 700-900 July 14, 1998 Sold for $750

901. **RV Futura** vase, green on an orange to tan ground, two long open buttresses, 15.5"h, mint 1200-1700 July 14, 1998 Sold for $1000

902. **RV Futura** vase, green geometric design outlined in blue on a light blue ground, 9"h, mint 500-700 July 14, 1998 Sold for $650

903. **RV Apple Blossom** vase, lime green ground with white, green and pink blossoms, green leaves and brown branches, 10"h, mint 200-300 July 14, 1998 Sold for $270

904. **RV Windsor** vase, mottled orange to brown with geometric green design around neck, 6"h, mint 200-300 July 14, 1998 Sold for $400

905. **RV Wincraft** box, mottled blue glaze with yellow flowers and green branch on lid, marked, 4"l x 2"h, mint 200-250 July 14, 1998 Sold for $110

Not Pictured:

906. **RV Donatello** ashtray, 4.25"h, minute chips; with a **RV Donatello** planter with underplate, 4.5"h, tiny chips to top; with a **RV White Rose** ewer, 6"h, hairline; with **RV Bleeding Heart** ewer, green, 7"h, chip 200-300 July 14, 1998 Sold for $220

907. **RV Pinecone** pedestal, green, 17"h, chips around bottom 300-500 July 14, 1998 Sold for $325

908. **RV Matt Green** compote, pedestal form with molded flowers and branches and geometric designs around top edge, in a green matt glaze, unmarked, 9"h, hairline from top edge 200-300 July 14, 1998 Sold for $140

909. **RV Raymor** dishes, 10 pieces, four dessert plates, two cups and two saucers all in light brown, covered dish in darker brown, all marked, tiny chip on lid of covered piece, 6.5"l x 2"h, other pieces mint 200-300 July 14, 1998 Sold for $350

910. **RV Ivory I** wallpocket, cream with orange highlights on Arts & Crafts stylized design, 11"l, ding to bottom edge 150-200 July 14, 1998 Sold for $120

911. **RV Columbine** vase, pink to green, 5.5"w; with a **RV Apple Blossom** vase, (not shown), two handles, pink, 5.5"w, both mint 200-250 July 15, 1998 Sold for $150

912. **RV Fuschia** vase, green to brown, 18.5"h, tight line to top 250-350 July 15, 1998 Sold for $500

913. **RV Wisteria** vase, two handles, 8"h, mint 550-750 July 15, 1998 Sold for $475

914. **RV Monticello** vase, two handles, brown, 4"h, mint 200-250 July 15, 1998 Sold for $90

915. **RV Dogwood** basket, green to brown with white dogwood, 8"h, mint 350-550 July 15, 1998 Sold for $400

916. **RV Falline** vase, brown, original label, two handles, 7.5"h, mint 650-850 July 15, 1998 Sold for $950

917. **RV Columbine** vase, brown to green, two handles, 9"dia., mint 200-300 July 15, 1998 Sold for $190

918. **RV Blackberry** vase, original label, 12"h, minor flakes hidden on foot 1200-1700 July 15, 1998 Sold for $1300

919. **RV Carnelian** vase, glaze in blue, green and lavender, two open handles, 9.5"w, mint 250-350 July 15, 1998 Sold for $350

920. **RV Columbine** baskets, one shown, pair, brown to green, marked, 7.5"h, one with line to handle, other small chip 100-200 July 15, 1998 Sold for $160

921. **RV Monticello** vase, two handles, brown, 5.5"h, flake to base 100-200 July 15, 1998 Sold for $190

922. **RV Dogwood** vase, green with white floral, 8"h, mint 300-400 July 15, 1998 Sold for $300

923. **RV Monticello** vase, two handles, brown, 5.5"h, mint 200-300 July 15, 1998 Sold for $220

924. **RV Baneda** vase, red with multi-color floral band, original label, 9"h, mint 550-750 July 15, 1998 Sold for $650

Not Pictured:

925. **RV Rozane Aztec** vase, Arts & Crafts design in squeezebag technique, impressed number, 8.5"h, firing bubbles, mint 300-500 July 14, 1999 Sold for $200

926. **RV Sunflower** vase, paper label, 6"h, mint 550-750 July 14, 1999 Sold for $550

927. **RV Rozane** vase, violet decoration, impressed number, artist signed J. Imlay, 6"h, minute flake 150-200 July 14, 1999 Sold for $300

928. **RV Moss** vase, pink to green, 8.5"h, tiny flakes; with a **RV Wincraft** vase, green hi-glaze with branch handles, pink flower, 6"h, mint 150-250 July 14, 1998 Sold for $240

929. **RV Cosmos** wallpocket, brown, 4.5"w x 6"h, mint; with a **RV Columbine** vase, orange to green, blue flower, 10.5"h, glaze flake; with a **RV Clematis** vase, green, 7.5"h, minute flake; with a **RV Rosecraft Panel** vase, green, 5.5"dia. x 4"h, glaze misses, mint 200-300 July 13, 1998 Sold for $550

930. **RV Rozane Mongol** vase, three handles, hi-glaze in red, wafer mark, 6.25"h, mint 700-900 June 7, 1998 Sold for $550

931. **RV Carnelian** vase, two-handled form, 5.5"h, mint 100-200 July 14, 1999 Sold for $180

932. **RV Carnelian** vase, two-handled form, 3"h, minor chip to rim; with a **RV Carnelian** flower frog, ink mark, 3"h, mint 100-200 July 14, 1999 Sold for $170

933. **RV Rozane** basket, floral decoration, red and green on cream ground, 11"h, factory line to handle, mint 150-250 July 14, 1999 Sold for $130

934. **RV Cosmos** vase, two-handled form, impressed mark, 4"h, green, mint 100-150 July 14, 1999 Sold for $90

935. **RV White Rose** vase, two-handled form, floral decoration, impressed mark, 7"h, mint 150-250 July 14, 1999 Sold for $120

936. **RV Dahlrose** vase, double-handled jardinere, 4"h, mint 100-200 July 14, 1999 Sold for $190

937. **RV Pinecone** vase, impressed mark, 4"h, mint 150-250 July 14, 1999 Sold for $150

938. **RV Foxglove** vase, double-handled form, raised mark, 16"h, mint 500-700 July 14, 1999 Sold for $750

939. **Roseville Sign**, blue, 4"h x 7.5"l, mint 2000-2500 July 14, 1999 Sold for $2800

940. **RV Carnelian** covered jar and mug, 7"h, mint 200-300 July 14, 1999 Sold for $100

941. **RV Cosmos** bowl, double-handled form, impressed mark, 7"dia, minor chip to inside lip 100-150 July 14, 1999 Sold for $50

942. **RV Cosmos** vase, double-handled form, impressed mark, 4"h, pink, mint 100-150 July 14, 1999 Sold for $110

943. **RV Carnelian** vase, flattened form, 6"h, mint 100-200 July 14, 1999 Sold for $60

Not Pictured:

944. **RV Luffa** lamp base, good mold, pottery 9"h, mint 250-350 July 13, 1998 Sold for $500

945. **RV** lamp base, green to blue matt with round flowers in purple, yellow and blue, slender green leaves, pottery 9.5"h, mint 300-500 July 13, 1998 Sold for $650

946. **RV Pinecone** bowl, blue, two handles, marked, 11"dia., minor flake to foot 200-300 July 13, 1998 Sold for $375

947. **RV Pinecone** vase, blue, 9"h, chip; with a **RV Pinecone** vase, blue, 6"dia., hairline 200-300 July 14, 1998 Sold for $375

948. **RV Moss** three arm candlestick, marked, 7"h, mint 200-300 July 14, 1998 Sold for $325

949. **RV Cherry Blossom** vase, orange with cream banding, white and yellow flowers with green leaves and brown branches, 5"h, mint 250-350 July 14, 1998 Sold for $280

950. **RV Dogwood II** vase, green with black branches and white flowers, 8"dia. x 4.5"h, mint 200-300 July 14, 1998 Sold for $210

951. **RV Wincraft** vase, mottled light blue top to dark blue base with white flowers and green leaves, wide flaring top, hi-glaze overall, marked, 12"h, mint 250-350 July 14, 1998 Sold for $210

952. **RV Rozane** vase, brown, green and orange ground with wild roses, artist signed, 11.25"h, mint 250-350 June 7, 1998 Sold for $350

953. **RV Sunflower** vase, 6"h, mint 600-800 June 6, 1999 Sold for $700

954. **RV Bittersweet** basket, green, 8"h, mint 150-250 July 14, 1998 Sold for $220

955. **RV Cosmos** vase, blue, two handles, marked, 6"h, mint; with a **RV Cosmos** vase, green with loop handles, nice form, marked, 5"h, mint 100-200 July 14, 1998 Sold for $200

956. **RV Vista** vase, molded landscape design, 11.5"h, repaired chips 200-300 July 13, 1998 Sold for $325

59

957. **RV Jonquil** jardinere and pedestal, jar 12"dia., overall height 28"h, pedestal has minor chip to inside bottom 1200-1700   July 14, 1999 Sold for $1200

958. **RV Mostique** jardinere and pedestal, stylized Arts & Crafts design, jar 11"dia., overall height 27", hairline to jar 700-900   July 14, 1999 Sold for $550

959. **RV Pinecone** jardinere and pedestal, green, marked, jar 14"dia., overall height 29", insignificant chips 900-1200   July 14, 1999 Sold for $1100

Not Pictured:

960. **RV Laurel** vase, 7"h, mint   200-300   July 14, 1999 Sold for $290

961. **RV Rosecraft** vase, stamp mark, 6"h x 7"w, mint 200-250   July 14, 1999 Sold for $250

962. **RV Pinecone** vase, marked, 8"w x 8"h, mint 200-300 July 14, 1999 Sold for $350

963. **RV Freesia** ewer, marked, 15.5"h, mint   450-650 July 14, 1999 Sold for $375

964. **RV Pinecone** jardinere, green, marked, 9"dia. x 8.5"h, mint   300-400   July 13, 1998 Sold for $325

965. **RV Baneda** vase, green/blue glaze with crystals, 6"h, mint   200-300   July 13, 1998 Sold for $325

966. **RV Blackberry** vase, two handles, paper label, 6.5"h, mint   300-400   July 13, 1998 Sold for $450

967. **RV Carnelian I** pitcher, blue with dark blue drip glaze, stamp mark, 15.5"h, mint   250-350   July 13, 1998 Sold for $475

968. **RV Blackberry** vase, two handles, paper label, 10"h, mint   1200-1700   July 13, 1998 Sold for $1100

969. **RV Cherry Blossom** vase, two small handles, orange with yellow stripes, 5.25"h, mint   250-350 July 13, 1998 Sold for $375

970. **RV Silhouette** vase, dark to light pink, marked, 8.5"h, water deposit line inside, mint   250-350   July 13, 1998 Sold for $450

971. **RV Blackberry** jardinere, 9.5"dia. x 8"h, mint   500-700 July 13, 1998 Sold for $900

972. **RV Pinecone** vase, brown, two handles, 11"h, minor flake to decoration, bruise to top   200-300 July 13, 1998 Sold for $425

973. **RV Blackberry** vase, two handles, paper label, 5"h, tiny flake   150-250   July 13, 1998 Sold for $375

974. **RV Blackberry** vase, two handles, 10"h, large chip on handle   400-600   July 13, 1998 Sold for $450

975. **RV Juvenile** bowl, rabbit decoration, 8"dia., repaired chips; with a **RV Juvenile** bowl, duck decoration, 8"dia.; and a **RV Juvenile** plate, rabbit decoration, 8"dia., mint   300-400   July 13, 1998 Sold for $250

976. **RV Ferella** lamp base, two handles, red, 11"h, original label, minor chip repair to foot   350-450   July 13, 1998 Sold for $500

977. **RV Snowberry** hanging basket, pink, 5.5"h, with chains, rough spot; with a **RV Snowberry** hanging basket, green, 5.5"h, mint   100-200   July 13, 1998 Sold for $210

978. **RV Bushberry** jardinere and pedestal, brown and orange, marked, 9"dia. x 25"h, repaired chip to top edge 500-700 July 13, 1998 Sold for $475

979. **RV Dahlrose** jardinere and pedestal, 11"dia. x 30"h, with minute flake to bottom, some wear to top 500-700 July 13, 1998 Sold for $850

980. **RV Pinecone** floor vase, brown/orange to yellow with green interior, marked, 21"h, repaired base 400-600 July 13, 1998 Withdrawn

981. **RV Clematis** jardinere and pedestal, green, jardinere is 9"dia. x 25"h, has peppering, and chip to top 500-700 July 13, 1998 Sold for $600

Not Pictured:

982. **RV Pinecone** vase, 10.5"h, small chip to top 300-400 June 6, 1999 Sold for $350

983. **RV Florentine** wallpocket, brown, good mold, stamp mark, 7"h, tiny glaze flake; with a **RV Florentine** wallpocket, brown, stamp mark, 8.5"h, mint 200-250 July 14, 1998 Sold for $200

984. **RV Blackberry** vase, paper label, 5"h, mint 250-350 July 13, 1998 Sold for $450

985. **RV Blackberry** vase, 5"dia. x 4"h, mint 200-300 July 13, 1998 Sold for $400

986. **RV Dogwood** basket, green, 9.5"h, mint 250-350 July 13, 1998 Sold for $250

987. **RV Sunflower** vase, two handles, 4"h, mint 400-500 July 13, 1998 Sold for $425

988. **RV Rosecraft Vintage** vase, brown, ink mark, 4"h, mint 100-150 July 13, 1998 Sold for $325

989. **RV Wisteria** vase, blue, two handles, 8"h, mint 700-900 July 13, 1998 Sold for $1300

990. **RV Sunflower** vase, two handles, 5"h, mint 400-500 July 13, 1998 Sold for $375

991. **RV Pinecone** bowl, blue, 14"w, mint 150-250 July 13, 1998 Sold for $350

992. **RV Ferella** vase, red, 5.5"h, mint 300-400 July 13, 1998 Sold for $475

993. **RV Wisteria** vase, brown, two handles, 8"h, mint 500-750 July 13, 1998 Sold for $700

994. **RV Dahlrose** hanging basket, 7"h, mint 200-300 July 13, 1998 Sold for $210

995. **RV Pinecone** bowl, brown, 9"w, mint 150-250 July 13, 1998 Sold for $220

996. **RV Baneda** vase, green, two handles, 4"h, small bruise to side 150-250 July 13, 1998 Sold for $300

997. **RV Jonquil** vase, two handles, 6.5"h, mint 300-400 July 13, 1998 Sold for $280

998. **RV Pinecone** vase, brown, two handles, marked, 12"h, repaired chips 150-250 July 14, 1998 Sold for $280

999. **RV Monticello** vase, tan, two handles, 5.25"h, mint 150-250 July 13, 1998 Sold for $260

1000. RV Sunflower vase, two handles, 5"h, small flake 350-450   June 7, 1998   Sold for $400

1001. RV Jonquil vase, 8"h, mint   300-400   June 7, 1998   Sold for $425

1002. Weller Coppertone vase, frog with leaves, green, brown and black matt glaze, stamp mark, 7"h, mint 450-650   June 7, 1998   Sold for $750

1003. RV Wisteria vase, 8"h, partial paper label, mint 400-600   June 7, 1998   Sold for $475

1004. RV Luffa vase, 7.5"h, mint   300-400   June 7, 1998   Sold for $300

1005. RV Jonquil strawberry jar, four small openings surround large circular opening, 6.5"h, mint 450-650   June 7, 1998   Sold for $450

1006. RV Sunflower bowl, 7.5"w, mint   550-750 June 7, 1998   Sold for $650

1007. RV Rosecraft Hexagon bowls, two, orange designs, one with two handles, 7.5"w, flake on handle, other 4"h, mint   200-250   June 7, 1998   Sold for $425

1008. RV Laurel vase, mottled peach ground, 9"h, mint 350-550   June 7, 1998   Sold for $350

1009. RV Jonquil vase, 7.5"h, mint   300-400   June 7, 1998 Sold for $300

1010. RV Laurel bowl, tan ground, floral, 6.5"w, mint 100-150   June 7, 1998   Sold for $110

1011. RV Laurel vase, mottled orange ground, 8"h, mint 200-250   June 7, 1998   Sold for $210

1012. RV Jonquil vase, 7.5"h, mint   350-450   June 7, 1998 Sold for $375

1013. RV Jonquil bowl, 7"w, mint   150-250   June 7, 1998 Sold for $250

1014. Rozane Fujiyama vase, incised and painted floral decoration, stamped mark, 11"h, flake to top 1000-1500   July 11, 2000   Sold for $1500

1015. Rozane Woodland vase, painted and incised orchid, wafer mark, 7.5"h, glaze missing at lip   450-650 July 11, 2000   Sold for $350

1016. RV Rozane vase, yellow roses, RP Co. mark, 8.5"h, with a **RV Rozane** vase, yellow floral on a dark green to brown ground, RP Co. mark, 11"h, both with damaged top   150-250   July 13, 1993   Sold for $180

1017. RV Rozane vase, dark green to brown hi-glaze with an orange floral decoration, RP Co. mark, 4"h, mint   50-100   July 13, 1993   Sold for $90

1018. RV Rozane vase, light brown to green and red background with white and green floral decoration, impressed mark, 8"h, mint   200-300   July 13, 1993   Sold for $260

1019. RV Rozane pitcher, orange cherries and green leaves, artist's initials RP Co. mark, 12.5"h, mint   200-300   July 13, 1993   Sold for $250

1020. RV Rozane ewer, yellow and brown floral, unmarked, 8"h, mint   100-150   July 13, 1993   Sold for $170

1021. RV Rozane vase, yellow rose with green leaves on a green, orange to dark brown ground, signed Myers on side, impressed RP Co. mark, 18"h, mint   400-600   July 13, 1993   Sold for $700

1022. RV Rozane vase, orange floral decoration, RP Co. mark, 5"h, mint   100-150   July 13, 1993   Sold for $100

1023. RV Rozane pitcher, orange and yellow berry decoration, wafer mark, artist signed, 12.5"h, small chip   100-200   July 13, 1993   Sold for $140

1024. RV Rozane vase, orange flowers, RP Co. mark, 3"h; with a **RV Rozane** vase, blue berries and orange and green leaves, signed Adams, wafer mark, 9.5"h, both restored   150-250   July 13, 1993   Sold for $150

Not Pictured:

1025. RV Rozane tankard, brown hi-glaze and a dog in a green collar design, artist initialed, impressed mark, 14"h, heavy crazing   450-650   July 14, 1998   Sold for $450

1026. RV Rozane Royal vase, gray to cream ground with blueberries, peach and green leaves and stems running length of vase, artist M. Timberlake, 8"dia. x 18"h, mint   1500-2500   July 13, 1993   Sold for $1700

63

1027. **RV Tuscany** vase, two handles, gray, 5"h, mint 150-250 June 8, 1997 Sold for $90

1028. **RV Rosecraft Vintage** jardinere, 12"w x 9"h, mint 300-400 June 8, 1997 Sold for $550

1029. **RV Zephyr Lily** vase, green ground, 7"h, minute nick to one flower 100-200 June 8, 1997 Sold for $70

1030. **RV Silhouette** planter, blue and green ground, 11"w, mint 100-200 June 8, 1997 Sold for $90

1031. **RV Bleeding Heart** jardinere, blue ground, 11.5"w x 8"h, tight line at top 200-300 June 8, 1997 Sold for $230

1032. **RV Rosecraft Vintage** bowl, 3", mint 50-100 June 8, 1997 Sold for $100

1033. **RV Apple Blossom** window box, pink, 14.5"w, mint 200-300 June 8, 1997 Sold for $80

1034. **RV Rosecraft Vintage** jardinere, 10"w x 7"h, mint 200-300 June 8, 1997 Sold for $170

1035. **RV Florentine** vase, 6"h, mint 100-150 June 8, 1997 Sold for $100

1036. **RV Tuscany** vase, pierced for flowers, pink, 5"h, mint 100-150 June 8, 1997 Sold for $80

Not Pictured:

1037. **RV Monticello** vase, brown, green, white and black matt, no mark, 7"dia. x 5"h, mint 250-350 July 16, 1997 Sold for $350

1038. **RV Moss** planter with tray, green and pink, 5"h, line to tray, planter mint 250-350 July 15, 1997 Sold for $350

1039. **RV Jonquil** vase, 7"h, mint 250-350 June 8, 1997 Sold for $290

1040. **RV Jonquil** basket, 9"h, mint 400-600 June 8, 1997 Sold for $650

1041. **RV Sunflower** vase, 9"h, mint 1000-1500 June 8, 1997 Sold for $1100

Not Pictured:

1042. **RV Futura** vase, pink, 8"h, line to rim 350-450 July 15, 1997 Sold for $230

1043. **RV Bleeding Heart** jardinere, blue and green, 7"h, flake to handle 250-350 July 15, 1997 Sold for $230

1044. **RV Jonquil** strawberry jar, five openings, not marked, 7"h, mint 300-400 July 15, 1997 Sold for $230

1045. RV Sunflower vase, two handles, 5"h, mint 400-600 June 8, 1997 Sold for $500

1046. RV Jonquil vase, two handles, 5"h, mint 200-300 June 8, 1997 Sold for $160

1047. RV Freesia vase, 8.5"h, mint 150-250 June 8, 1997 Sold for $100

1048. RV Rozane 1917 vase, green ground, 8"h, mint 250-350 June 8, 1997 Sold for $210

1049. RV Snowberry vase, pink ground, 4"h, mint 100-200 June 8, 1997 Sold for $70

1050. RV Columbine vase, pink ground, two handles, 3"h, mint 100-200 June 8, 1997 Sold for $80

1051. RV Imperial basket, 8"h, mint 150-250 June 8, 1997 Sold for $150

1052. RV Columbine vase, brown ground, two handles, 3"h, mint 100-200 June 8, 1997 Sold for $100

1053. RV Iris vase, brown and yellow ground, 4", mint 150-250 June 8, 1997 Sold for $100

1054. RV Snowberry vase, two handles, pink ground, 7.5"h, mint 150-250 June 8, 1997 Sold for $110

1055. RV Fuschia bowl, blue and tan ground, two handles, 8.5"h, mint 100-150 June 8, 1997 Sold for $210

1056. RV Ivory vase, two handles, bruise to bottom rim, 5"h, mint 100-150 June 8, 1997 Sold for $60

1057. RV Sunflower vase, two handles, 5"h, mint 400-600 June 8, 1997 Sold for $550

Not Pictured:

1058. RV Ferella vase, pink and green matt, no mark, 4"h, filled hidden chip to base 200-300 July 16, 1997 Sold for $220

1059. RV Sunflower vase, 8", mint 900-1200 June 8, 1997 Sold for $1200

1060. RV Sunflower vase, two handles, paper label, 6", mint 600-800 June 8, 1997 Sold for $650

1061. RV Sunflower vase, 10", mint 1000-1500 June 8, 1997 Sold for $2000

Not Pictured:

1062. RV Baneda vase, green, not marked, 9.5"h, minute flake to bottom edge 250-350 July 15, 1997 Sold for $250

1063. RV Sunflower vase, brown, yellow and green, two handles, no mark, 6"h, mint 500-700 July 16, 1997 Sold for $500

1064. RV Pinecone basket, blue, 10"h, mint   300-400
June 8, 1997 Sold for $500

1065. RV Orian vase, blue, 7"h, mint   250-350
June 8, 1997 Sold for $160

1066. RV Fuschia vase, green, two handles, 6.5"h, mint
150-250   June 8, 1997 Sold for $150

1067. RV Freesia vase, blue, 5"h, mint   150-250
June 8, 1997 Sold for $100

1068. RV Futura candlestick, 4"h, paper label, mint
250-350   June 8, 1997 Sold for $375

1069. RV Water lily bowl, pink, 8"h, mint   150-250
June 8, 1997 Sold for $120

1070. RV Rosecraft Vintage jardinere, 7"h, tight line at top
100-200 June 8, 1997 Sold for $175

1071. RV Bleeding Heart vase, pink, 4"h, mint   150-250
June 8, 1997 Sold for $120

1072. RV Tourmaline vase, blue matt glaze, 4.5"h, mint
150-250 June 8, 1997 Sold for $100

1073. RV Dahlrose bowl, 10.5"h, mint   150-250
June 8, 1997 Sold for $250

1074. RV Ixia flower pot, 5"h, mint   150-250
June 8, 1997 Sold for $100

1075. RV White Rose basket, green, 8"h, mint   250-350
June 8, 1997 Sold for $180

Not Pictured:

1076. RV Pinecone vase, blue, two handles, 7"h, mint
200-300   July 15, 1997 Sold for $300

1077. RV Moss vase, blue ground, 9.5"h, mint   200-300
July 15, 1997 Sold for $290

1078. RV Bushberry vase, green, two handles, 12.5"h, mint
250-350   July 15, 1997 Sold for $650

1079. RV Pinecone pitcher, brown, #415-9"h, mint   300-400
July 15, 1997 Sold for $375

1080. RV Freesia lamps, pair, light and dark green, 13"h, both
mint   400-600 July 15, 1997 Sold for $1000

1081. RV Futura vase, green and blue geometric design, not
marked, 10"h, mint   700-900 July 16, 1997
Sold for $800

1082. RV Zephyr Lily vase, blue, #139-12"h, mint   600-800
July 15, 1997 Sold for $290

1083. RV Wisteria vase, bulbous form, paper
label, 8"w x 6"h, mint   700-900
July 15, 1997   Sold for $600

1084. RV Monticello vase, brown, orange band
with white and black design, handles, not
marked, 5"h, mint   200-300
July 15, 1997   Sold for $270

1085. RV Baneda vase, two handles, paper
label, 9"h, mint   600-800 July 15, 1997
Sold for $750

1086. RV Falline vase, two handles, not marked,
8"w x 6"h, mint   700-900 July 15, 1997
Sold for $600

1087. **RV Bleeding Heart** basket, pink ground, 12"h, mint 250-350 June 8, 1997 Sold for $400

1088. **RV Dahlrose** vase, two handles, 8"h, mint 250-350 June 8, 1997 Sold for $180

1089. **RV Zephyr Lily** vase, two handles, 7"h, mint 150-250 June 8, 1997 Sold for $80

1090. **RV Apple Blossom** vase, green, two handles, 10.5"h, mint 200-300 June 8, 1997 Sold for $175

1091. **RV Bushberry** bowl, green, 3"h, mint 100-150 June 8, 1997 Sold for $90

1092. **RV Pinecone** vase, blue, 8.5"h, mint 300-400 June 8, 1997 Sold for $700

1093. **RV Futura** hanging basket, brown, 5.5"d, mint 250-350 June 8, 1997 Sold for $300

1094. **RV Foxglove** shell, green, 6"h, mint 100-200 June 8, 1997 Sold for $200

1095. **RV Cosmos** ewer, blue, 10"h, mint 200-300 June 8, 1997 Sold for $300

1096. **RV Jonquil** hanging basket, 7"w, mint 300-400 June 8, 1997 Sold for $450

1097. **RV Magnolia** vase, green, 6"h, mint 100-200 June 8, 1997 Sold for $80

1098. **RV Iris** basket, brown, 10"h, mint 350-450 June 8, 1997 Sold for $325

Not Pictured:

1099. **RV Morning Glory** vase, two handles, green and blue ground, 4.5"h x 11"w, mint 300-400 July 15, 1997 Sold for $500

1100. **RV Futura** vase, two-handled form, red ground, 4"h x 6"w, mint 300-400 July 15, 1997 Sold for $300

1101. **RV Futura** vase, orange and yellow with green thistles, two handles, 15.5"h, chip to base, line to handle 350-550 July 16, 1997 Sold for $350

1102. **RV Carnelian** vase, green with brown drip, ink mark, 15"h, chip to top 250-350 July 16, 1997 Sold for $325

1103. **RV Pinecone** pedestal, green, 20.5"h, mint 400-600 July 16, 1997 Sold for $290

1104. **RV Magnolia** pitcher, orange, #1327, 9"h, mint 150-250 July 15, 1997 Sold for $220

1105. **RV Cherry Blossom** console bowl, brown and cream with white flowers, 10"l x 3"h, mint 300-400 June 8, 1997 Sold for $300

1106. **RV Luffa** vase, 7.5"h, mint 250-350 June 8, 1997 Sold for $220

1107. **RV Falline** vase, two handled form, paper label, 12"h, mint 900-1100 June 8, 1997 Sold for $1300

1108. **RV Jonquil** vase, two loop handles, unmarked, 5"h, mint 250-350 June 8, 1997 Sold for $180

1109. RV **Ming Tree** ewer, green, 10"h, mint   150-250
June 8, 1997 Sold for $100

1110. RV **Apple Blossom** basket, pink, 8.5"h, mint   250-350
June 8, 1997 Sold for $150

1111. RV **Dahlrose** vase, 8"h, mint   250-350   June 8, 1997
Sold for $200

1112. RV **Teasel** vase, 6"h, mint   150-250   June 8, 1997
Sold for $100

1113. RV **Snowberry** urn, pink, two handles, 6.5"h, mint
150-250   June 8, 1997 Sold for $110

1114. RV **Jonquil** bowl with frog, 10.5"w, mint 300-400
June 8, 1997 Sold for $550

1115. RV **Dahlrose** vase, 6"h, mint   200-300   June 8, 1997
Sold for $130

1116. RV **Russco** urn, green, 6"h, mint   250-350
June 8, 1997 Sold for $110

1117. RV **Blackberry** vase, two handles, 6"h, chip to handle
250-350   June 8, 1997 Sold for $260

1118. RV **Futura** bowl, 8"d, mint   350-550   June 8, 1997
Sold for $400

1119. RV **Magnolia** basket, brown, 8"h, mint   250-350
June 8, 1997 Sold for $150

1120. RV **Dahlrose** bud vase, 8"h, mint   200-300
June 8, 1997 Sold for $110

Not Pictured:

1121. RV **Pinecone** ashtray, blue, 2.5"h, mint   100-150
July 15, 1997 Sold for $220

1122. RV **Thornapple** flower frog, blue, marked, 5"h, mint
100-150   July 15, 1997 Sold for $240

1123. RV **Teasel** vase, ivory and peach marked, 15"h, minute
flakes to base   350-450   July 15, 1997 Sold for $270

1124. RV **Peony** mugs, six, green, #2-3.5"h, all mint
300-400   July 15, 1997 Sold for $210

1125. RV **Bushberry** vase, blue, 10"h, mint   150-250
July 16, 1997 Sold for $325

1126. RV **Peony** basket, pink, yellow and green, 12"h, mint
150-250   July 16, 1997 Sold for $300

1127. RV **Laurel** vase, yellow, 6"h, mint   250-350
July 16, 1997 Sold for $400

1128. RV **Jonquil** vase, two handles, paper label, 12"h, mint   1500-1700 June 8, 1997 Sold for $850

1129. RV **Jonquil** vase, two handles, not marked, 6"w x 3"h, mint   250-350 June 8, 1997 Sold for $130

1130. RV **Dogwood** vase, green with white floral decoration, stamp mark, 6"h, mint   300-500 June 8, 1997 Sold for $200

1131. RV **Baneda** vase, two handles, not marked, 7"h, mint 500-700   June 8, 1997 Sold for $450

1132. RV Mock Orange basket, green ground, 10.5"h, mint 250-350 June 8, 1997 Sold for $260

1133. RV Foxglove vase, green and pink ground, 6"h, mint 150-250 June 8, 1997 Sold for $110

1134. RV Jonquil vase, two handles, 7.5", mint 250-350 June 8, 1997 Sold for $325

1135. RV Futura vase, two handles, blue ground, 7"h, tight hairline 350-450 June 8, 1997 Sold for $550

1136. RV Juvenile cup, rabbit design, 3"h, mint 150-250 June 8, 1997 Sold for $350

1137. RV Sunflower hanging basket, 7.5"w x 4.5"d, mint 800-1100 June 8, 1997 Sold for $1000

1138. RV Primrose vase, pink ground, two handles, 7.5"h, mint 150-250 June 8, 1997 Sold for $130

1139. RV Silhouette planter, white ground, 11", mint 100-200 June 8, 1997 Sold for $100

1140. RV Blackberry bowl, 8"w x 3"h, tight minor line at top 250-350 June 8, 1997 Sold for $200

1141. RV Dahlrose vase, two handles, 8"h, harmless unchipped chip under vase 150-250 June 8, 1997 Sold for $140

1142. RV Snowberry candlesticks, blue ground, 5"h, mint 150-250 June 8, 1997 Sold for $130

1143. RV Foxglove basket, pink and green ground, 12"h, mint 250-350 June 8, 1997 Sold for $500

Not Pictured:

1144. RV Jonquil vase, bulbous form, not marked, 5.5"h, mint 250-350 July 15, 1997 Sold for $280

1145. RV Cherry Blossom vase, orange and cream, not marked, 7.5"h, mint 250-350 July 15, 1997 Sold for $375

1146. RV Futura vase, green with blue, pink and yellow balloon design around top, four open buttresses, 8.5"h, mint 800-1100 June 8, 1997 Sold for $1100

1147. RV Moss flower frog, blue, 4"h, mint 100-150 July 15, 1997 Sold for $350

1148. RV Sunflower vase, two handles, 6"h, mint 500-700 June 8, 1997 Sold for $425

1149. RV Sunflower vase, 6"h x 7"w, mint 700-900 June 8, 1997 Sold for $650

1150. RV Sunflower vase, two handles, 8"h, mint 900-1200 June 8, 1997 Sold for $1100

Not Pictured:

1151. RV Sunflower vase, yellow, brown, green and blue, no mark, 5"h, mint 400-600 July 16, 1997 Sold for $400

1152. RV Sunflower vase, low form, two handles, 4"h x 8"w, mint 650-850 July 15, 1997 Sold for $500

1153. RV Sunflower vase, not marked, 4"h, mint 350-450 July 15, 1997 Sold for $375

1154. RV White Rose vase, pink and green ground, two handles, 8"h, mint 200-300   June 8, 1997 Sold for $200

1155. RV Cremona vase, green ground, 8"h, mint 200-300 June 8, 1997 Sold for $180

1156. RV Futura jardinere, two handles, orange and green ground, 9"w x 6"h, mint 350-550   June 8, 1997 Sold for $210

1157. RV Bushberry vase, orange and green ground, 6.5"h, mint 100-150   June 8, 1997 Sold for $100

1158. RV Pinecone pitcher, green, 10.5"h, mint 350-550 June 8, 1997 Sold for $400

1159. RV Jonquil vase, two handles, 8"h, mint 300-400 June 8, 1997 Sold for $400

1160. RV Baneda vase, green, two handles, 5"h, mint 350-550   June 8, 1997 Sold for $400

1161. RV Zephyr Lily vase, blue, two handles, 10.5"h, mint 150-250   June 8, 1997 Sold for $150

1162. RV Cremona vase, pink ground, 5"h, mint 100-150 June 8, 1997 Sold for $60

1163. RV Sunflower console bowl, two handles, 13"w x 3.5"h, mint 750-950   June 8, 1997 Sold for $900

1164. RV Gardenia ewer, green, 11"h, mint 150-250 June 8, 1997 Sold for $130

1165. RV Moss vase, pink and green ground, 7.5"h, mint 200-250   June 8, 1997 Sold for $260

1166. RV Sunflower vase, blue, green and yellow, 4"h, mint 400-600   July 16, 1997 Sold for $375

1167. RV Wisteria vase, blue, green and purple, 10"h, mint 900-1200   July 16, 1997 Sold for $1300

1168. RV Jonquil vase, brown and green, 8"h, mint 300-400   July 16, 1997   Sold for $350

1169. RV Dutch candleholder, scene of Dutch boy and girl, not marked, 7"h, line in the making   150-250
June 8, 1997   Sold for $350

1170. RV Burmese candlesticks, pair, green with gold highlights, marked, 8"h, mint   300-500   June 8, 1997
Sold for $200

1171. RV Russco vase, white matt glaze, line design, silver label, 6.5"h, mint   150-250   June 8, 1997
Sold for $100

1172. RV Persian bowl, yellow and pink floral design with green leaves on cream ground, 6.5"dia. x 3"h, tiny flake and hairline   100-200   June 8, 1997   Sold for $90

1173. RV Futura vase, four arms joining top to base in brown and blue top on a green base, not marked, 5"square top x 4.25"h, mint   300-400   June 8, 1997   Sold for $400

1174. RV Tuscany bowl with two candlesticks, pink and green, all not marked, bowl 11"l, sticks 4"h, all mint   300-400   June 8, 1997   Sold for $160

1175. RV Silhouette vase, nude in panel, orange and brown, marked, 10"h, repaired chip   200-300   June 8, 1997
Sold for $240

1176. RV Blackberry vase, good color and mold, not marked, 7"dia. x 3"h, mint   300-400   June 8, 1997
Sold for $325

1177. RV Morning Glory vase, white with purple and yellow flowers, not marked, 4.5"h, mint   350-450
June 8, 1997   Sold for $350

1178. RV Victorian vase, purple/gray with banded decoration, not marked, 7.5"h, mint   350-450   June 8, 1997
Sold for $375

1179. RV Russco vase, green and yellow crystalline glaze, not marked, 8"h, mint   350-550
June 8, 1997   Sold for $140

1180. RV Carnelian vase, two curved handles at top, pink and yellow glaze with green and purple drip, not marked, 7"h, mint   250-350
June 8, 1997   Sold for $350

1181. RV Russco vase, flaring top and two handles at base, orange and gold crystalline glaze, paper label, 8"h, mint   300-400   June 8, 1997
Sold for $130

1182. RV Russco vase, pillow vase with two pointed handles in orange and gold with gray highlights inside, 7"w x 7"h, mint   250-350
June 8, 1997   Sold for $130

71

1183. **RV Poppy** vase, pink and yellow ground, two handles, 4"h, mint 100-200 June 8, 1997 Sold for $90

1184. **RV White Rose** basket, pink and green ground, 10"h, mint 250-350 June 8, 1997 Sold for $220

1185. **RV Laurel** vase, yellow, 9.5"h, mint 250-350 June 8, 1997 Sold for $290

1186. **RV Futura** vase, four feet, salmon, blue and green ground, 7.5"h, mint 450-650 June 8, 1997 Sold for $500

1187. **RV Magnolia** vase, two handles, green and brown ground, 8"h, mint 200-300 June 8, 1997 Sold for $160

1188. **RV Baneda** hexagon bowl, two handles, 14"w, mint 600-800 June 8, 1997 Sold for $475

1189. **RV Ixia** vase, yellow and brown ground, 7.5"h, mint 150-250 June 8, 1997 Sold for $110

1190. **RV Jonquil** vase, two handles, 6.5"h, mint 250-350 June 8, 1997 Sold for $230

1191. **RV Fuschia** vase, yellow and brown ground, two handles, original label, 6.5"h, mint 150-250 June 8, 1997 Sold for $160

1192. **RV Fuschia** vase, green and brown ground, 7"h, mint 150-250 June 8, 1997 Sold for $150

1193. **RV White Rose** basket, blue ground, 10.5"h, mint 250-350 June 8, 1997 Sold for $260

1194. **RV Sunflower** vase, two handles, 4"h, mint 400-600 June 8, 1997 Sold for $350

1195. **RV Cremona** vase, pink and yellow matt glaze, swirled green and yellow leaf and berry decoration, paper label, 10"h, mint 300-400 June 8, 1997 Sold for $200

1196. **RV Moderne** bowl, pink/white and brown matt, impressed mark, 11"l x 4"h, mint 200-400 June 8, 1997 Sold for $140

1197. **RV Wisteria** vase, two handles, paper label, 9"h, mint 700-900 June 8, 1997 Sold for $1200

1198. **RV Luffa** vase, two small handles, 6"h, mint 300-500 June 8, 1997 Sold for $260

1199. RV Fuschia vase, blue, 8", mint   150-250
June 8, 1997 Sold for $325

1200. RV Pinecone vase, green, 7", mint   200-250
June 8, 1997 Sold for $120

1201. RV Wisteria vase, blue, 8", mint   300-400
June 8, 1997 Sold for $700

1202. RV Fuschia bowl, green, 3", mint   100-150
June 8, 1997 Sold for $130

1203. RV Pinecone basket, brown, 10", mint   300-400
June 8, 1997 Sold for $500

1204. RV Sunflower vase, 6" x 8.5", mint   800-1100
June 8, 1997 Sold for $950

1205. RV Dogwood II vase, 10", mint   250-350
June 8, 1997 Sold for $600

1206. RV Iris vase, blue, 7.5", mint   100-200   June 8, 1997
Sold for $100

1207. RV Columbine basket, 8", mint   200-300
June 8, 1997 Sold for $210

1208. RV Bleeding Heart bowl, pink, 3", mint   100-200
June 8, 1997 Sold for $100

1209. RV Jonquil vase, 4", mint   150-250   June 8, 1997
Sold for $130

1210. RV Foxglove vase, green and pink, 8", mint   150-250
June 8, 1997 Sold for $140

1211. RV Pinecone vase, green, 6.5", mint   150-250
June 8, 1997 Sold for $110

1212. RV Dogwood vase, white and green
dogwood decoration, stamp mark,
6.75"h, mint   300-500   June 8, 1997
Sold for $300

1213. RV Dogwood vase, white and green
dogwood decoration, stamp mark,
12.25"h, mint   600-800   June 8, 1997
Sold for $700

1214. RV Jonquil vase, two handles, not
marked, 5.5"h, mint   250-350
June 8, 1997 Sold for $210

73

1215. RV Apple Blossom vase, pink, branch handles, 6"h, mint 150-200 June 8, 1997 Sold for $120

1216. RV Clematis bookends, pair, blue, raised mark, 5"w x 5"h, tiny flakes on each 150-250 June 8, 1997 Sold for $110

1217. RV Apple Blossom hanging basket, blue, 7.5"dia. x 5", mint 200-300 June 8, 1997 Sold for $250

1218. RV Carnelian II vase, handles, pink and green drip glaze over blue, 7"w x 5"h, mint 150-250 June 8, 1997 Sold for $150

1219. RV Freesia jardinere, blue, raised mark, tiny flake 250-350 June 8, 1997 Sold for $300

1220. RV Futura vase, star shape on round base, pink and green hi-glaze, not marked, 8"h, one glaze miss, mint 450-550 June 8, 1997 Sold for $450

1221. RV Ixia candleholders, green matt with yellow and pink flowers, marked, 2"h, mint 100-150 June 8, 1997 Sold for $90

1222. RV Teasel vase, light blue, 8"h, mint 200-300 June 8, 1997 Sold for $150

1223. RV Rosecraft Hexagon vase, green matt with cream design in alternating panels, stamp mark, 4.25"h, mint 250-350 June 8, 1997 Sold for $450

1224. RV Juvenile saucer, cream with yellow rabbits over green band, not marked, 5.25"dia., minute chips around edge 100-200 June 8, 1997 Sold for $50

1225. RV Wincraft bookends, green, 6.5"h, minute chip on bottom 150-250 June 8, 1997 Sold for $70

1226. RV Water lily conch shell, orange to brown, 6"h, mint 100-200 June 8, 1997 Sold for $80

Not Pictured:

1227. RV Rozane vase, standard glaze with sterling overlay, orange and yellow blossom with green leaves on caramel and dark brown ground, no mark, 5"h, minute flakes 900-1200 July 16, 1997 Sold for $400

1228. RV Futura vase, orange with purple mottling, blue and yellow flowers at top and green leaves on square base, 5"h, mint 350-450 June 8, 1997 Sold for $350

1229. RV Futura vase, green and pink molded floral design on flattened flaring form with two open buttresses, pink to deep rose ground, 6"w x 4"h, mint 450-650 June 8, 1997 Sold for $280

1230. RV Futura vase, brown cylindrical body under yellow flaring neck with four buttresses, 10"h, repaired chip to base 600-800 June 8, 1997 Sold for $375

Not Pictured:

1231. RV Foxglove pedestal bowl, blue, two handles, marked, 11"dia. x 4"h, mint 150-250 June 8, 1997 Sold for $300

1232. RV Magnolia bowl, green, marked, 3"h, unchipped chip to base   50-100   June 8, 1997   Sold for $30

1233. RV White Rose vase, two handles, green to blue, marked, 4"h, mint   50-100   June 8, 1997 Sold for $60

1234. RV Apple Blossom low bowl, green with branch handles, marked, 16"l x 2.5"h, chip to one handle   100-150   June 8, 1997   Sold for $60

1235. RV White Rose vase, pink to green, marked, 6"h, mint   100-150   June 8, 1997   Sold for $60

1236. RV Apple Blossom wallpocket, green with branch handle, marked, 8.5", mint   100-200   June 8, 1997 Sold for $170

1237. RV Clematis vase, orange to brown, marked, 7.5"h, mint   100-200   June 8, 1997   Sold for $80

1238. RV Florentine jardinere, brown, 7.5"dia. x 6.5"h, chip to top   100-150   June 8, 1997   Sold for $110

1239. RV Freesia vase, two handles, green, marked, 7.5"h, mint   100-200   June 8, 1997   Sold for $150

1240. RV Florentine vase, brown, two handles, stamp mark, 8"h, chip to base, hairline   100-150   June 8, 1997 Sold for $60

1241. RV Corinthian wallpocket, green and cream, not marked, 12.5"l, mint   100-200   June 8, 1997 Sold for $230

1242. RV Magnolia vase, orange to brown, marked, 6"h, mint   100-150   June 8, 1997   Sold for $80

1243. RV Freesia console bowl, blue, marked, 13.5"l x 3.5"h, chip to top edge   100-150   June 8, 1997   Sold for $40

1244. RV White Rose vase, orange to green, marked, 6"h, mint   100-150   June 8, 1997   Sold for $90

1245. RV Bittersweet vase, green, marked, 3.5"h, mint 50-100   June 8, 1997   Sold for $50

1246. RV Pinecone planter, brown, marked, 3.5"h, chip to top edge   100-150   June 8, 1997   Sold for $60

1247. RV Futura vase, blue, green and yellow molded floral design on tan and brown ground, two open handles, 6"h, mint   450-650   June 8, 1997   Sold for $400

1248. RV Futura bowl, green geometric designs with pink, blue, green and yellow balloons, 9"w x 3.5"h, mint 500-700   June 8, 1997   Sold for $350

1249. RV Futura vase, blue, yellow and green molded floral design on brown and tan ground, 10"h, two minute flakes on handles   600-800   June 8, 1997 Sold for $800

Not Pictured:

1250. RV Bittersweet jardinere, green with orange berries, green leaves, marked, 7"dia. x 6"h, mint   150-250 June 8, 1997   Sold for $350

75

1251. RV Zephyr Lily vase, orange to green, marked, 16"h, mint   300-400   June 8, 1997 Sold for $260

1252. RV Snowberry planter with underplate, blue, marked, 5.5"h, heavy water deposit to bottom and plate   150-250   June 8, 1997 Sold for $130

1253. RV Snowberry bud vase, pink, marked, 7.5"h, water deposit   50-100   June 8, 1997 Sold for $50

1254. RV Apple Blossom bowl, pink, marked, 11"l x 4.75"h, mint   100-200   June 8, 1997 Sold for $70

1255. RV Foxglove vase, blue, marked, 3"h, water deposit ring   50-100   June 8, 1997 Sold for $120

1256. RV Bushberry vase, orange to brown, marked, 4.25"h, mint   100-150   June 8, 1997 Sold for $60

1257. RV Gardenia console bowl, gray to lavender, marked, 15.5"l x 2.5"h, minor glaze flake to top edge   150-250   June 8, 1997 Sold for $90

1258. RV Pinecone bowl, blue, marked, 7.5"dia. x 2.5"h, unchipped chip to bottom and heavy water deposit   100-200   June 8, 1997 Sold for $70

1259. RV Columbine vase, pink to green, marked, 3.5"h, minute chip to top   50-100   June 8, 1997 Sold for $30

1260. RV Snowberry vase, pedestal form, blue, marked, 8.5"h, glaze flakes to top edge   50-100   June 8, 1997 Sold for $60

1261. RV Clematis vase, green with pink flowers, marked, 4"h, mint   50-100   June 8, 1997 Sold for $50

1262. RV Zephyr Lily basket, green, marked, 8.5"h, mint   100-200   June 8, 1997 Sold for $100

1263. RV Foxglove vase, pink, marked, 3"h, mint   50-100   June 8, 1997 Sold for $70

1264. RV Thornapple bud vase, orange to brown, marked, 7.5"h, mint   100-150   June 8, 1997 Sold for $240

1265. RV Zephyr Lily vase, green, marked, 16"h, mint   300-400   June 8, 1997 Sold for $375

1266. RV Water lily planter, blue to green, marked, 5"h, heavy water deposit around bottom   100-150   June 8, 1997 Sold for $30

1267. RV Futura vase, incised decoration of pink crocuses with green and blue highlights on blue to tan ground, four buttresses at base, 9"h, mint   900-1200   June 8, 1997 Sold for $1000

1268. RV Futura vase, blue and green leaves on a light blue ground on a trapezoidal base of blue, 7"h, mint   800-1100   June 8, 1997 Sold for $850

1269. RV Futura vase, bulbous base with tiered, flaring neck covered in a mottled blue and gunmetal glaze, 10"h, minute flake to top rim and repaired chip, tight hairline   500-700   June 8, 1997 Sold for $650

1270. RV Cosmos vase, green to brown, marked, 12.5"h, mint 200-300   June 8, 1997   Sold for $275

1271. RV Snowberry vase, blue, marked, 6"dia. x 5"h, mint 100-150   June 8, 1997   Sold for $100

1272. RV Topeo bowl, green to lavender, paper label, 13"l x 4"h, mint 200-300   June 8, 1997   Sold for $100

1273. RV Rozane basket, yellow with multicolored flowers, marked, 6.5"w x 6"h, line to bottom   100-150   June 8, 1997   Sold for $60

1274. RV Moderne compote, white to brown, marked, 6"dia. x 6.5"h, mint 150-250   June 8, 1997   Sold for $160

1275. RV Velmoss vase, blue, paper label, 6.25"h, mint 100-200   June 8, 1997   Sold for $150

1276. RV Zephyr Lily wallpocket, green, 8.5"l, tiny chip to back   100-150   June 8, 1997   Sold for $80

1277. RV Water lily cookie jar, blue to green, marked, 10.5"h, mint 250-350   June 8, 1997   Sold for $400

1278. RV Dahlrose vase, not marked, 8.5"h, glaze bubbles, mint 250-350   June 8, 1997   Sold for $130

1279. RV Zephyr Lily wallpocket, green, marked, 8.5"l, mint 100-200   June 8, 1997   Sold for $160

1280. RV Iris vase, green to blue, marked, 7.5"dia. x 6"h, mint 100-200   June 8, 1997   Sold for $240

1281. RV Pinecone footed basket, blue, marked, 6.5"w x 6"h, mint 200-300   June 8, 1997   Sold for $700

1282. RV Cosmos vase, blue, marked, 9.5"h, mint 100-200   June 8, 1997   Sold for $130

1283. RV Bushberry vase, orange to brown, branch handles, marked, 10.5"h, mint 150-250   June 8, 1997   Sold for $ 180

1284. RV Futura vase, blue and green flaring four-sided form with buttresses below molded green floral design, 4"h, mint 450-650   June 8, 1997   Sold for $400

1285. RV Futura vase, narrow pocket form with molded blue floral design on yellow and tan ground, 6"h, mint 400-600   June 8, 1997   Sold for $400

1286. RV Futura vase, flaring four-sided form with round base and green geometric design on a blue ground, 10"h, mint 900-1200   June 8, 1997   Sold for $1200

77

1287. RV Clematis basket, brown, 7"h, mint 100-200
July 15, 1997 Sold for $100

1288. RV Gardenia hanging basket, white and green, 6"h, mint 250-350 July 15, 1997 Sold for $190

1289. RV Bittersweet basket, pink, 10"w, mint 100-200
July 15, 1997 Sold for $150

1290. RV White Rose vase, blue, 3"h, mint 50-100
July 15, 1997 Sold for $50

1291. RV Freesia basket, green, 10"h, mint 150-250
July 15, 1997 Sold for $160

1292. RV Foxglove bowl, blue, 4"h, mint 70-120
July 15, 1997 Sold for $170

1293. RV Freesia basket, green, 8"h, mint 150-250
July 15, 1997 Sold for $140

1294. RV Foxglove vase, pink, 3"h, mint 50-100
July 15, 1997 Sold for $70

1295. RV Clematis hanging basket, blue, 5"h, mint 150-250
July 15, 1997 Sold for $130

1296. RV Fuschia vase, pink, partial silver label, 6"h, mint 100-200 July 15, 1997 Sold for $170

Not Pictured:

1297. RV Freesia covered jar, blue, 8"h, mint 250-350
July 15, 1997 Sold for $450

1298. RV Bushberry pitcher, orange, 9"h, mint 250-350
July 15, 1997 Sold for $500

1299. RV Laurel vase, green, orange, brown and pink, no mark, 6"h, mint 150-250 July 16, 1997 Sold for $270

1300. RV Cherry Blossom vase, blue, green, light and dark pink, no mark, 5"h, mint 250-350 July 16, 1997 Sold for $325

1301. RV Futura vase, narrow form with geometric design in dark blue against lighter blue ground, 6.5"w x 5"h, bruise to top 250-350 June 8, 1997 Sold for $200

1302. RV Futura jardinere, pink molded leaves with purple geometric design on a green ground, 9"w x 6"h, flake at base 400-600 June 8, 1997 Sold for $200

1303. RV Futura vase, flaring form with two open handles above round green two-tiered base, green geometric designs at top, orange ground, 12.5"h, mint 900-1200 June 8, 1997 Sold for $1200

1304. RV Magnolia double bud vase, green, 4.5"h, mint 75-120   July 15, 1997   Sold for $70

1305. RV Freesia basket, green, white and purple, 8"h, mint 150-250   July 15, 1997   Sold for $150

1306. RV Gardenia vase, white, brown and green, 3.5"h, mint 70-120   July 15, 1997   Sold for $60

1307. RV Apple Blossom planter, blue, 8"w, mint 100-200 July 15, 1997   Sold for $100

1308. RV Apple Blossom vase, pink, 10"h, mint 100-200 July 15, 1997   Sold for $150

1309. RV Water lily floor vase, orange, brown and yellow, 14"h, mint 300-400   July 15, 1997   Sold for $300

1310. RV Juvenile bowl, rabbits, ink mark, 8"dia., some wear, otherwise mint 150-250   July 15, 1997   Sold for $80

1311. RV Apple Blossom vase, pink and white, 10"h, mint 100-200   July 15, 1997   Sold for $180

1312. RV Fuschia vase, blue, 3"h, mint 150-250 July 15, 1997   Sold for $130

1313. RV Freesia basket, brown, 8"h, mint 150-250 July 15, 1997   Sold for $100

1314. RV Clematis double bud vase, orange, 5"h, mint 70-120   July 15, 1997   Sold for $70

Not Pictured:

1315. RV Matt Green bud vases, pair, double vases, 8"w x 4.5"h, bruise to one 200-300   July 15, 1997 Sold for $280

1316. RV Clematis jardinere and pedestal, orange and yellow, jardinere 8", all 24.5"h, both mint 700-900 July 15, 1997   Sold for $550

1317. RV Silhouette vase, orange, two handles, nude, 6"h x 9"dia., chip to handle 150-250   July 15, 1997 Sold for $350

1318. RV Victorian Art vase, brown matt glaze, not marked, 10"h, repaired chips 150-250   July 15, 1997 Sold for $220

1319. RV Futura vase, Pink Twist, six-sided with blue and green geometric design on a pink and rose ground design, 8"h, mint 450-650   June 8, 1997   Sold for $600

1320. RV Futura bowl, Aztec, trapezoidal form with geometric design, green and orange with brown base, 8"w x 4"h, mint 500-700   June 8, 1997 Sold for $550

1321. RV Futura vase, Football Urn, flaring shoulder below two handles, green, brown and orange, 9"h, mint 900-1200 June 8, 1997   Sold for $950

1322. RV Cosmos vase, blue, #649-4"h, mint 70-120
July 15, 1997 Sold for $140

1323. RV Water lily vase, brown and yellow, #74-7"h, mint
100-200 July 15, 1997 Sold for $120

1324. RV Water lily ewer, blue and white, #10-6"h, mint
150-250 July 15, 1997 Sold for $90

1325. RV Gardenia vase, brown and tan, #687-12"h, mint
300-400 July 15, 1997 Sold for $180

1326. RV Pinecone console bowl, blue, #323-15"w, mint
250-350 July 15, 1997 Sold for $400

1327. RV Peony jardinere, pink and yellow, #661-6"h, mint
150-250 July 15, 1997 Sold for $150

1328. RV Pinecone vase, green, 12.5"h, mint 300-400
July 15, 1997 Sold for $350

1329. RV Bittersweet vase, pink and gray, #812-5"h, mint
70-120 July 15, 1997 Sold for $60

1330. RV Pinecone pitcher, brown, #415, 9"h, mint
300-400 July 15, 1997 Sold for $400

1331. RV Water lily vase, pink and green, #174-6"h, mint
70-120 July 15, 1997 Sold for $130

1332. RV Clematis vase, blue and white, #106-7"h, mint
100-150 July 15, 1997 Sold for $70

1333. RV Iris vase, blue, #367-4"h, mint 100-200
July 15, 1997 Sold for $120

1334. RV Pinecone floor vase, brown, #807-15"h, chip to base
400-500 July 15, 1997 Sold for $500

1335. RV Bushberry hanging basket, orange, 5"h, mint
250-350 July 15, 1997 Sold for $170

1336. RV Pinecone bowl, blue, #429-10"w, mint 150-250
July 15, 1997 Sold for $300

1337. RV Magnolia basket, blue, #384, 8"h, mint 150-250
July 15, 1997 Sold for $120

1338. RV White Rose hanging basket, orange and green,
4.5"h, mint 150-250 July 15, 1997 Sold for $200

1339. RV Peony floor vase, green and white, #68-14"h, chip
to base 100-150 July 15, 1997 Sold for $130

1340. RV Zephyr Lily bowl, brown and green, #470-5"h,
mint 100-150 July 15, 1997 Sold for $110

1341. RV Pinecone double vase, green, #473-8"h, mint
150-250 July 15, 1997 Returned

1342. **RV Snowberry** teapot, pink, 7"h, chip to spout; with a **RV Snowberry** creamer and sugar, pink, creamer #1-C, 3.5"h, sugar #1-S, 3"h, both mint   250-500
July 15, 1997 Sold for $250

1343. **RV Foxglove** floor vase, pink, #55-16"h, chip to handle   300-400   July 15, 1997 Sold for $375

1344. **RV Dahlrose** vase, brown and green, 6"h, mint   100-200   July 15, 1997 Sold for $120

1345. **RV Poppy** wallpocket, pink, #1281, 8.5"h, mint   200-300   July 15, 1997 Sold for $750

1346. **RV Carnelian II** vase, pink, ink mark, 8"h, chip and line to base   200-300   July 15, 1997 Sold for $190

1347. **RV Gardenia** vase, green and white, #681-6"h, mint   100-150   July 15, 1997 Sold for $70

1348. **RV Zephyr Lily** vase, brown and yellow, 15"h, chip to base   300-400   July 15, 1997 Sold for $ 300

1349. **RV Peony** creamer and sugar, pink, #3-C, sugar #3-S, 6"w, both mint; with a **RV Peony** teapot, pink, #3, 8"h, mint   200-350   July 15, 1997 Sold for $400

1350. **RV Jonquil** vase, two handled form, excellent color and mold, 8"h, mint   350-450   July 16, 1997 Sold for $500

1351. **RV Foxglove** vase, green, 3"h, mint   50-100
July 16, 1997 Sold for $70

1352. **RV Luffa** jardinere, two handles, 11"dia. x 8"h, mint   600-800   July 16, 1997 Sold for $375

1353. **RV Moss** vase, two handles, 14.5"h, chips to back   400-600   July 16, 1997 Sold for $400

1354. **RV Bushberry** bowl, green, 4"h, mint   70-120
July 16, 1997 Sold for $100

1355. **RV Blackberry** jardinere, two handles at top, 11"w x 8"h, mint   800-1100   July 16, 1997 Sold for $750

1356. **RV Fuschia** vase, brown and yellow, 3.5"h, mint   50-100   July 16, 1997 Sold for $80

1357. **RV Baneda** vase, green, two handles, 8"h, mint   450-650   July 16, 1997 Sold for $700

Not Pictured:

1358. **RV Fuschia** wallpocket, blue, #282-8"h, mint   150-250   July 15, 1997 Sold for $800

1359. **RV Rosecraft Panel** vase, green, stamp mark, 6"h, mint 150-250 July 15, 1997 Sold for $200

1360. **RV White Rose** vase, blue to green, marked, 4"h, hairline to top and water deposits around bottom 50-100 July 15, 1997 Sold for $30

1361. **RV Peony** vase, green, marked, 7.5"h, mint 100-200 July 15, 1997 Sold for $80

1362. **RV Zephyr Lily** vase, green, marked, 7.5"h, mint 100-200 July 15, 1997 Sold for $130

1363. **RV Foxglove** vase, pink, marked, 6"h, mint 100-150 July 15, 1997 Sold for $120

1364. **RV Gardenia** vase, gray to lavender, marked, 6"h, mint 100-150 July 15, 1997 Sold for $100

1365. **RV Water lily** bowl, pink to green, marked, 7"l x 3"h, mint 100-150 July 15, 1997 Sold for $60

1366. **RV Clematis** bowl, green, marked, 6.5"dia. x 3"h, mint 100-150 July 15, 1997 Sold for $60

1367. **RV Silhouette** wallpocket, green, marked, 8"l, mint 200-300 July 15, 1997 Sold for $140

1368. **RV Gardenia** vase, green, marked, 6.5"h, minute chip to bottom edge 70-120 July 15, 1997 Sold for $40

1369. **RV Clematis** vase, orange to brown, marked, 6"h, mint 100-150 July 15, 1997 Sold for $60

1370. **RV Snowberry** basket, blue, marked, 7"h, mint 150-250 July 15, 1997 Sold for $130

1371. **RV Snowberry** vase, blue, marked, 6.5"h, mint 100-150 July 15, 1997 Sold for $90

1372. **RV Cosmos** vase, green to brown, marked, 5.5"dia. x 6"h, chip to top edge   50-100 July 15, 1997 Sold for $150

1373. **RV Futura** vase, yellow tulip on green stems with green leaves against a mottled tan and blue ground, two long open buttresses, 12.75"h, repaired chips 800-1100 July 15, 1997 Sold for $700

1374. **RV Futura** vase, green and blue floral against a blue and tan ground, flaring top over two open buttresses, 7"h, mint 800-1100 July 15, 1997 Sold for $950

1375. **RV Futura** vase, green thistles on an orange to tan ground, two long open buttresses, 15.5"h, mint 1200-1700 July 15, 1997 Sold for $1100

1376. **RV Dogwood II** vase, open work at top, white and black floral on green ground, 14"h, mint   300-500
Withdrawn

1377. **RV Windsor** vase, blue with green leaf decoration, 5.25"h, mint   150-200   June 8, 1997   Sold for $350

1378. **RV Bittersweet** double bud vase, signed, 6"h, mint 100-200   June 8, 1997   Sold for $140

1379. **RV Teasel** vase, caramel and cream, 6"h, mint   100-200 June 8, 1997   Sold for $130

1380. **RV Wincraft** vase, pinecone design in brown, hi-glaze, marked, 6"h, mint   150-250   June 8, 1997   Sold for $80

1381. **RV Moderne** console bowl, aqua with gold highlights on Deco design, impressed marks, 10"l x 3"h, mint 250-350   June 8, 1997   Sold for $90

1382. **RV Foxglove** basket, green, signed, 9"h, mint   250-350 June 8, 1997   Sold for $160

1383. **RV Pinecone** vase, green with pinecone and twig handle, impressed marks, 4"h, mint   150-250 June 8, 1997   Sold for $110

1384. **RV Laurel** vase, broad form with two closed handles in yellow and black, incised 9, 8"h, mint   200-300 June 8, 1997   Sold for $300

1385. **RV Pinecone** bowl, oval form in green and ivory, impressed mark, 9"h, mint   200-250   June 8, 1997 Sold for $250

1386. **RV Dahlrose** vase, brown, green and ivory, two handles, 8"h, mint   150-200   June 8, 1997 Sold for $270

1387. **RV Futura** vase, seagulls in a light green against a gray to orange ground with green blades of grass, tapering, cylindrical form, 10"h, mint   1200-1700 July 15, 1997   Sold for $1200

1388. **RV Futura** vase, flaring form with tiered neck in green over peach, 10"h, mint   1000-1500 July 15, 1997   Sold for $1300

1389. **RV Futura** vase, ribbed form with flaring base covered in a emerald green hi-glaze, 9"h, mint 1700-2200   July 15, 1997   Sold for $1800

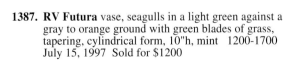

83

1390. **RV Futura** vase, geometric design in pink and green hi-glaze, 8.5"h, hairline to top   450-650   July 15, 1997 Sold for $220

1391. **RV Futura** vase, round form with four feet on square base in mottled green over orange and blue, 7.5"h, repaired chip   450-650   July 15, 1997 Sold for $240

1392. **RV Futura** vase, dark green and lime green hi-glaze over two-handled form with flared, tiered neck, 9"h, mint   600-800   July 15, 1997 Sold for $600

1393. **RV Futura** vase, three sided form with light blue geometric design against navy blue ground, 8"h, mint 550-750   July 15, 1997 Sold for $550

1394. **RV Futura** vase, tapered and ribbed cylindrical form with green geometric design on a light blue ground with four darker blue buttresses, 7.5"h, hairline and chip to foot   300-400   July 15, 1997 Sold for $350

1395. **RV Futura** vase, molded floral in green and blue against a blue and orange ground, 5"h, repaired chip 350-450   July 15, 1997 Sold for $500

1396. **RV Futura** vase, green and pink hi-glaze, 8"h, mint 400-600   July 15, 1997 Sold for $325

1397. **RV Futura** jardinere, lavender, yellow and green molded leaves with blue molded geometric design on an orange to green ground, 12"dia. x 8"h, deteriorating repairs   350-450   July 15, 1997 Sold for $200

1398. **RV Futura** vase, round ribbed form with blue, green and yellow molded floral design against a tan to orange ground, 8"h, mint   500-700   July 15, 1997 Sold for $600

1399. **RV Futura** vase, flaring form in orange with green buttresses, 8"h, mint   550-750   July 15, 1997 Sold for $550

1400. **RV Futura** jardinere, yellow, pink and green leaves against an orange ground with blue geometrics, 9"dia. x 6"h, repaired chips   300-400   July 15, 1997 Sold for $170

1401. **RV Futura** vase, green hi-glaze with gunmetal highlights, round body with tiered and ribbed neck, 12.5"h, mint   1000-1500   July 15, 1997 Sold for $1000

1402. **RV Futura** vase, two-handled form with tiered neck in orange above green flaring base, 7"h, crack to base 150-250   July 15, 1997 Sold for $170

1403. **RV Futura** vase, mottled green ground with blue highlights and brown pinecones with green leaves, two buttress form with flared top, 10"h, chip to base and repaired chip to top   550-750   July 15, 1997 Sold for $350

1404. **RV Dogwood** jardinere and pedestal, not marked, jardinere 10"dia. x 11"h, pedestal is 17"h, both mint 800-1100   July 15, 1997 Sold for $1300

1405. **RV Vista** jardinere and pedestal, scene, not marked, jardinere 12"dia. x 10.5"h, pedestal is 18"h, pedestal has minor chip to bottom   800-1100   July 15, 1997 Sold for $1000

1406. **RV Futura** vase, molded green floral decoration on an orange and green ground, four sided form, 6.5"h, mint 400-600   July 15, 1997 Sold for $375

1407. **RV Futura** vase, four-sided flaring form covered in a blue hi-glaze with gunmetal crystals, 6"h, mint 400-600   July 15, 1997 Sold for $350

1408. **RV Futura** urn, tiered neck in pink with two open handles above flared base in blue, 7"h, mint   400-600 July 15, 1997 Sold for $425

1409. **RV Futura** vase, geometric design in green and gray against a blue ground, 6"h, chip to base   300-400 July 15, 1997 Sold for $350

1410. **RV Futura** vase, four-sided flaring form with geometric design in rose, green and pink above a round base with green scarabs, 7"h, small flake to bottom   250-350 July 15, 1997 Sold for $270

1411. **RV Futura** vase, molded thistle decoration in green and red against a pink to purple ground, two buttresses, 8"h, mint   700-900   July 15, 1997 Sold for $1000

1412. **RV Futura** jardinere, molded leaves in pink with purple geometric designs on a green ground, 12"dia. x 9"h, repaired chips   450-650   July 15, 1997 Sold for $220

1413. **RV Futura** vase, three-sided form over round base with green geometric design outlined in blue against a light blue ground, 9"h, mint   600-800 July 15, 1997 Sold for $750

1414. **RV Futura** vase, bulbous tiered form with flared lip covered in a blue and tan matt glaze, 7"h, repaired chip to base   350-550   July 15, 1997 Sold for $650

1415. **RV Futura** vase, cylindrical form with orange ground, green geometric decoration above two handles, 6.5"h, mint   350-550   July 15, 1997 Sold for $350

1416. **RV Futura** vase, four-sided form covered in a blue and orange glaze with green buttresses, 8"h, mint   650-850 July 15, 1997 Sold for $850

1417. **RV Futura** vase, bulbous bottom with green hi-glaze below tiered neck with pink and green hi-glaze, 8"h, mint   400-600   July 15, 1997 Sold for $425

1418. **RV Futura** jardinere and pedestal, molded and painted Deco design of colorful leaves in yellow, lavender and green with blue arrows, ground shades from orange to green, jar 15"dia. x 10.5"h, pedestal 18"h, pedestal has small flake on bottom   1250-1750   July 15, 1997 Sold for $2100

1419. **RV Magnolia** jardinere and pedestal, blue and pink, jardinere 8", all 24"h, flakes to rim of jardinere, pedestal is mint   700-900   July 15, 1997 Sold for $750

85

1420. RV Pinecone vase, blue, 6"h, flakes to base, hairlines 100-200   July 15, 1997   Sold for $190

1421. RV Freesia basket, green, 8"h, chip to rim   100-200 July 15, 1997   Sold for $80

1422. RV Clematis console bowl, orange, 10"w, chip to handle   70-120   July 15, 1997   Sold for $40

1423. RV Water lily pitcher, brown and orange, 15"h, hidden chip to base, flake to side   200-300   July 15, 1997 Sold for $190

1424. RV Cosmos bowl, blue, 6"h, flake to blossom   50-100 July 15, 1997   Sold for $160

1425. RV Apple Blossom floor vase, blue, 18"h, line to rim 300-400   July 15, 1997   Sold for $350

1426. RV Moss console bowl, 8"dia., flake to handle 100-200   July 15, 1997   Sold for $140

1427. RV Water lily vase, pink and green, 12"h, chip to side 200-300   July 15, 1997   Sold for $120

1428. RV Bushberry basket, orange, 8"h, chip to base 100-150   July 15, 1997   Sold for $120

1429. RV Columbine vase, orange, 6"h, chip to base 100-200   July 15, 1997   Sold for $110

Not Pictured:

1430. RV Rozane Light vase, peach and white pansy, green to cream ground, three handles, footed, not marked, 10"h, mint   450-650   June 8, 1997   Sold for $500

1431. RV Clemana vase, handles, green, 12.5"h, repaired chip; with **RV Ivory II** candlestick, green, paper label, 5.5"h, mint   150-250   July 15, 1997   Sold for $350

1432. RV Futura vase, red with floral decoration on slender branches, green leaves, square footed base, unmarked, 9"h, mint   1000-1500   July 15, 1997 Sold for $1300

1433. RV sign, pink matt glaze, 6"l x 2"h, mint 1500-2000   July 15, 1997 Sold for $2200

1434. RV Rozane Pattern figurine, fish and waves in light to dark brown matt glaze, marked, 5.25"h, mint   200-300 July 15, 1997   Sold for $190

Not Pictured:

1435. RV Futura vase, ribbed form with blue and green molded floral on green and peach ground, 8.5"h, flake on rim 700-900   June 8, 1997   Sold for $650

1436. RV Sunflower vase, two-handled form, 5"h, mint 350-550 July 16, 1997 Sold for $350

1437. RV Russco vase, two handles, brown and tan, 7"h, mint 200-250 July 16, 1997 Sold for $160

1438. RV Cherry Blossom vase, two-handled form, brown, paper label, 10"h, mint 650-850 July 16, 1997 Sold for $550

1439. RV Sunflower hanging basket, 7"dia. x 4.5"h, mint 900-1200 July 16, 1997 Sold for $850

1440. RV Dahlrose jardinere, 13"dia. x 9"h, repaired chip to top of handle 300-500 July 16, 1997 Sold for $250

1441. RV Tourist bowl, scene of car being pulled by horses, 7"w x 3.5"h, repair to chip at top 900-1200 July 16, 1997 Sold for $800

1442. RV Cremona vase, pink and green matt glaze, 10"h, mint 250-350 July 16, 1997 Sold for $190

1443. RV Moss vase, green to brown, 8.5"h, mint 350-400 July 16, 1997 Sold for $325

1444. RV Ceramic Design wallpocket, cream matt glaze with green leaves outlined in black, no mark, 10"h, mint 250-350 July 16, 1997 Sold for $450

Not Pictured:

1445. RV Bleeding Heart vase, green and pink matt, 6"h, mint 200-300 July 16, 1997 Sold for $250

1446. RV Cremona flower frog, blue, marked, 4.5"h, mint 50-100 July 15, 1997 Sold for $200

1447. RV Magnolia cups, set of six, blue, marked, 3"h, some have chips 200-300 July 15, 1997 Sold for $200

1448. RV Moss vase, blue, marked and paper label, 6.5"h, mint 200-250 July 15, 1997 Sold for $200

1449. RV Pinecone planter, brown, marked, 10"l x 3.5"h, mint 200-300 July 15, 1997 Sold for $210

1450. RV Sunflower vase, green and yellow, 5"h, mint 400-600 July 16, 1997 Sold for $450

1451. RV Sunflower vase, green and yellow, 10"h, mint 900-1200 July 16, 1997 Sold for $950

1452. RV Sunflower vase, green, yellow and blue, paper label, 6"h, mint 500-700 July 16, 1997 Sold for $400

Not Pictured:

1453. RV Pinecone vase, brown with two twig handles at neck, impressed mark, 16"h, mint 450-650 July 16, 1997 Sold for $600

For more details please call:
(513) 321-6742

1454. RV Cherry Blossom vase, brown, green, cream and white, no mark, 5"h, mint 250-350 July 16, 1997 Sold for $210

1455. RV Wisteria vase, blue, green and purple, gold label, no mark, 4"h, mint 250-350 July 16, 1997 Sold for $400

1456. RV Wisteria vase, brown, yellow, green and lavender, no mark, 5"h, mint 300-400 July 16, 1997 Sold for $375

1457. RV Baneda vase, green, brown and blue, paper label, no mark, 6"h, mint 300-400 July 16, 1997 Sold for $325

1458. RV Dahlrose console bowl and candlesticks, pair, green, brown and yellow, no mark, bowl 10"dia. x 3.5"h, candlesticks 5.5"w x 3.5"h, all mint 350-550 July 16, 1997 Sold for $600

1459. RV Baneda vase, pink, green, brown and blue, no mark, 7"h, mint 400-500 July 16, 1997 Sold for $450

1460. RV Baneda vase, pink, green, brown and blue, no mark, 8"h, mint 400-500 July 16, 1997 Sold for $650

1461. RV Cherry Blossom vase, brown, white, yellow and green, no mark, 7"h, mint 400-500 July 16, 1997 Sold for $700

1462. RV Baneda vase, green, blue and brown, no mark, 6"h, mint 300-400 July 16, 1997 Sold for $270

1463. RV Topeo vase, light blue, green and pink, no mark, 6"h, mint 250-350 July 16, 1997 Sold for $220

1464. RV Jonquil vase, brown, green, yellow and white, no mark, 5"h, mint 250-350 July 16, 1997 Sold for $170

1465. RV Wisteria vase, brown, yellow, green and lavender, no mark, 6"dia. x 4"h, mint 250-350 July 16, 1997 Sold for $270

Not Pictured:

1466. RV Carnelian II vase, rose and brown glaze with blue and lavender drip, two handles, not marked, 10"h, mint 250-350 July 15, 1997 Sold for $270

1467. RV Wisteria vase, two-handled form with semi-gloss lavender flowers against a brown, yellow to green ground, paper label, 10.5"h, mint 900-1200 July 16, 1997 Sold for $750

1468. RV Morning Glory vase, purple, yellow and green on white ground, no mark, 12.5"h, mint 1000-1500 July 16, 1997 Sold for $950

1469. RV Sunflower vase, yellow, green, blue and brown, no mark, 9"h, mint 900-1200 July 16, 1997 Sold for $800

Not Pictured:

1470. RV Futura vase, pink and green Art Deco design on green rectangular base, two green handles, not marked, 8"h, chipped at base 250-350 July 15, 1997 Sold for $280

1471. RV Foxglove vase, green and pink, 6"h, repaired chip to rim   100-200   July 16, 1997   Sold for $40

1472. RV Silhouette basket, orange, 10"h, chips to base   100-200   July 16, 1997   Sold for $80

1473. RV Foxglove vase, blue and yellow, 4"h, flake to rim   70-120   July 16, 1997   Sold for $50

1474. RV Magnolia floor vase, green, 15"h, hidden chip to base   300-400   July 16, 1997   Sold for $270

1475. RV Primrose vase, orange and yellow, 7"h, small chip to base   150-250   July 16, 1997   Sold for $90

1476. RV Zephyr Lily bowl, green, 10"dia., chip to rim   100-150   July 16, 1997   Sold for $60

1477. RV Water lily cookie jar, 10"h, mint   250-350   July 16, 1997   Sold for $250

1478. RV Bushberry vase, green and brown, 7"h, base has been ground, flakes to base   100-200   July 16, 1997   Sold for $60

1479. RV Freesia floor vase, orange and brown, 15"h, chip to base   300-400   July 16, 1997   Sold for $230

1480. RV Bushberry vase, brown and orange, 4"h, chips to rim and base   50-100   July 16, 1997   Sold for $30

1481. RV Silhouette basket, orange, 10"h, chips to base   100-200   July 16, 1997   Sold for $70

1482. RV Pinecone vase, green, 7"h, flake to base and rim   100-200   July 16, 1997   Sold for $80

Not Pictured:

1483. RV Florentine umbrella stand, ivory and brown, #298-18"h, chip to base   400-600   July 15, 1997   Sold for $350

1484. RV Bushberry umbrella stand, orange, 20"h, chip to base   400-600   July 15, 1997   Sold for $475

1485. RV Futura bowl, green geometric designs with pink, blue, green and yellow balloons, 9"w x 3.5"h, mint   500-700   June 8, 1997   Sold for $300

1486. RV Rozane Woodland vase, beige flowers, wafer mark, 10.25"h, chip repairs at base   500-700   July 15, 1997   Sold for $300

1487. RV Rozane Della Robbia teapot, carved and incised design stylized flowers with inscriptions, pale green hi-glaze to blue/green textured ground, Rozane wafer mark, 8"w x 4"h, mint   1000-1500   July 15, 1997   Sold for $1100

1488. RV Rozane Egypto Aladdin's lamp, green and gunmetal mottled glaze, wafer mark, 5"h, small chip to base   200-300   July 15, 1997   Sold for $170

1489. RV Rozane Woodland vase, square shape with protruding bottom, tan to brown finish, shiny incised decoration of yellow and orange flowers with green leaves, orange hi-glaze interior, wafer mark, 11"h, mint   900-1200   July 15, 1997   Sold for $550

For more details please call:
(513) 321-6742

1490. **RV Sunflower** vase, green, blue, yellow and brown, 5"h, mint   400-500   July 16, 1997   Sold for $400

1491. **RV Imperial I** basket, brown and green, 8.5"h, mint 250-350   July 16, 1997   Sold for $180

1492. **RV Baneda** lamp base, green, blue, yellow and brown, 10.5"h, mint   600-800   July 16, 1997   Sold for $1500

1493. **RV Wisteria** vase, purple, blue, green and brown, no mark, 6"h, mint   350-450   July 16, 1997   Sold for $600

1494. **RV Baneda** console bowl, green, blue, brown and yellow, two handles, gold foil label, 11"w x 3"h, mint 300-400   July 16, 1997   Sold for $300

1495. **RV Baneda** vase, two handles, pink, blue, yellow, brown and green, 7"h, mint   350-450   July 16, 1997 Sold for $400

1496. **RV Wisteria** vase, brown, green, purple and yellow, no mark, 10.5"h, mint   800-1100   July 16, 1997 Sold for $550

1497. **RV Baneda** vase, two handles, green, blue, yellow and brown, 7"h, mint   350-450   July 16, 1997 Sold for $1100

1498. **RV Sunflower** vase, green, brown, blue and yellow, 5"h, mint   400-500   July 16, 1997   Sold for $450

1499. **RV Moss** vase, two handles, green, blue and brown, 9"h, tiny chips to base   250-350   July 16, 1997 Sold for $180

1500. **RV Pinecone** basket, green and brown, 10"h, mint 400-500   July 16, 1997   Sold for $270

1501. **RV Green Matt** bowl, raised stylized floral design in green matt, 3.5"h, mint   150-250   July 16, 1997 Sold for $120

Not Pictured:

1502. **RV Wisteria** vase, 6"h, mint   400-600   July 16, 1997 Sold for $425

1503. **RV Velmoss** vase, rose matt glaze with green leaf design, 9"h, mint   350-550   July 16, 1997 Sold for $240

1504. **RV Baneda** vase, 9"h, mint   650-850   July 16, 1997 Sold for $475

1505. **RV Wisteria** vase, 8"h, mint   700-900   July 16, 1997 Sold for $600

1506. **RV Futura** vase, green and brown matt, two handles, paper label, 9"dia. x 9"h, mint 900-1200   July 16, 1997 Sold for $1300

1507. **RV** sign, light aqua matt glaze, 9.5"w x 4"h, repair to bottom corner   1200-1700 July 16, 1997   Sold for $1500

1508. **RV Futura** vase, yellow hi-glaze over brown matt, no mark, 10"h, chip at base and rim   400-600   July 16, 1997 Sold for $350

1509. RV Baneda vase, pink with banded design, 7"h, mint 400-500   July 16, 1997 Sold for $375

1510. RV Laurel vase, orange, 6"h, mint   250-350 July 16, 1997 Sold for $220

1511. RV Pinecone vase, two handles, 10", mint   350-450 July 16, 1997 Sold for $260

1512. RV Jonquil vase, handled form, 3"h, mint   150-250 July 16, 1997 Sold for $120

1513. RV Cherry Blossom jardinere, brown and cream banded floral, 10"dia. x 9.5"h, mint   700-900 July 16, 1997 Sold for $500

1514. RV Wisteria vase, 8"w x 6.5"h, mint   650-850 July 16, 1997 Sold for $600

1515. RV Jonquil vase, handled and bulbous form, 4"h, mint 150-250   July 16, 1997 Sold for $140

1516. RV Moss vase, footed pedestal base, handles, good color, 9.5"h, mint   250-350   July 16, 1997 Sold for $280

1517. RV Blackberry vase, 7"w x 6"h, mint   450-650 July 16, 1997 Sold for $450

1518. RV Russco vase, yellow to orange glaze, 8.5"h, mint 250-350   July 16, 1997 Sold for $150

Not Pictured:

1519. RV Cosmos vase, blue, #948-7"h, mint   100-200 July 15, 1997 Sold for $230

1520. RV Pinecone candleholders, pair, brown, 5"h, mint 250-350   July 15, 1997 Sold for $350

1521. RV Baneda vase, green, two handles, not marked, 6"h, line to top   150-250   July 15, 1997 Sold for $240

1522. RV Futura vase, vertical form with stacked flaring cones over round base with yellow, blue, green and lavender geometric decoration on a brown ground, 10.5"h, mint   700-900 June 8, 1997 Sold for $400

1523. RV Futura vase, floral design on top sides, brown with blue matt, 9"w x 6.25"h, mint   600-800   June 8, 1997 Sold for $500

1524. RV Futura vase, four-sided flaring form with lobes at base, geometric design, orange and brown matt, 12"h, mint   700-900   June 8, 1997 Sold for $900

1525. RV Sunflower vase, green, partial paper label, 6"h, mint 300-400   June 2, 1996   Sold for $550

1526. RV Dahlrose vase, green and brown, paper label, 8"h, mint 150-250   June 2, 1996   Sold for $200

1527. RV Ferella vase, pink, 6"h, repairs to rim   100-150 June 2, 1996   Sold for $250

1528. RV Cherry Blossom vase, brown and cream, 7"h, mint 300-400   June 2, 1996   Sold for $325

1529. RV Wisteria vase, brown and blue, 8.5"h, mint 500-700   June 2, 1996   Sold for $1500

1530. RV Topeo vase, red hi-glaze, 7"h, minor scratches to surface 150-250   June 2, 1996   Sold for $130

1531. RV Laurel vase, yellow, 6.5"h, roughness to base in making   150-250   June 2, 1996   Sold for $200

1532. RV Jonquil vase, brown and green, 8"dia. x 7"h, mint 350-450   June 2, 1996   Sold for $425

1533. RV Panel vase, fan form with different nude on each side, green, 6"h, mint   250-350   June 2, 1996 Sold for $325

Not Pictured:

1534. RV Fuschia ewer, green and pink floral design on brown and yellow ground, impressed mark, 10"h, mint 100-200   July 16, 1996   Sold for $395

1535. RV bank, pig in brown, green and tan hi-glaze, impressed marks, 6.5"w x 4"h, mint   100-150 July 16, 1996   Sold for $200

1536. RV Jonquil planter, built-in flower frog, not marked, 6"h, water deposits inside   250-350   July 15, 1997 Sold for $240

1537. RV Dutch pitcher and six mugs, two Dutch men on pitcher, scenes with children on mugs, pitcher 11"h, mugs 5"h, all have chips   300-400   July 15, 1997 Sold for $425

1538. RV Luffa vase, two-handled form, caramel and green with white blossoms, 7"h, mint   400-600   July 16, 1996 Sold for $240

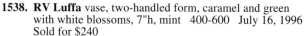

1539. RV Pinecone floor vase, green, impressed mark, 15"h, mint   800-1100   June 2, 1996 Sold for $1100

1540. RV Pinecone vase, brown, 8.5"h, mint 300-500   June 2, 1996   Sold for $325

1541. RV Futura vase, pink and lavender matt, paper label, 8"h, mint   400-600   June 2, 1996 Sold for $850

1542. RV Futura vase, rounded base also squared handles with terraced neck in green hi-glaze, 9"h, mint 400-600   June 2, 1996 Sold for $600

1543. RV Futura candlestick, hourglass form with two squared handles, caramel and brown matt glaze, paper label, 4"h, mint   200-300   June 2, 1996 Sold for $350

1544. RV Futura vase, two buttressed handles in pinecone design, mottled green, yellow, blue and tan glaze, 10.5"h, mint   600-800   June 2, 1996 Sold for $700

1545. RV Futura vase, two-handled with terraced base and neck, peach and green matt glaze, 6.5"h, hairline 200-300   June 2, 1996 Sold for $170

1546. RV Futura vase, tapered four-sided form with rounded sections atop square base, peach and gray matt glaze, 12.5"h, mint   600-800 June 2, 1996 Sold for $650

1547. RV Futura wallpocket, two-handled triangular form in caramel, green, yellow and blue matt glaze, original paper label, 8"h, mint   250-350 June 2, 1996 Sold for $550

1548. RV Futura vase, with two handles rising to flared rim, green floral decoration against a blue matt ground, 7"h, mint   400-600   June 2, 1996 Sold for $900

1549. RV Futura vase, raised geometric decoration from circular base in peach, blue and green matt glaze, mint   300-500   June 2, 1996 Sold for $425

1550. RV Futura vase, cut-corner form with blue and green floral design on a mottled caramel and gray   matt ground, 5"h, small chip to base   200-300 June 2, 1996 Sold for $160

1551. RV Futura vase, four buttresses support bullet form, dark and light blue matt glaze with green high-lights, 8"h, small chip to base   400-600   June 2, 1996 Sold for $350

1552. RV Wisteria vase, two-handled form in tan and green, gold paper label, 15.5"h, minute chip and repair 900-1200   June 2, 1996 Sold for $950

1553. RV Wisteria vase, rounded form with closed handles, blue and green, gold paper label, 6.5"dia. x 5"h, mint 300-400   June 2, 1996 Sold for $500

1554. RV Morning Glory vase, white, yellow, lavender and
green, gold foil label, 7.5"h, mint 300-400
July 17, 1996 Sold for $300

1555. RV Cherry Blossom vase, blue, pink, maroon and
green, 7"dia. x 5"h, mint 250-350 July 17, 1996
Sold for $300

1556. RV White Rose vase, in shades of pink and green,
raised mark, 10"h, mint 150-250 July 17, 1996
Sold for $80

1557. RV Florentine vase, two handles, tan, green, brown and
pink, ink mark, 8.5"h, mint 100-150 July 17, 1996
Sold for $90

1558. RV Thornapple ewer, pink, green and white, 15"h,
mint 300-500 July 17, 1996 Sold for $350

1559. RV Thornapple vase, light blue, white and green,
impressed mark, 6"h, mint 100-200 July 17, 1996
Sold for $100

1560. RV Dahlrose vase, two handles, brown, cream and
green, no mark, 8"h, mint 200-300 July 17, 1996
Sold for $325

1561. RV Orian vase, two handles, tan, green and blue,
original paper label, 6.5"h, mint 150-250
July 17, 1996 Sold for $110

1562. RV Peony vase, raised mark, pink, green, yellow and
brown, 8"h, mint 100-200 July 17, 1996
Sold for $160

Not Pictured:

1563. RV Thornapple triple candleholders, pair, green to
blue, marked, 6"h, minute fake to each 200-300
June 8, 1997 Sold for $375

1564. RV Cherry Blossom vase, two small handles, brown
and cream with white flowers, not marked, 4"h, mint
250-350 June 8, 1997 Sold for $325

1565. Rozane Della Robbia vase, flattened form with incised
decoration of large-petaled blossom with curving leaves
in light green hi-glaze against a cut-ground of darker
green, artist signed, wafer mark, 7"w x 3"d x 7.5"h, mint
2500-3500 July 17, 1996 Sold for $3500

Not Pictured:

1566. RV Rozane Della Robbia vase, pedestal vase with two
curled handles, figures circling vase, colors of orange,
green and white with hi-glaze, 12"h, restored
2500-3500 July 13, 1993 Sold for $3500

1567. RV Rozane Della Robbia pitcher, scene on each side of
Roman in chariot pulled by horses, turquoise with
brown, border of alternating squares of green and blue,
wafer mark, 10"h, a few glaze flakes 3000-4000
July 17, 1991 Sold for $2500

1568. RV Futura vase, four-sided twisted form with leaf decoration in caramel and green drip glaze, 6.5"h, mint 300-400 June 2, 1996 Sold for $280

1569. RV Futura vase, squared form on round base in pink and green matt glaze, original paper label, 7"h, mint 400-600 June 2, 1996 Sold for $300

1570. RV Futura vase, rectangular form on broad base with open handles in pink and green hi-glaze, 8"h, mint 500-700 June 2, 1996 Sold for $600

1571. RV Futura vase, angular base supports rounded form in gray, blue and green, paper label, 7.5"h, tiny chip to base 400-600 June 2, 1996 Sold for $375

1572. RV Futura vase, squat, flattened form with open handles atop broad base in pink and green matt glaze, 7"w x 4"h, mint 300-400 June 2, 1996 Sold for $375

1573. RV Futura vase, round form rises to terraced neck in gunmetal, light and dark green hi-glaze, 10.5"h, mint 700-900 June 2, 1996 Sold for $700

1574. RV Futura candlesticks, pair, squared form with leaf design in caramel, aqua and gray drip glaze, original paper label, 4"h, hidden chip to one base 200-300 June 2, 1996 Sold for $210

1575. RV Futura vase, square base and four legs support swollen body in mottled green, peach and blue matt glaze, 7.5"h, hairline 200-300 June 2, 1996 Sold for $300

1576. RV Futura vase, bulbous base supports tall terraced neck in green matt glaze and pink hi-glaze, 8.5"h, chip to base 200-300 June 2, 1996 Sold for $325

1577. RV Futura vase, geometric form with two squared handles and terraced neck in caramel and gray/green matt glaze, 7"h, hidden chip to base 200-300 June 2, 1996 Sold for $200

1578. RV Futura vase, flattened rectangular form on broad base in ivory, carmel, green and blue matt glaze, paper label, 6"h, mint 300-400 June 2, 1996 Sold for $280

1579. RV Rozane Mongol vase, three feet support bulbous base with three open handles from shoulder to neck, deep red hi-glaze, 11"h, mint 1000-2000 June 2, 1996 Sold for $1500

Not Pictured:

1580. RV Rozane Mongol vase, large form with wide, flared rim in dark red hi-glaze, wafer mark, 14.5"h, several minute flakes 1000-1500 July 15, 1996 Sold for $800

95

1581. RV Windsor two-handled form with green and yellow leaf decoration against a mottled violet/blue ground, large foil label, 5"h, repaired lip   100-150
July 16, 1996 Sold for $110

1582. RV Baneda vase, two-handled form with floral design against a pink mottled ground, foil label, 6"h, mint   350-450   July 16, 1996 Sold for $450

1583. RV Windsor bowl, two handles with yellow and green Arts & Crafts decoration, 7"dia. x 3"h, flakes to base and interior   100-150   July 16, 1996 Sold for $80

1584. RV Baneda vase, broad, two-handled form with floral design against a pink mottled ground, 6.5"dia. x 5"h, mint   300-400   July 16, 1996 Sold for $550

1585. RV Sunflower vase, mustard and green floral on caramel, green and blue ground, great mold, 8.5"h, mint   800-1100   July 16, 1996 Sold for $1450

1586. RV Rosecraft Hexagon vase, six-sided form with orange design on brown ground, ink mark, 6"dia. x 4"h, mint   150-250   July 16, 1996 Sold for $300

1587. RV Windsor vase, rounded form with wide, flared rim in yellow and green geometric design, mottled blue and lavender ground, 6.5"h, mint   300-400   July 16, 1996 Sold for $300

1588. RV Clemana vase, chalice form with two tiny handles, pink, white and green floral design on blue ground, 7"h, mint   250-350   July 16, 1996 Sold for $400

1589. RV Baneda vase, tapered form with two tiny handles, pink mottled glaze, large foil label, 6"h, mint   350-450   July 16, 1996 Sold for $325

Not Pictured:

1590. Lonhuda vase, collie sitting on grass, all in shades of green, yellow, and brown, signed by A.D.F., impressed marks, 8"w x 7.5"h, hairline and repair to foot   1000-1500   July 16, 1996   Sold for $1500

1591. RV Futura vase, flaring four-sided form with bulbous base, in green and blue, 10"h, mint   800-1100
July 17, 1996 Sold for $750

1592. RV Futura vase, cylindrical body with geometric design above four geometric columns, green and blue, 7.5"h, mint   600-800   July 17, 1996 Sold for $650

1593. RV Dogwood II bud vase, white and black floral on dark green ground, 8"h, mint 200-300 July 16, 1996 Sold for $150

1594. RV Fuschia vase, two handles, green and white floral design on blue ground, 4"h, mint 150-250 July 16, 1996 Sold for $200

1595. RV Dogwood II wallpocket, white and black floral on green ground, 10"h, repaired chip to top 100-200 July 16, 1996 Sold for $150

1596. RV Sunflower vase, two tiny handles at rim, 8.5"h, mint 800-1100 July 16, 1996 Sold for $700

1597. RV Rosecraft Vintage vase, large form with tan berries and leaves on a brown matt ground, ink mark, 10"h, mint 350-550 July 16, 1996 Sold for $650

1598. RV Rosecraft Vintage wall pocket, two-handled form with tan berries and leaves on a brown matt ground, ink mark, 9"h, chip to bottom 150-250 July 16, 1996 Sold for $170

1599. RV Dogwood II vase, white and black floral on green ground, 8"h, chip to rim 100-150 July 16, 1996 Sold for $80

1600. RV Fuschia flower frog, footed form with two handles in caramel, green and white floral design on blue ground, 3"h, glaze miss to edge, mint; with **RV Fuschia** candlesticks, pair, caramel, green and white floral design on blue ground, 5"h, one with handle repair 100-200 July 16, 1996 Sold for $260

Not Pictured:

1601. RV Sunflower vase, two handles, green, yellow and brown, partial paper label, 6"h, mint 200-300 July 17, 1996 Sold for $325

1602. RV Wisteria vase, green and purple floral decoration, backed by shades of blue and brown, paper label, 10"h, mint 600-800 July 16, 1996 Sold for $1000

1603. RV Carnelian II vase, two-handled form in mottled green, teal and gray, 7"dia x 7.5"h, mint 300-400 July 16, 1996 Sold for $550

1604. RV Carnelian II vase, mottled rose, teal, green and tan, 9"h, mint 350-450 July 16, 1996 Sold for $600

1605. RV Carnelian II vase, two-handled form in mottled rose, teal, green and tan, 8"dia. x 6"h, mint 250-350 July 16, 1996 Sold for $300

97

For more details please call:
(513) 321-6742

1606. RV Carnelian II vase, mottled purple and green over mottled pink, tan and caramel matt glaze, 5"h, mint 150-250 July 16, 1996 Sold for $250

1607. RV Pinecone vase, green, brown and yellow matt glaze, 10"dia. x 7"h, flakes to base 200-300 July 16, 1996 Sold for $160

1608. RV Snowberry plate, green, brown and white on pink and blue ground, impressed mark, 5.25"dia., mint 50-100 July 16, 1996 Sold for $70

1609. RV Carnelian II candlesticks, two, mottled deep rose, caramel and tan matt glaze, ink mark, 5"dia. x 3"h, mint 100-200 July 16, 1996 Sold for $150

1610. RV Pinecone vase, green, brown and yellow matt glaze, impressed mark, 15"h, mint 400-600 July 16, 1996 Sold for $600

1611. RV Pinecone vase, green, brown and yellow matt glaze, impressed mark, 6"h, mint 200-250 July 16, 1996 Sold for $200

1612. RV Pinecone ashtray, green, caramel and dark brown, raised mark, 4.5"w, mint 100-150 July 16, 1996 Sold for $90

1613. RV Laurel vase, green and black on coral matt ground, 7"dia. x 6"h mint 200-300 July 16, 1996 Sold for $200

Not Pictured:

1614. RV Jonquil vase, broad-waisted form with two handles, 7.5"h, mint 400-600 July 16, 1996 Sold for $375

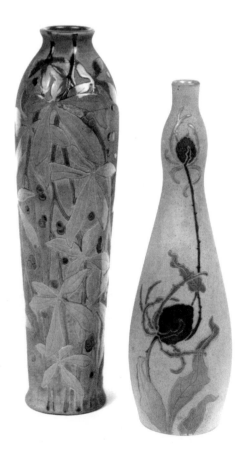

1615. RV Woodland vase, mustard leaves and caramel berries on brown stems against an unglazed ground, wafer mark, 13"h, repaired chips at base 1000-1500 July 16, 1996 Sold for $950

1616. RV Woodland vase, thistle blossoms and jagged curling leaves on thorned branches, all in shades of yellow and brown against an unglazed ground, wafer mark, 11.5"h, mint 1000-1200 July 16, 1996 Sold for $650

Not Pictured:

1617. RV Woodland vase, four-sided form in bisque finished with incised hi-glaze floral decoration in caramel, yellow, brown and light green, wafer mark, 11.5"h, minute repaired chips to base 700-900 July 15, 1996 Sold for $800

1618. RV Matt Green jardinere, four small handles rising from shoulder to neck in green matt glaze, 7"dia. x 5.5"h, minute chip to neck, hairline   150-250 June 2, 1996 Sold for $120

1619. RV Matt Green wallpocket, panels of stylized tulips in green matt glaze, 15"h, repairs to back   150-250 June 2, 1996 Sold for $210

1620. RV Egypto vase, geometric design and two open handles at neck covered in a thick green matt glaze, wafer mark, 5.5"h, mint   300-400   June 2, 1996 Sold for $450

1621. RV Egypto jug, one-handled form with ribbed and bead design in thick dark green matt glaze, 12.5"h, minor glaze flaws, mint   400-600   June 2, 1996 Sold for $450

1622. RV Matt Green vase, three-footed form covered in a thick green matt glaze, 7"dia. x 5"h, rough base, mint 200-300   June 2, 1996 Sold for $90

1623. RV Matt Green planter, squared, footed form with stylized flower and rivet design in dark green matt glaze, 5.5"w x 4.5"h, mint   150-250   June 2, 1996 Sold for $110

1624. RV Egypto jug, squat, three-spouted form with open handle covered in thick green matt glaze, wafer mark, 7.5"w x 5"d x 5"h, chip to base   200-300   June 2, 1996 Sold for $325

1625. RV Woodland vase, incised floral decoration in hi-glaze caramel, olive and dark brown against a perforated cream bisque ground, 10.5"h, mint 900-1200   June 2, 1996 Sold for $1000

1626. RV Fuji vase, intricate stylized glaze pattern of flowers in teal, navy, caramel and light green on tan bisque ground, wafer mark, 10"h, chip to base 900-1200   June 2, 1996 Sold for $850

1627. RV Woodland vase, incised floral decoration in hi-glaze caramel and green against a perforated gray to rust bisque ground, 9"h, minor flakes to rim and base   800-1100   June 2, 1996 Sold for $400

99

1628. RV Moss candelabra, three candleholders, green and tan, 7"h, mint 150-250 July 15, 1996 Sold for $160

1629. RV Gardenia candlesticks, pair, brown, white and green, raised mark, 2"h, mint 50-100 July 15, 1996 Sold for $70

1630. RV Magnolia cookie jar, blue, pink, cream and black, raised mark, 8"h, minute flakes 300-400 July 15, 1996 Sold for $290

1631. RV Donatello bowl, large low form in green, ivory and brown, 12"dia. x 3"h, mint 100-200 July 15, 1996 Sold for $70

1632. RV Rozane basket, green, pink, yellow, lavender and aqua, ink mark, 13"h, repair to handle 150-250 July 15, 1996 Sold for $90

1633. RV Clematis cookie jar, caramel, green and mustard, raised mark, 8"h, jar mint, minute chip to lid 250-350 July 15, 1996 Sold for $280

1634. RV Donatello vase, narrow form with open handle and two spouts in green, ivory and brown, 8.5"h, minute chips to edge, handle repaired 100-150 July 15, 1996 Sold for $80

1635. RV Donatello vase, green, ivory and brown, 6.5"h, minute hidden flake to base 50-100 July 15, 1996 Sold for $210

Not Pictured:

1636. RV Rozane pitcher, pink fruit on brown branches and gray/green leaves against a green to cream ground, hi-glaze, artist signed, wafer mark, 10.5"h, mint 300-400 June 2, 1996 Sold for $325

1637. RV Rozane vase, decoration of yellow blossom with brown center atop green, brown and yellow stems and leaves on a green, and dark brown ground, initialed C. C. on side, impressed marks, 12.5"h, chip to base 150-250 July 15, 1996 Sold for $220

1638. RV Pauleo vase, tulips in dark orange, yellow, black and salmon among green leaves and stems against a mottled orange, yellow, pink and green ground, 19"h, mint 1200-1700 July 15, 1996 Sold for $1500

1639. RV Pauleo vase, purple berries and violet, green, yellow, red and pink leaves on green branches against a lavender to orange ground, 17"h, mint 1200-1700 July 15, 1996 Sold for $900

1640. RV Dahlrose vase, two small handles at shoulder to rim, brown, 6"h, mint   100-150   June 2, 1996 Sold for $100

1641. RV Dahlrose triple bud vase, green and brown, 7.5"w x 6"h, mint   100-200   June 2, 1996 Sold for $180

1642. RV Dahlrose pocket vase, rectangular shape with two handles, brown, 8.5"w x 2.5" x 6"h, minute flakes to rim 100-200   June 2, 1996 Sold for $80

1643. RV Dahlrose candlesticks, pair, brown, 3.5"h, mint 100-200   June 2, 1996 Sold for $130

1644. RV Dahlrose vase, squared form with flared rim, brown, 6"h, mint   150-250   June 2, 1996 Sold for $160

1645. RV Dahlrose vase, large form with open handles, brown and green, paper label, 12.5"h, hidden chip to base 300-500   June 2, 1996 Sold for $350

1646. RV Dahlrose wallpocket, brown and green with open handles, 8.5"h, mint   150-250   June 2, 1996 Sold for $260

1647. RV Dahlrose vase, two-handled form with narrow base, brown and green, 8.5"h, mint   150-250   June 2, 1996 Sold for $210

1648. RV Dahlrose console bowl, brown and green, 10.5"w x 6"d x 4.5"h, mint   150-250   June 2, 1996 Sold for $190

1649. RV Dahlrose vase, rounded form with handles, brown, 5"dia. x 4"h, mint   100-150   June 2, 1996 Sold for $150

Not Pictured:

1650. RV Rozane vase, rose floral decoration, in shades of ivory, green and brown, impressed mark, artist signed, 9"h, mint   150-250   July 16, 1996 Sold for $250

1651. RV Rozane vase, floral, in green, tan and brown, no signature, 7"h, mint   200-300   July 16, 1996 Sold for $450

1652. RV Falline vase, light to dark brown and green, 9.5"h, mint   700-900   June 2, 1996 Sold for $700

1653. RV Falline vase, brown and green, gold paper label, 15.5"h, repaired   400-600   June 2, 1996 Sold for $200

101

1654. **RV Futura** vase, twisted four-sided form with green leaves and linear, geometric decoration, mottled green and tan matt glaze, 6.5"h, mint 300-400 July 15, 1996 Sold for $300

1655. **RV Futura** vase, circular base supports four-sided form with rose, pink and gray/green geometric decoration, 7.5"h, mint 400-600 July 15, 1996 Sold for $500

1656. **RV Futura** vase, four-sided, flared form atop circular base in light blue and green matt glaze, 10"h, mint 800-1100 July 15, 1996 Sold for $850

1657. **RV Futura** vase, rounded form with terraced neck in dark green and mint green hi-glaze, 7.5"dia. x 10"h, mint 700-900 July 15, 1996 Sold for $650

1658. **RV Futura** vase, two-handled form with ivory and green floral design against a rose matt ground, 6.5"w x 4"d, mint 400-500 July 15, 1996 Sold for $550

1659. **RV Futura** vase, four buttressed handles support terraced and flared rim, mottled brown and vivid yellow matt glaze, 10"h, mint 800-1100 July 15, 1996 Sold for $650

1660. **RV Futura** vase, terraced geometric design rises from circular base supporting tapered form in green, blue/gray and peach matt glaze, 8"h, mint 500-700 July 15, 1996 Sold for $475

1661. **RV Futura** vase, six-sided base supports flattened form with delicate blue and yellow floral design on a mottled caramel and tan ground, 6"h, minute line at rim 200-300 July 15, 1996 Sold for $210

Not Pictured:

1662. **RV Futura** vase, circular base supports scalloped and flared form in green hi-glaze, 6"dia. x 9"h, rim chip 1000-1500 July 15, 1996 Sold for $450

1663. **RV Futura** vase, cut-corner base supports four-sided, flared form in a gray over aqua matt glaze, 6.5"h, mint 300-400 July 15, 1996 Sold for $375

1664. **RV Futura** jardinere, taupe, pink and blue, 9"dia. x 6"h, mint 200-300 July 16, 1996 Sold for $325

1665. **RV Futura** hanging basket, yellow and green leaves and blue triangles on rust ground, 7.5"dia. x 4.5"h, mint 250-350 July 16, 1996 Sold for $210

1666. **RV Futura** vase, angular base supports round form with triangular shapes in green, blue and ivory, 7.5"h, mint 700-900 July 15, 1996 Sold for $800

1667. **RV Futura** vase, circular base supports scalloped and flared form in green hi-glaze, 6"dia. x 9"h, rim chip 1000-1500 July 15, 1996 Sold for $450

1668. **RV Futura** vase, cut-corner base supports four-sided, flared form in a gray over aqua matt glaze, 6.5"h, mint 300-400 July 15, 1996 Sold for $375

1669. RV Futura vase, terraced triangular base supports three-sided form in light and dark blue, 8"h, minute chip to edge   250-350   July 15, 1996   Sold for $300

1670. RV Morning Glory pillow vase, two-handled form in white with lavender, brown, yellow and green floral decoration, 7.5"h, repair to rim   150-200 July 15, 1996   Sold for $100

1671. RV Florane wallpocket, caramel shaded into brown, ink mark, 10"h, mint   100-200   July 15, 1996 Sold for $140

1672. RV Zephyr Lily vase, two-handled form in blue, 9"h, repaired rim and base   50-100   July 15, 1996 Sold for $60

1673. RV Baneda vase, two-handled form in mottled pink matt with caramel, blue, green and tan floral design, 8"h, mint   300-500   July 15, 1996   Sold for $600

1674. RV Russco hanging basket, three-handled form in mottled tan matt glaze, 7"dia., mint   100-150 July 15, 1996   Sold for $130

1675. RV Pinecone vase, blue, 7"h, mint   200-250 July 15, 1996   Sold for $300

1676. RV Fuschia vase, two-handled form in brown with green and pink floral design, impressed marks, 8.5"h, mint   100-200   July 15, 1996   Sold for $170

1677. RV Moderne double bud vase, light blue, 9"h, mint 50-100   July 15, 1996   Sold for $60

Not Pictured:

1678. RV Carnelian II vase, two handle, pink and tan, 8"dia. x 5"h, mint   100-200   July 16, 1996   Sold for $210

1679. RV Wisteria vase, brown, purple and green, two handles, 6"h, mint   200-300   July 16, 1996 Sold for $260

1680. RV Freesia vase, green, cream and lavender, 8"h, mint 100-150   July 16, 1996   Sold for $200

1681. RV Rozane Woodland vase, tapered form with incised, hi-glaze decoration in caramel and yellow on a beige, ground in bisque finish, wafer mark, initialed H.S. and E.T., 9"h, mint   800-1000   July 16, 1996 Sold for $1200

1682. RV Aztec vase, tapered four-sided form with stylized, hi-glaze Arts & Crafts design in cream and blue/gray on a blue ground, impressed 8, 10.5"h, minor chips to edge 600-800   July 16, 1996   Sold for $500

1683. RV Rozane Woodland vase, twisted shape with ground in beige cork-type bisque finish, incised and hi-glazed design of blossoms, buds, stems and leaves in olive, gold and brown, wafer mark, 10.5"h, chips to underside 600-800   July 16, 1996   Sold for $425

103

1684. RV Bushberry window box, two handles, blue, green and brown, 8"w, chip to rim, repair to handle 150-250 July 16, 1996 Sold for $60

1685. RV Bushberry basket, blue, green and brown, 8"h, minute flake to base; with a **RV Bushberry** cornucopia not pictured, blue, green and brown, 8.5"dia. x 5"h, repair to rim 150-200 July 16, 1996 Sold for $110

1686. RV Bushberry ashtray, blue, green and brown, 6.5"dia. x 2.5"h, mint 100-150 July 16, 1996 Sold for $200

1687. RV Bushberry vase, two handles, blue, green and brown, 9"h, chip to rim; with a **RV Bushberry** double bud vase, not pictured, blue, green and brown, 4.5"h, minute flake to base 150-200 July 16, 1996 Sold for $200

1688. RV Bushberry bowl, blue, green and brown, 10"dia. x 2.5"h, repair to handles 100-150 July 16, 1996 Sold for $110

1689. RV Bushberry ewer, blue, green and brown, 15"h, repairs to handle and spout 150-250 July 16, 1996 Sold for $300

1690. RV Bushberry pitcher, blue, green and brown, 9"h, mint 200-300 July 16, 1996 Sold for $325

1691. RV Bushberry bowl, blue, green and brown, 6"w, mint 100-150 July 16, 1996 Sold for $80

1692. RV Bushberry mug, blue, green and brown, 3.5"h, mint 100-150 July 16, 1996 Sold for $160

1693. RV Bushberry bowl, blue, green and brown, 10"w, mint 150-200 July 16, 1996 Sold for $200

1694. RV Bushberry vase, blue, green and brown, 7"h, mint 100-200 July 16, 1996 Sold for $110

Not Pictured:

1695. RV Apple Blossom bowl, 10"dia. x 2.5"h, mint; with a **RV Apple Blossom** basket, blue, marked, 11"l x 8"h, mint 200-300 July 13, 1998 Sold for $325

1696. RV Bleeding Heart vase, green, 6"h, mint; with a **RV Thornapple** bowl, 5.5"dia. x 3"h, mint 200-300 July 13, 1998 Sold for $250

1697. RV Wisteria vase, lavender and green floral on brown and yellow ground, foil label, 6.5"dia. x 5"h, mint 300-400 June 2, 1996 Sold for $375

1698. RV Wisteria vase, lavender and green floral on brown and yellow ground, foil label, 8.5"dia x 6.5"h, mint 600-800 June 2, 1996 Sold for $800

1699. RV Bleeding Heart basket, green, pink and white on caramel ground, impressed mark 8"h, mint   150-250 July 16,1996 Sold for $375

1700. RV Pinecone vase, green and brown on blue ground, impressed mark, 7"h, mint   150-200   July 16,1996 Sold for $240

1701. RV Pinecone basket, green and brown, raised mark 11"h, repair to handle   100-200   July 16,1996 Sold for $120

1702. RV Morning Glory vase, lavender and yellow blossoms on green ground, 6.5"h, mint   300-400 July 16,1996 Sold for $325

1703. RV Pinecone vase, green and brown on blue and white ground, gold paper label, 10.5"h, mint   300-400 July 16,1996 Sold for $475

1704. RV Vista wallpocket, green and purple on blue ground, 9.5"h, hairline   100-150   July 16,1996 Sold for $230

1705. RV Pinecone vase, green and brown on blue ground, impressed mark 6"h, mint   100-150   July 16,1996 Sold for $240

1706. RV Pinecone vase, green and brown against a green and white ground, 8"w x 5"d x 8.5"h, mint   250-350 July 16,1996 Sold for $260

1707. RV Carnelian II vase, mottled purple and green drip over mottled pink, tan and caramel matt glaze, 7"h, mint 150-200   July 16,1996 Sold for $325

1708. RV Pinecone basket, green, brown and cream, raised mark 6"h, mint   150-200   July 16,1996 Sold for $210

1709. RV Futura vase, terraced geometric design rises from circular base supporting tapered form in green, blue/gray and peach matt glaze, 8"h, mint   500-700   July 16, 1996 Sold for $700

1710. RV Futura vase, four-sided cone form supported by four columns, peach with green mottling, original label, 5"h, mint   300-400 July 16, 1996 Sold for $500

Not Pictured:

1711. RV Futura vase, green, peach and gray, 8"h, minute hairline to rim   150-200 July 16, 1996 Sold for $220

1712. RV Bushberry tea set, teapot with creamer and sugar, blue, green and brown, teapot, 10.5"w x 5.5"h, all mint 250-350 July 16, 1996 Sold for $500

1713. RV Bushberry footed vase, two handles blue, green and brown, 6"h, mint 70-150 July 16, 1996 Sold for $80

1714. RV Bushberry candlesticks, blue, green and brown, C.S., 2"h, mint 70-150 July 16, 1996 Sold for $90

1715. RV Bushberry vase, two handles, blue, green and brown, 15"h, mint 350-550 July 16, 1996 Sold for $750

1716. RV Bushberry vase, two handles, blue, green and brown, 6"h, mint 70-150 July 16, 1996 Sold for $90

1717. RV Bushberry console bowl, blue, green and brown, 10"w, mint 150-200 July 16, 1996 Sold for $80

1718. RV Bushberry flower frog, blue, green and brown, 4.5"h, mint 50-100 July 16, 1996 Sold for $110

1719. RV Bushberry cornucopia, blue, green and brown, 6"h, mint 100-150 July 16, 1996 Sold for $70

Not Pictured:

1720. RV Lotus vase, yellow and brown hi-glaze, 10"h, mint 250-350 July 15, 1996 Sold for $275

1721. RV Wisteria vase, two-handled form, lavender and green floral on brown and yellow ground, 6.5"dia. x 4"h, mint 250-350 July 15, 1996 Sold for $375

1722. RV Wincraft vase, cream and green floral design on mottled blue ground, 14"h, mint 250-350 July 15, 1996 Sold for $600

1723. RV Blackberry vase, broad, two-handled form, large foil label, 6"dia. x 4"h, mint 250-350 July 15, 1996 Sold for $375

1724. RV Fuschia bowl, two handles, green, brown, pink and white, 9"dia., mint 150-200 July 17, 1996 Sold for $350

1725. RV Pinecone ashtray, brown and green, 5"w, mint 100-200 July 17, 1996 Sold for $200

1726. RV Pinecone basket, brown and green, 13"w x 10"h, mint 300-500 July 17, 1996 Sold for $700

1727. RV Ferella vase, two handles, mottled pink, brown, green and cream, partial paper label, 5"h, mint 250-350 July 17, 1996 Sold for $250

1728. RV Water lily covered jar, orange, yellow and green, 8"h, minute flake to handle, hairlines to inside of lid 200-300 July 17, 1996 Sold for $260

1729. RV Fuschia vase, two handles, brown, pink, green and white, 10"h, mint 200-300 July 17, 1996 Sold for $250

1730. RV Baneda vase, two handles, green, caramel and blue, 9"h, mint 300-400 July 17, 1996 Sold for $550

1731. RV Cherry Blossom vase, caramel, cream, green, white and yellow, gold foil label, 7"dia. x 5"h, mint 250-350 July 17, 1996 Sold for $260

1732. RV Bushberry planter, with dish, green, 5"h, mint 100-200 July 16, 1996 Sold for $240

1733. RV Bushberry vase, green, 8"h, mint 100-200 July 16, 1996 Sold for $210

1734. RV Zephyr Lily vase, blue, two handles, 6.25"h, mint; with a **RV Zephyr Lily** candlesticks, pair, blue, 5"h, mint 200-300 July 13, 1998 Sold for $210

1735. RV Pinecone vase, green and brown with two open handles, impressed mark, 10"h, mint 250-350 July 16, 1996 Sold for $375

1736. RV Clemana bowl, green and blue, impressed mark, 6"dia. x 4"h, mint 100-200 July 16, 1996 Sold for $210

1737. RV Rosecraft Panel vase, green, cream and brown, 4"h x 7"dia., ink mark, mint 150-200 July 16, 1996 Sold for $210

1738. RV Rosecraft Black wallpocket, black, 9"h, mint 100-200 July 15, 1996 Sold for $230

1739. RV Bushberry double cornucopia, blue, green and brown, 8"w, mint   100-200   July 16, 1996
Sold for $150

1740. RV Bushberry vase, two handles, blue, green and brown, 10"w, F.B., mint   150-200   July 16, 1996
Sold for $110

1741. RV Bushberry console bowl, two handles, blue, green and brown, 14"w, mint   150-200   July 16, 1996
Sold for $150

1742. RV Bushberry basket, blue, green and brown, 10"h, mint   150-250   July 16, 1996   Sold for $280

1743. RV Bushberry footed vase, two handles, blue, green and brown, 8"h, mint   100-200   July 16, 1996
Sold for $110

1744. RV Bushberry vase, flattened form, blue, green and brown, 9"h, mint   100-200   July 16, 1996
Sold for $210

1745. RV Bushberry console bowl, two handles, blue, green and brown, 12"w, mint   100-200   July 16, 1996
Sold for $130

1746. RV Bushberry ewer, blue, green and brown, 6"h, mint   100-200   July 16, 1996   Sold for $100

Not Pictured:

1747. RV Pinecone vase, green, 7"h, mint   200-300
July 16, 1996   Sold for $210

1748. RV Wisteria vase, blue, purple and green, two handles, 6"h, mint   200-300   July 16, 1996   Sold for $475

1749. RV Panel vase, pink, light and dark green, ink mark, 8"h, mint   100-150   July 16, 1996   Sold for $220

1750. RV Dawn vase, green, 6"h, mint   100-200
July 16, 1996   Sold for $220

1751. RV Iris wallpocket, two handles, pink, 8"h, mint   150-200   July 15, 1996   Sold for $450

1752. RV Fuschia wallpocket, two handles, brown, 8"h, mint   150-200   July 15, 1996   Sold for $450

1753. RV Ferella candlesticks, pair, large cup surrounds candleholder, deep rose, 4"h, mint   200-300
July 15, 1996   Sold for $450

1754. RV Ferella bowl, flower frog built in, pink, 10"dia. x 3.5"h, mint   200-300   July 15, 1996   Sold for $475

1755. RV Sunflower vase, blue to green to brown, 6"h, mint   250-350   July 15, 1996   Sold for $375

1756. RV Jonquil vase, two small handles, brown, green, white and yellow, no mark, 6"h, mint   200-300
July 17, 1996   Sold for $200

1757. RV White Rose ewer, pink, green and white, 15"h, mint   300-500   July 17, 1996   Sold for $290

1758. RV Bleeding Heart basket, handle encircles bowl, pink, raised mark, 10", mint   200-300   June 2, 1996
Sold for $260

1759. RV Apple Blossom tea set, teapot with lid, creamer and sugar, pink, raised mark, teapot 7"h, creamer 2.5"h, mint   250-350   June 2, 1996   Sold for $270

1760. RV Vista floor vase, green, purple and light blue, molded landscape decoration, ink mark, 18"h, line in base in making   800-1100   July 17, 1996
Sold for $550

1761. RV Sunflower vase, yellow, green, blue and brown, 4"h, mint   350-450   July 16, 1997   Sold for $325

1762. RV Baneda vase, green, blue, brown and yellow, gold foil label, 6"h, mint   350-450   July 16, 1997
Sold for $400

1763. RV Monticello basket, brown, black, white and green, 6.5"h, mint   300-400   July 16, 1997   Sold for $500

1764. RV Pinecone vase, green, two handles, 4"h, mint
150-250   July 17, 1996 Sold for $120

1765.RV Cremona vase, twisting vines, leaves and berries in
green and yellow on a mottled pink ground, paper label,
12.5"h, mint   250-350   July 17, 1996 Sold for $190

1766. RV Wisteria vase, lavender floral design on blue and
brown ground, 6"h, mint   200-300   July 17, 1996
Sold for $550

1767. RV Futura jardinere, two-handled form with geometric
decoration in yellow, green, lavender and blue on an
orange to gray ground, 11.5"dia. x 8"h, mint   500-700
July 17, 1996 Sold for $525

1768. RV Ferella vase, two-handled form with green and
yellow floral design on mottled brown ground, 4"h, mint
250-350   July 17, 1996 Sold for $300

1769. RV Dogwood vase, cream, green and brown floral
design on olive ground, ink mark, 6"h, mint
200-300   July 17, 1996 Sold for $200

1770. RV Cremona vase, twisting vines, leaves and berries in
green and yellow on a mottled pink ground, paper label,
12.5"h, mint   250-350   July 17, 1996 Sold for $170

1771. RV Monticello vase, broad two-handled form, 6"dia. x
5"h, mint   200-300   July 17, 1996 Sold for $290

Not Pictured:

1772. RV Pinecone wall shelves, pair, brown, 8.5"w x 5"d x
5.5"h, mint   400-600   July 16, 1996 Sold for $475

1773. RV Pinecone triple bud vase, brown, 8.5"h, mint
250-350   July 16, 1996 Sold for $300

1774. RV Pinecone basket, twig handle, brown, 10"h, mint
300-400   June 2, 1996 Sold for $400

1775. RV Pinecone ewer, twig handle, green, 15"h, mint
500-700   June 2, 1996 Sold for $900

Not Pictured:

1776. RV Pinecone tumblers, pair, green, 5.5"h, mint
350-450   July 14, 1998 Sold for $270

1778. RV Pinecone vase, blue, two handles, 10.5"h, mint
300-400   July 14, 1998 Sold for $400

1779. RV Pinecone vase, brown, 12"h, repaired chip to base
200-300   July 16, 1996 Sold for $270

1780. RV Pinecone vase, brown, 6"h, mint   200-300
July 16, 1996 Sold for $230

1781.RV Blackberry vase, two-handled form with deep violet berries on a green and brown ground, 8.5"h, mint 600-800   July 17, 1996   Sold for $1200

1782.RV Tourmaline vase, broad-shouldered form in blue and pale green mottled matt glaze, 5"h, mint   150-250 July 17, 1996   Sold for $90

1783. RV Russco vase, two-handled form in tan over caramel matt glaze, 7"h, mint   250-350   July 17, 1996 Sold for $200

1784. RV sign, self-standing ceramic sign reads Roseville in pale yellow on a blue ground, 8"w x 5"h, mint 1500-2000   July 17, 1996   Sold for $2700

1785. RV Cremona vase, twisting vines, leaves and berries surround broad shoulder in a pale pink mottled matt glaze, 10.5"h, mint   200-300   July 17, 1996 Sold for $150

1786. RV Russco vase, two-handled form in tan over caramel matt glaze, 7"h, mint   250-350   July 17, 1996 Sold for $140

1787. RV Normandy vase, multicolored floral design on mint green and cream matt, 6"h, base chips   50-100 July 17, 1996   Sold for $70

1788. RV Ferella vase, two-handled form with green and yellow floral design on mottled brown ground, 8"h, mint 500-700   July 17, 1996   Sold for $700

Not Pictured:

1789. RV Blackberry vase, brown, green and black, no mark, 6"h, mint   350-450   July 16, 1997   Sold for $425

1790. RV Bleeding Heart vase, 8"h, mint   100-150 July 16, 1997   Sold for $200

1791. RV Peony floor vase, yellow and green, 15"h, mint 300-400   July 16, 1997   Sold for $300

1792. RV Rozane vase, hunting dog with pheasant in his mouth, wafer mark and partial paper label, 10"w x 10"h, mint   500-700   July 13, 1993   Sold for $275

1793. RV Freesia vase, blue, 15", mint   200-300 July 13, 1993   Sold for $300

1794. RV Pinecone basket, green, gold paper label, 12.5"w x 9.5"d x 10"h, mint 600-800   June 2, 1996   Sold for $900

1795. RV Pinecone vase, brown and yellow, impressed mark, 14"h, mint   500-700 June 2, 1996   Sold for $500

1796. RV Cherry Blossom vase, two-handled form, caramel and cream with white blossoms, 10"h, mint   800-1100 July 15, 1996 Sold for $700

1797. RV Cherry Blossom vase, two-handled form, caramel and cream with white blossoms, foil label, 8"dia. x 8"h, mint   700-900   July 15, 1996 Sold for $600

1798.RV Dogwood I jardinere and pedestal, green, cream and black, 28"h, minute flake to base of pedestal, jardinere mint   700-900   July 16, 1996 Sold for $8520

1799. RV Clematis jardinere and pedestal, green, pink and yellow, jardinere with unchipped chip to base, flake to side, pedestal 25"h with minute flake to base   700-900 July 16, 1996 Sold for $400

1800. RV Blackberry vase, green, brown and black, 12.5"h, mint   1000-1500 June 2, 1996 Sold for $ 1500

1801. RV Blackberry basket, green, brown, black and yellow, 8"h, mint   400-600 June 2, 1996 Sold for $850

1802. RV Carnelian I ewer, aqua drip over light pink, ink mark, 15"h, mint   400-600   June 2, 1996 Sold for $350

1803. RV Carnelian II vase, mottled green, pink, purple and light blue drip over pink, tan and caramel, 14"h, mint 600-800   June 2, 1996 Sold for $850

1804. RV Bushberry jardinere and pedestal, blue, green and brown, jardinere 8"h, both 24.5"h, both mint 1000-1500   July 16, 1996 Sold for $1100

1805. RV Bushberry umbrella stand, two handles, blue, green and brown, 20"h, small flaws on bottom rim 700-900   July 16, 1996 Sold for $800

1806. RV Cherry Blossom vase, two-handled form, caramel and cream with white blossoms, 7"h, mint 500-700 June 2, 1996 Sold for $375

1807. RV Cherry Blossom vase, large two-handled form with pink and yellow blossoms on deep rose branches against a pink and gray/green ground, 11"h, mint   900-1200 June 2, 1996 Sold for $1200

111

1808. RV Morning Glory vase, lavender and yellow floral on green ground, 7.5"h, mint   300-400   July 17, 1996 Sold for $375

1809. RV Cherry Blossom vase, caramel and cream with white blossoms, 5"dia. x 5"h, mint   250-350 July 17, 1996 Sold for $260

1810.RV Jonquil vase, yellow, white and green floral design, 7.5"h, mint   300-400   July 17, 1996 Sold for $325

1811. RV Luffa jardinere, 11"dia. x 8"h, mint   700-900 July 17, 1996 Sold for $475

1812. RV Blackberry vase, large foil label, 6"dia. x 4"h, mint 250-350   July 17, 1996 Sold for $375

1813. RV Luffa vase, caramel and green with white blossoms, 7"h, mint   200-300   July 17, 1996 Sold for $250

1814.RV Sunflower vase, wide rim, 7.5"dia. x 4"h, mint 500-700   July 17, 1996 Sold for $500

1815. RV Dahlrose vase, 8.5"h, chip to top   100-200 July 17, 1996 Sold for $200

Not Pictured:

1816. RV Cherry Blossom jardinere, brown, yellow, white and green, 11"dia. x 8"h, mint   700-900 July 16, 1997 Sold for $500

1817. RV Falline vase, brown and green, gold foil label, 7"h, mint   550-750   July 16, 1997 Sold for $550

1818. RV Apple Blossom vase, blue, white and brown, 10"h, mint   150-200   July 16, 1996 Sold for $210

1819. RV Luffa wallpocket, green and brown, gold label, 8"h, mint   200-300   July 15, 1997 Sold for $700

1820. RV Magnolia floor vase, blue, #97-14"h, mint 250-350   July 15, 1997 Sold for $425

1821. RV Moderne bowl, aqua with gold highlights, 15"w x 6.5"d x 4.5"h, minor base chips   200-300 June 10, 1995 Sold for $210

1822. RV Carnelian II vase, green, lavender and tan drip matt glaze over rose, caramel and gray, 8"dia. x 9"h, mint   400-500 July 16, 1996 Sold for $750

1823. RV Carnelian II vase, mottle green, teal and gray, 10"h, mint   400-500 July 16, 1996 Sold for $650

1824.RV Wisteria vase, two-handled form, lavender and green floral on brown and yellow ground, foil label, 7"h, mint 500-700   July 15, 1996   Sold for $450

1825.RV Luffa vase, two-handled form, caramel and green with white blossoms, 6.5"dia. x 6"h, mint   400-600   July 15, 1996   Sold for $300

1826.RV Jonquil vase, two-handled form, yellow, white and green floral design, 8"h, mint   350-450   July 15, 1996   Sold for $400

1827.RV Carnelian II vase, two-handled form in mottled rose, teal, green and tan, 8"dia x 8"h, mint   400-600   July 15, 1996   Sold for $550

1828.RV Cherry Blossom vase, two-handled form, caramel and cream with white blossoms, 5"dia. x 5"h, mint 250-350   July 15, 1996   Sold for $325

1829.RV Sunflower vase, broad-shouldered form with short rim, 7"dia. x 6"h, mint   500-700   July 15, 1996   Sold for $750

1830.RV Monticello vase, two-handled form with caramel, white, black and green stylized decoration, 7"h, mint 350-450   July 15, 1996   Sold for $325

Not Pictured:

1831. RV Wisteria jardinere, 9"h x 12.5"w, chip to base 900-1200   June 8, 1997   Sold for $1000

1832. RV Wisteria vase, green, brown and purple, foil label, 5"h, mint   350-450   July 16, 1997   Sold for $375

1833. RV Blackberry vase, green, tan and black, gold foil label, 6"h, flake to one berry   200-300   July 17, 1996   Sold for $260

1834. RV Columbine jardinere and pedestal, pink and green on pink and gray ground, raised mark 10"h, all 31"h, repair to pedestal, chip to base of jardinere   600-800 July 16, 1996   Sold for $500

1835. RV Bushberry jardinere and pedestal, blue, green and brown, jardinere 10"h, both 30"h, minute chip to base of jardinere and pedestal   800-1100   July 16, 1996 Sold for $1100

Not Pictured:

1836. RV Mostique jardinere and pedestal, blue, yellow, brown hi-glaze on a textured tan ground, ink mark, 28"h, hidden chips to base of jardinere   500-700 July 16, 1996   Sold for $650

1837. RV Florentine jardinere and pedestal, brown and green matt glaze, ink mark, 28"h, both with minor chips 400-600   July 16, 1996   Sold for $550

For more details please call:
(513) 321-6742

1838. RV Pinecone vase, green, two handles, 7"h, mint 150-250 June 10, 1995 Sold for $120

1839. RV Imperial bowl, two-handled form with brown, blue, green and red ground, 9.5"dia., mint 150-250 June 10, 1995 Sold for $90

1840. RV Dogwood II wallpocket, white blossoms on green and black, 10"h, minute chip 150-250 June 10, 1995 Sold for $100

1841. RV Gardenia vase, gray, mint 100-150 June 10, 1995 Sold for $100

1842. RV Imperial vase, brown, blue, green and red ground, 14"h, base chip 200-300 June 10, 1995 Sold for $110

1843. RV Gardenia vase, brown, 8", mint 100-150 June 10, 1995 Sold for $80

1844. RV Imperial basket, brown, blue, green and red ground, 10"h, mint 200-300 June 10, 1995 Sold for $230

1845. RV Pinecone vase, green with two wide, branch handles, 8.5"h, mint 150-250 June 10, 1995 Sold for $200

Not Pictured:

1846. RV Topeo vase, green to blue matt glaze, 12"h, mint 250-350 June 12, 1995 Sold for $475

1847. RV Cherry Blossom vase, caramel and tan, foil label, 5"h, mint 300-400 June 12, 1995 Sold for $425

1848. RV Morning Glory vase, white with lavender and yellow flowers, 10"h, chip repair to top 250-350 June 10, 1995 Sold for $180

1849. RV Morning Glory vase, green with pink and yellow flowers, two-handled form, foil label, 14.5"h, mint 1000-1500 June 10, 1995 Sold for $1200

Not Pictured:

1850. RV Morning Glory basket, white, paper label, 10.5"h, mint 400-600 June 12, 1995 Sold for $700

1851. RV Morning Glory vase, pink, yellow and green floral on ivory ground, 6"h, minute base flakes 200-300 June 12, 1995 Sold for $210

1852. RV Dogwood II vase, green, 8"h, mint 300-400
June 10, 1995 Sold for $160

1853. RV Clemana vase, green, two handles, 4"h, mint
150-250 June 10, 1995 Sold for $140

1854. RV Fuschia vase, blue, two handles, 9"h, mint
200-300 June 10, 1995 Sold for $300

1855. RV Tuscany candlesticks, pair, gray, 4"dia. x 4"h,
mint 100-200 June 10, 1995 Sold for $60

1856. RV Zephyr Lily vase, blue, two handles, 15"h, repair
to base 300-500 June 10, 1995 Sold for $220

1857. RV Jonquil vase, two-handled, 8.5"h, mint 400-500
June 10, 1995 Sold for $650

1858. RV Morning Glory vase, white, two handles, 7"dia. x
4"h, mint 300-500 June 10, 1995 Sold for $260

1859. RV Carnelian II vase, mottled blue and green, two
handles, 7"h, mint 150-250 June 10, 1995
Sold for $170

Not Pictured:

1860. RV Falline vase, brown, two handles, 7", repaired chip
to handle 250-350 July 14, 1998 Sold for $325

1861. RV Foxglove vase, blue with cream and pink blossoms,
four-handled form on circular base, 14"h, minute base
chip 300-400 June 10, 1995 Sold for $ 250

1862. RV Thornapple triple candleholders, pair, brown, 6"w
x 6"h, one with paper label, both mint 200-300
June 10, 1995 Sold for $270

1863. RV Blackberry vase, two-handled form,
12.5"h, mint 1000-1500 June 10, 1995
Sold for $1500

1864. RV Blackberry vase, two-handled form,
6"dia. x 4"h, mint 300-400 June 10, 1995
Sold for $325

Not Pictured:

1865. RV Blackberry vase, violet berries on
caramel, yellow and green ground, 5"h, mint
300-400 June 10, 1995 Sold for $300

1866. RV Fuschia hanging basket, two handles,
brown, paper label, 6"dia., mint 150-250
June 12, 1995 Sold for $400

1867. RV Vista jardinere, 10"h, mint 500-700
June 12, 1995 Sold for $500

115

1868. RV Luffa vase, two-handled form in green and caramel, 8.5"h, minute firing flaw at base   200-300 June 10, 1995 Sold for $190

1869. RV Dogwood vase, green, ink mark, 6"h, mint 200-300   June 10, 1995 Sold for $200

1870. RV Wisteria vase, pink blossoms on green, brown and yellow ground, 8.5"h, mint   500-600 June 10, 1995 Sold for $650

1871. RV Baneda vase, pink with caramel, green, yellow and blue floral decoration, 9.5"h, mint   400-600 June 10, 1995 Sold for $550

1872. RV Panel vase, brown, ink mark, 8"h, mint   200-300 June 10, 1995 Sold for $180

1873. RV Mostique vase, blue, caramel, white and teal against a gray ground, 8.5"h, mint   200-300 June 10, 1995 Sold for $250

1874. RV Windsor vase, two-handled form in mottled orange, 7"h, mint   300-400 June 10, 1995 Sold for $260

Not Pictured:

1875. RV Dogwood II vase, green, 8"h, mint   250-350 June 10, 1995 Sold for $325

1876. RV Fuschia basket with attached frog, brown, 8"h, mint 200-300   June 10, 1995 Sold for $240

1877. RV Pinecone vase, green, bulbous form with two branch handles on a square base, paper label, 7"dia. x 7"h, mint 200-300   June 10, 1995 Sold for $250

1878. RV Imperial II wallpocket, red and blue hi-glaze, 6"h, mint   200-300 June 12, 1995 Sold for $375

1879. RV Ferella console bowl, mottled rose and aqua matt glaze, 12.5"w x 6"h, mint   350-550 June 12, 1995 Sold for $650

1880. RV Rozane Mara vase, molded blossoms and leaves atop vertical stems covered in an iridescent glaze of violet, blue, rose, green and gold, 10.5"h, mint 1500-2000 June 12, 1995 Sold for $2100

Not Pictured:

1881. RV Rozane vase, orange floral decoration and green leaves, marked, artist signed Gussie Gerwick, 6.5"w x 13"h, mint   250-350 July 13, 1998   Sold for $350

1882. RV Rozane paperweight, pansy decoration, wafer mark, artist signed V. Adams, 4"w x 1"h, mint 150-200   July 13, 1998   Sold for $230

1883. RV Pinecone vase, green, two handles, 7"h, mint 200-300 June 10, 1995 Sold for $160

1884. RV Mostique vase, yellow, green and blue hi-glaze on gray matt, 10"h; with an **RV Mostique** bowl, mustard, brown, blue and green hi-glaze on gray matt, 8"dia., vase mint, bowl with scratches to interior 200-300 June 10, 1995 Sold for $325

1885. RV Bushberry teapot, green, 11"dia. x 5.5"h; with an **RV Bushberry** creamer, 5.5"dia. x 2"h, teapot is mint, creamer has chips to base 200-300 June 10, 1995 Sold for $130

1886. RV Baneda vase, two-handled form in pink mottled glaze, paper label, 9.5"h, mint 400-600 June 10, 1995 Sold for $400

1887. RV Blackberry jardinere, brown, yellow, green and caramel with deep purple berries, 6"h, mint 500-700 June 10, 1995 Sold for $400

1888. RV Bittersweet hanging basket, tan and brown, 6"dia., mint 150-200 June 10, 1995 Sold for $130

1889. RV Creamware Colonial humidor, colonial gents in brown, with long pipes, on a brick red band against a cream crackle glaze ground, 5.5"h, chip to lid 200-250 June 10, 1995 Sold for $260

Not Pictured:

1890. RV Mostique vase, 15"h, mint 300-400 June 12, 1995 Sold for $475

1891. RV Morning Glory vase, lavender and yellow blossoms on green, two handles, 10.5"h, mint 900-1200 June 10, 1995 Sold for $1300

1892. RV Sunflower wall pocket, mustard blossoms on blue, green and brown ground, 7.5"h, cracked 200-300 June 10, 1995 Sold for $210

1893. RV Sunflower vase, large mustard blossoms on blue, green and brown ground, 9"h, mint 700-900 June 10, 1995 Sold for $1400

Not Pictured:

1894. RV Sunflower vase, blue, green, yellow and brown, paper label, 5"h, mint 400-600 July 16, 1997 Sold for $350

1895. RV Sunflower wallpocket, 7"h, mint 600-800 June 12, 1995 Sold for $1000

1896. RV Dogwood II vase, green, 9"h, mint 150-250
June 10, 1995 Sold for $110

1897. RV Monticello vase, brown, two handles, 7"h, mint
200-300 June 10, 1995 Sold for $300

1898. RV Cherry Blossom vase, pink with two handles, 5"h,
mint 250-350 June 10, 1995 Sold for $350

1899. RV Bushberry vase, green and caramel, 14"h, base
chip 250-350 June 10, 1995 Sold for $210

1900. RV Imperial II vase, aqua and lavender hi-glaze, 5"h,
mint 150-250 June 10, 1995 Sold for $210

1901. RV Carnelian II vase, two handles, maroon and green,
6.5"h, mint 100-200 June 10, 1995 Sold for $325

1902. RV Baneda vase, green, broad waist with two handles,
6"h, mint 250-350 June 10, 1995 Sold for $300

1903. RV Blackberry vase, two-handled wide form, 5"h, mint
300-400 June 10, 1995 Sold for $300

1904. RV Dogwood II vase, green, 8"h, mint 200-300
June 10, 1995 Sold for $150

Not Pictured:

1905. RV Luffa candlesticks, brown and green, 5"h, mint
150-250 June 10, 1995 Sold for $250

1906. RV Pinecone vase, green with two pinecone needle
handles, 10.5"h, mint 250-350 June 10, 1995
Sold for $260

1907. RV Pinecone hanging basket, blue, 6"dia., minute chip to
one handle 100-200 July 16, 1996 Sold for $230

1908. RV Rozane Woodland vase, hi-glaze
blossoms in caramel and mustard with dark
brown centers on olive green twisting stems
against a tan matt ground, wafer mark, 11"h,
mint 1200-1700 June 10, 1995
Sold for $1300

1909. RV Rozane Crystalis vase, three squared
handles supporting cylindrical neck covered
in a mottled mustard, ivory and olive matt
glaze, incised marks, 6.5"dia. x 4"h, mint
1000-1500 June 10, 1995 Sold for $1000

Not Pictured:

1910. RV Rozane Crystalis vase, covered in a
mottled tan, light and dark blue matt glaze,
no mark, 13.5"h, repair to foot 1500-2500
July 16, 1997   Sold for $1200

1911. RV Ferella vase, two-handled form in mottled rose glaze, 6"h, mint 400-500 June 10, 1995 Sold for $425

1912. RV Ivory Florentine jardinere, green, cream and caramel, 10.5"dia. x 8"h, mint 150-250 June 10, 1995 Sold for $120

1913. RV Water lily vases, pair, blue, two-handled, 4"h, both mint 100-200 June 10, 1995 Sold for $120

1914. RV Vista vase, green, two handles, violet and pale blue, 12"h, mint 400-600 June 10, 1995 Sold for $550

1915. RV Apple Blossom vase, green, two branch handles, 6"h, mint 100-200 June 10, 1995 Sold for $80

1916. RV Ivory Florentine jardinere, green, cream and caramel, 10.5"dia. x 8"h, minute chip on inner rim 100-200 June 10, 1995 Sold for $120

1917. RV Ferella flower pot, brown with attached underplate, paper label, 5"h, mint 300-500 June 10, 1995 Sold for $450

Not Pictured:

1918. RV Lotus vase, blue and cream hi-glaze, 10"h, mint 300-500 June 10, 1995 Sold for $220

1919. RV Carnelian II vase, 12"h, mint 300-400 June 12, 1995 Sold for $900

1920. RV Blackberry bowl, two handles, caramel, yellow and green with violet berries, 8"dia. x 3"h, mint 300-400 June 10, 1995 Sold for $375

1921. RV Rozane Fujiyama vase, hi-glaze blossoms and buds in mustard, tan and caramel on narrow, bowed stems and jagged leaves of olive and vivid green against a beige matt ground, marked Fujiyama, 11"h, minute flake at rim 1000-1500 June 10, 1995 Sold for $950

1922. RV Rozane Woodland vase, hi-glaze olive green stylized vertical stems supporting blue blossoms against a matt ground of blue to tan to green, wafer mark, 11"h, mint 1200-1700 June 10, 1995 Sold for $1100

Not Pictured:

1923. RV Rozane Woodland vase, beige bisque finish, incised and hi-glaze geometric decoration in caramel and yellow, wafer mark, initialed H.S. and E.T., 9"h, mint 800-1100 June 12, 1995 Sold for $750

1924. RV Tourmaline vase, pink and pale blue mottled matt glaze, 4.5"h, mint   100-200   June 10, 1995 Sold for $110

1925. RV Laurel vase, broad form with two closed handles in yellow and black, incised 9, 8"h, mint   200-300 June 10, 1995 Sold for $220

1926. RV Panel wallpockets, pair, dark green matt, 9.5"h, one with hairline, one with chips to rim   100-200 June 10, 1995 Sold for $110

1927. RV Cherry Blossom vase, two-handled form, pink and yellow blossoms on a teal and pink ground, 5"dia. x 4"h, mint   200-300   June 10, 1995   Sold for $375

1928. RV Baneda vase, green with caramel, blue and yellow decoration, 9.5"h, mint   300-400   June 10, 1995 Sold for $450

1929. RV Wisteria bowl, pink blossoms against a brown and green ground, 5.5"dia. x 2.5"h, mint   200-250 June 10, 1995   Sold for $200

1930. RV Water lily vase, two-handled form in brown and caramel, 8", mint   150-200   June 10, 1995 Sold for $200

1931. RV Tourmaline vase, hi-glaze aqua, yellow and rose over olive and aqua matt, 4.5"h, mint   100-200 June 10, 1995   Sold for $200

Not Pictured:

1932. RV Moss bowl and candlesticks, 14"l x 4", mint 250-350   June 12, 1995   Sold for $290

1933. RV Zephyr Lily ewer, orange and green, 16"h, mint 250-350   June 12, 1995   Sold for $210

1934. RV Bushberry lemonade set, pitcher and five cups, orange and brown, 11"h, mint   500-750   June 12, 1995 Sold for $450

1935. RV Dahlrose vase, 8.5"h, mint   200-300   June 12, 1995 Sold for $220

1936. RV Apple Blossom jardinere and pedestal, pink, jardinere, 10.5"dia., pedestal, 16.5"h, jardinere is mint, pedestal with base chip   400-600   June 12, 1995 Sold for $700

1937. RV Apple Blossom jardinere and pedestal, green, jardinere, 10.5"dia., pedestal 16.5"h, both mint   700-900 June 12, 1995   Sold for $850

Not Pictured:

1938. RV Pinecone jardinere and pedestal, green, jardinere 11"dia., pedestal 17"h, mint   900-1200   June 12, 1995 Sold for $1000

1939. RV Ixia jardinere and pedestal, white and yellow blossoms against a pink and green ground, jardinere, 10"dia., pedestal 17"h, jardinere mint, pedestal with glaze flaw and tight line   500-700   June 12, 1995 Sold for $1100

1940. RV Luffa vase, two handles, caramel, green and yellow, 8.5"h, mint   300-400   June 12, 1995 Sold for $250

1941. RV Cremona vase, light green with darker green drip over berries, leaves and vines, unmarked, 6.5"dia. x 4"h, small chip to bottom   50-100   June 12, 1995 Sold for $90

1942. RV Futura vase, terraced form in tan and blue matt glaze, 7"h, mint 400-600   June 12, 1995 Sold for $650

1943. RV Futura vase, four small buttressed handles at shoulder, yellow and brown drip glaze, 10"h, base chip 300-500   June 12, 1995 Sold for $350

1944. RV Matt Color vase, horizontal ribs in matt white glaze, 5"h, base chips   50-100   June 12, 1995 Sold for $30

1945. RV Topeo vase, light blue mottled matt glaze, 9"h, mint   250-350   June 12, 1995   Sold for $450

1946. RV Moderne vase, cream matt glaze, paper label, 5.5"h, mint   100-200   June 12, 1995   Sold for $180

Not Pictured:

1947. RV Futura hanging basket, green, yellow and blue geometric shapes on a tan ground, 7"dia., mint   300-400 June 12, 1995   Sold for $325

1948. RV Futura vase, terraced form with two handles in pink and gray hi-glaze, foil label, 8"h, base chips   400-500 June 12, 1995   Sold for $400

1949. RV Futura vase, pink with green, two handles, 6.5"w x 4"h, mint   300-400   June 12, 1995   Sold for $350

1950. RV Futura vase, star-shaped form on terraced pedestal in pink and gray/green hi-glaze, 8.5"h, mint   350-450 June 12, 1995   Sold for $350

1951. RV Rozane Royal vase, blossoms atop stems and leaves in white, pale green and dark green against a green ground, signed M. Timberlake, wafer mark, 14"h, mint   1200-1700   June 12, 1995   Sold for $1700

1952. RV Rozane Royal vase, iris blossoms with curling petals atop vertical stems and leaves in dark blue, violet, medium blue and white against a cream to blue ground, signed Walter Meyers, impressed marks, 16"h, tight line at rim and base, repair to lip   1000-1500 June 12, 1995   Sold for $1200

Not Pictured:

1953. RV Rozane Royal vessel with lid, matching pitcher, both in brown, yellow and green berries on green and yellow thorny branches and leaves, on a dark brown to olive green ground, chocolate pot 10"h, pitcher 3.5"h, both mint   250-350   June 12, 1995   Sold for $500

1954. **RV Donatello** double bud vase, two handles, 7"h, mint 200-300 June 12, 1995 Sold for $300

1955. **RV Cherry Blossom** jardinere, caramel and cream, 10"dia. x 8"h, mint 600-800 June 12, 1995 Sold for $400

1956. **RV Wincraft** vase, yellow and green with white flower, 10"h, mint 150-200 June 12, 1995 Sold for $100

1957. **RV Decorated Persian** hanging basket, floral design in green, red, lavender and yellow on a cream ground, 9"dia. x 8"h, hairlines 300-400 June 12, 1995 Sold for $300

1958. **RV Decorated Persian** pedestal, floral design in green, olive, yellow and deep red on a cream ground, 17.5"h, minor base chip 300-400 June 12, 1995 Sold for $240

1959. **RV Rosecraft Panel** vase, violet blossoms and green stems and leaves on a dark green ground, ink mark, 10.5", chip to rim 100-200 June 12, 1995 Sold for $125

1960. **RV Donatello** jardinere, white and green with cherub design, ink mark, 11"dia. x 9"h, minute chip at rim 100-200 June 12, 1995 Sold for $110

1961. **RV Pinecone** vase, brown with single branch handle, 4"h, mint 200-300 June 12, 1995 Sold for $180

1962. **RV Rozane Light** vase, caramel, peach and ivory rose blossoms and buds on light green and teal thorned stems and leaves on a dark brown to ivory ground, signed J. Imlay, wafer mark, 15"h, mint 900-1200 June 12, 1995 Sold for $600

Not Pictured:

1963. **RV Futura** vase, four-sided form on circular pedestal in pink and gray matt, 7"h, mint 300-500 June 12, 1995 Sold for $325

1964. RV Creamware Nursery Plate, Higgeldy-Piggeldy, 7.5"h, mint 100-150 July 13, 1994 Sold for $110

1965. RV Juvenile bowl, banded design of five chicks, 8"dia., mint 100-150 July 13, 1994 Sold for $110

1966. RV Juvenile cup, duck with hat, RV mark, 3"h, mint 100-150 July 13, 1994 Sold for $120

1967. RV Juvenile plate, duck with hat, RV mark, 7.5"dia., mint 100-150 July 13, 1994 Sold for $100

1968. RV Juvenile cereal bowl, Sun Bonnet Girl design, RV mark, 6"dia., mint 100-150 July 13, 1994 Sold for $140

1969. RV Juvenile egg cup, chick design, 4"h, mint 100-150 July 13, 1994 Sold for $150

1970. RV Juvenile bowl, decoration of three puppies, RV mark, 8"dia., mint 100-150 July 13, 1994 Sold for $160

1971. RV Juvenile bowl, duck with hat, RV mark, 8"dia., mint 100-150 July 13, 1994 Sold for $130

Not Pictured:

1972. RV Blackberry vase, two handles, 6.5"h, mint 250-350 June 10, 1995 Sold for $350

1973. RV Blackberry vase, two handles, 9"h, mint 350-450 June 10, 1995 Sold for $550

1974. RV Futura vase, egg shape atop base and four feet in shades of peach and green, 7.5"h, base chip 300-500 June 12, 1995 Sold for $300

1975. RV Mostique jardinere, 9"h, mint 250-350 June 12, 1995 Sold for $425

1976. RV Sunflower vase, two-handled form with broad waist, paper label, 5.5"h, mint 300-500 July 15, 1996 Sold for $500

1977. RV Jonquil vase, broad-waisted form with two handles and wide rim, 5"h, mint 250-350 July 15, 1996 Sold for $325

1978. RV Cherry Blossom vase, two-handled form, caramel and cream with white blossoms, 5"h, mint 250-350 July 15, 1996 Sold for $230

1979. RV Rozane vase, orange and yellow floral decoration wrapping around the top and trailing down the front, green leaves, artist signed on side CL Leffler, impressed Rozane RPCo., 15.5"h, mint 1700-2700 July 13, 1994 Sold for $1700

Not Pictured:

1980. RV Rozane vase, rose blossoms and buds in caramel, orange and tan atop thorny stems and leaves in green, impressed marks, 20"h, chips to base, body and neck 500-700 June 12, 1995 Sold for $700

123

1981. RV Wisteria vase, pink blossoms against a dark blue, green and caramel ground, 8.5"h, mint   300-400 June 10, 1995 Sold for $375

1982. RV Carnelian vase, green on green drip, 12.5"h, minor base chips   200-250   June 10, 1995 Sold for $210

1983. RV Morning Glory vase, green, paper label, 6"h, repair to handle and rim   150-250   June 10, 1995 Sold for $230

1984. RV Dogwood wallpockets, pair, green, ink mark, 9.5"h, one with hairline, one mint   200-250   June 10, 1995 Sold for $210

1985. RV Blackberry jardinere, paper label, 9.5"dia. x 7"h, minor flake at base   250-350   June 10, 1995 Sold for $400

1986. RV Luffa vase, brown and green, 8"h, repair to rim 100-150   June 10, 1995 Sold for $160

1987. RV Ixia vase, green, 15"h, repaired base chip   100-150 June 10, 1995 Sold for $210

1989. RV Vista basket, landscape design in green, blue and lavender, 9.5"h, repair to handle   100-150 June 10, 1995 Sold for $150

Not Pictured:

1990. RV Cherry Blossom jardinere, two handles, brown with cream bands and floral design, 11"dia. x 8"h, mint 650-850   July 14, 1998 Sold for $600

1991. RV Florentine wallpockets, three, two 7"l and one 8", one stamped, two with paper labels, one with flake 250-350   July 14, 1998 Sold for $240

1992. RV Water lily cookie jar, brown to orange with yellow flower, 10.5"h, mint   300-500   June 12, 1995 Sold for $450

1993. RV Baneda vase, pink with banded decoration, 6.5"h, mint   400-600   June 12, 1995 Sold for $750

1994. RV Velmoss Scroll vase, cream with stylized red roses and green leaves, 8"h, mint 100-150 June 12, 1995 Sold for $230

1995. RV Jonquil vase, brow with white and yellow flowers, paper label, 5"h, mint 150-250 June 12, 1995 Sold for $260

1996. RV Ferella bowl with flower frog, brown, 9.5"dia., mint 250-350 June 12, 1995 Sold for $375

1997. RV Rosecraft Panel vase, green, 9.25"h, mint 150-250 June 12, 1995 Sold for $270

1998. RV Wincraft candlesticks, white hi-glaze with green and brown highlights, 2"h, mint 70-120 June 12, 1995 Sold for $40

1999. RV Apple Blossom hanging basket, 6"h, mint 150-250 June 12, 1995 Sold for $190

2000. RV Topeo vase, red, paper label, 6"h, mint 150-250 June 12, 1995 Sold for $230

Not Pictured:

2001. RV Foxglove ewer, yellow, green and pink on blue ground, 15"h, mint 250-350 July 16, 1997 Sold for $400

2002. RV sign, blue and cream matt glaze, 8"w x 4"h, mint 1700-2700 July 16, 1997 Sold for $2100

2003. RV Baneda vase, green, blue and brown, 5"h, mint 350-450 July 16, 1997 Sold for $375

2004. RV Fuschia ewer, blue, pink, green and white, 10"h, mint 150-250 July 16, 1997 Sold for $325

2005. RV Pinecone window box, green, 15"l, mint 200-300 June 10, 1995 Sold for $210

2006. RV Jonquil vase, white and yellow blossoms with green stems, two-handled form, 6.5"h, mint 300-400 June 10, 1995 Sold for $400

2007. RV Pinecone window box, brown, 15"l, mint 200-300 June 10, 1995 Sold for $210

2008. RV Cherry Blossom vase, brown, 8"h, mint 600-800 June 12, 1995 Sold for $600

2009. RV Orion vase, brown with blue hi-glaze, 6.5"h, mint 250-350 June 12, 1995 Sold for $120

125

2010. RV Teasel vase, orange with green design, 5"h, mint 100-150 June 11, 1994 Sold for $110

2011. RV Columbine vase, rose and green, 4"h, mint 50-100 June 11, 1994 Sold for $100

2012. RV Sunflower vase, brown and green with yellow flowers, 5"h, mint 200-250 June 11, 1994 Sold for $200

2013. RV Cherry Blossom vase, brown and cream, 7"h, mint 200-300 June 11, 1994 Sold for $325

2014. RV Primrose vase, brown, yellow and green with white flowers, 4"h, chips to handle 50-100 June 11, 1994 Sold for $30

2015. RV Freesia vase, blue with cream, white and green, 4"h, mint 50-100 June 11, 1994 Sold for $100

2016. RV Montacello vase, green, blue and brown with white and black designs, 5"h, mint 100-200 June 11, 1994 Sold for $160

Not Pictured:

2017. RV Artcraft vase, blue, green and caramel, four buttressed handles, 4"h, mint 150-250 June 12, 1995 Sold for $300

2018. RV Freesia vase, orange with yellow floral decoration and greenery, 18", mint 300-400 July 13, 1994 Sold for $350

2019. RV Poppy vase, gray with large white and green poppies, 15", mint 250-350 July 13, 1994 Sold for $300

2020. RV Foxglove vase, blue, 13"h, mint 150-250 July 13, 1994 Sold for $325

2021. RV Dahlrose bowl, green and brown with white flowers, 4"h, mint 150-250 June 11, 1994 Sold for $90

2022. RV Clemana bowl, brown, 4.5"h, mint 100-200 June 11, 1994 Sold for $125

2023. RV Topeo vase, red hi-glaze, 7.5"h, mint 150-250 June 11, 1994 Sold for $225

2024. RV Panel vase, dark green with lighter green and lavender floral panel, 6"h, mint 100-200 June 11, 1994 Sold for $180

2025. RV Wisteria vase, brown with purple and green decoration, 6"h, repaired rim 100-150 June 11, 1994 Sold for $80

2026. RV Primrose vase, blue with white flowers, 4"h, mint 100-150 June 11, 1994 Sold for $80

2027. RV Dogwood II basket, green with white and black floral design, 5"h, mint 100-200 June 11, 1994 Sold for $125

Not Pictured:

2028. RV Jonquil bowl and frog, 10.5"dia., mint 100-200 July 10, 1994 Sold for $260

2029. RV Donatello double bud vase, basket shape with handle between openings, 7"h, mint 100-200 July 13, 1994 Sold for $230

2030. RV Thornapple bowl, green and blue with white floral design, 6"dia. x 3"h, mint 75-125 June 11, 1994 Sold for $50

2031. RV Baneda vase, green and blue with orange cherry decoration, 6"h, mint 200-250 June 11, 1994 Sold for $350

2032. RV Blackberry vase, green and brown with blackberry decoration, 5"h, mint 200-250 June 11, 1994 Sold for $275

2033. RV Wisteria vase, brown and green with purple wisteria, 5"h, mint 200-250 June 11, 1994 Sold for $275

2034. RV Jonquil vase, brown and green with white and yellow floral design, 4"h, mint 150-200 June 11, 1994 Sold for $200

2035. RV Luffa vase, green and brown with green design, 8"h, mint 150-200 June 11, 1994 Sold for $120

2036. RV Montacello vase, browns with white and black designs, 5"h, mint 100-150 June 11, 1994 Sold for $185

Not Pictured:

2037. RV Blackberry vase, 6"h, mint 200-300 July 13, 1994 Sold for $250

2038. RV Blackberry vase, 6"h, mint 200-300 July 13, 1994 Sold for $425

2039. RV Blackberry vase, 4.5"h, mint 150-250 July 13, 1994 Sold for $325

2040. RV Futura wallpocket, Art Deco design in orange and blue, black RV sticker, 8.5"h, mint 150-250 June 11, 1994 Sold for $290

2041. RV Futura vase, Art Deco shape narrowing at bottom with stylized design in shades of blue, paper label, 6"h, repaired chip 200-300 June 11, 1994 Sold for $280

2042. RV Futura vase, stylized floral decoration, shades of blue and orange, 7"w x 5"h, mint 300-500 June 11, 1994 Sold for $400

2043. RV Futura vase, Art Deco design in orange and brown, 12"h, repaired chips 300-500 June 11, 1994 Sold for $325

2044. RV Futura vase, rectangular base, red and pink with stylized floral decoration, 6.5"w x 4"h, mint 250-350 June 11, 1994 Sold for $350

2045. RV Futura vase, triangular shape narrowing to round base, dark blue Art Deco design on lighter blue ground, 9"h, repaired chips 250-350 June 11, 1994 Sold for $225

2046. RV Futura candlesticks, shades of blue, green and tan, 4.5"h, mint 250-350 June 11, 1994 Sold for $250

Not Pictured:

2047. RV Futura vase, olive and lime green hi-glaze, 5.5"h, tight hairline 600-800 July 14, 1998 Sold for $900

127

2048. RV Normandy hanging basket, cream and green with banded decoration, 7"dia., mint 100-200 June 11, 1994 Sold for $180

2049. RV Ming Tree vase, white hi-glaze with green tree and brown branch handle, 14.5"h, mint 150-250 June 11, 1994 Sold for $260

2050. RV Fuschia bowl, green and pink floral decoration, 8"dia., mint 50-100 June 11, 1994 Sold for $75

2051. RV Cremona vase, pink with green floral design, 12"h, mint 150-250 June 11, 1994 Sold for $200

2052. RV Matt Color vase, aqua, 6"h, mint 50-100 June 11, 1994 Sold for $100

2053. RV Bushberry vase, brown, 12.5"h, mint 150-250 June 11, 1994 Sold for $120

2054. RV Bleeding Heart bowl, two handles, rose and green glaze, scalloped top, 13"w, mint 100-150 June 11, 1994 Sold for $140

Not Pictured:

2055. RV Snowberry teapot with lid, sugar and creamer, blue, all mint 250-350 July 10, 1994 Sold for $280

2056. RV Imperial II vase, aqua and yellow mottled hi-glaze, 7"h, mint 250-350 June 10, 1995 Sold for $210

2057. RV Fuschia vase, brown and green, 8.5"h, mint 100-150 June 11, 1994 Sold for $115

2058. RV Apple Blossom hanging basket, pink to brown with white flowers, 8"dia., mint 150-200 June 11, 1994 Sold for $150

2059. RV Velmoss vase, green crystalline glaze, 6"h, mint 100-150 June 11, 1994 Sold for $60

2060. RV Blackberry basket, arched handle, green with blackberry decoration, 8"h, mint 250-350 June 11, 1994 Sold for $800

2061. RV Earlam bowl, blues, green and brown, 4"h, mint 100-200 June 11, 1994 Sold for $160

2062. RV Foxglove vase, pink and blue with white floral design, 4.5"h, mint 100-150 June 11, 1994 Sold for $60

2063. RV Teasel vase, cream to brown, 8"h, mint 150-250 June 11, 1994 Sold for $70

Not Pictured:

2064. RV Foxglove vase, pink, 16"h, minute flake to handle 200-300 June 11, 1994 Sold for $210

2065. RV Bushberry mugs, 15, blue, 4"h, mint 200-300 July 10, 1994 Sold for $500

2066. RV Pinecone vase, green, two-handled, 6.5"h, mint 150-250 June 10, 1995 Sold for $230

2067. RV Jonquil bowl, brown and green with white flowers, 12"w x 4"h, mint 150-250 June 11, 1994 Sold for $180

2068. RV Morning Glory vase, white with pink and green flowers, 4.5"dia. x 6.25"h, mint 200-300 June 11, 1994 Sold for $230

2069. RV Panel vase, dark green with lavender and green floral design in panels, 9"h, mint 150-250 June 11, 1994 Sold for $250

2070. RV Laurel urn, yellow, orange and black, 6.5"h, mint 150-250 June 11, 1994 Sold for $190

2071. RV Dahlrose bowl, brown and green with white flowers, 4.5"h, mint 150-250 June 11, 1994 Sold for $125

Not Pictured:

2072. RV Jonquil vase, 5.5"dia. x 4"h, mint 100-200 July 10, 1994 Sold for $200

2073. RV Pinecone vase, green, 8.5"h, mint 150-250 June 10, 1995 Sold for $250

2074. RV Dahlrose window box, brown, green, cream and orange, 15"w x 7"h, repaired chips 150-300 June 10, 1995 Sold for $200

2075. RV Artcraft vase, brown and green, 6.5"d x 5.25"h, mint 150-250 June 11, 1994 Sold for $300

2076. RV Futura vase, green glossy glaze, double handles, 9"h, mint 400-600 June 11, 1994 Sold for $400

2077. RV Futura jardinere, gray, pink and purple with Art Deco style leaves, 7"h, mint 500-700 June 11, 1994 Sold for $260

2078. RV Futura vase, funnel shape on square base supported by slender columns, yellow, blue and green matt, 4"h, mint 250-350 June 11, 1994 Sold for $350

2079. RV Futura vase, blue, green and yellow matt, 8"h, mint 400-600 June 11, 1994 Sold for $500

2080. RV Futura vase, brown, blue and green matt, 6"h, mint 300-500 June 11, 1994 Sold for $450

2081. RV Artcraft vase, blue to green and brown, 4"h, mint 150-250 June 11, 1994 Sold for $225

Not Pictured:

2082. RV Futura vase, blue and brown matt, 7"h, mint 450-650 July 14, 1998 Sold for $750

2083. **RV Tuscany** bowl with frog, pink gloss glaze with green, 10"w x 3"h, mint 100-150 June 11, 1994 Sold for $75

2084. **RV Victorian Art Pottery** vase, brown with stylized design, 7"h, mint 250-350 June 11, 1994 Sold for $450

2085. **RV Zephyr Lily** candleholders, green, 5"h, mint 100-150 June 11, 1994 Sold for $115

2086. **RV Moss** vase, pink and green, 13"h, minute base flake 300-400 June 11, 1994 Sold for $400

2087. **RV Cosmos** candlesticks, brown, 5"h, mint 100-150 June 11, 1994 Sold for $130

2088. **RV Russco** urn vase, blue, 7"h, mint 100-200 June 11, 1994 Sold for $60

2089. **RV Cremona** bowl, pink, blue and green, oval shape, 10"dia. x 3"h, mint 100-150 June 11, 1994 Sold for $60

Not Pictured:

2090. **RV Cremona** vase, green and blue floral design on mottled pink ground, 10.5"h, mint 250-350 June 12, 1995 Sold for $210

2091. **RV Wisteria** vase, handled form, 10"h, mint 300-500 July 13, 1993 Sold for $250

2092. **RV Mostique** jardinere and pedestal, tan ground with dark brown and green design, 28"h, repair to base 500-700 June 11, 1994 Sold for $275

2093. **RV Dahlrose** jardinere and pedestal, brown and green with white floral design, 24.5"h, mint 700-900 June 11, 1994 Sold for $600

2094. **RV Normandy** jardinere and pedestal, green and white line design with floral design on brown band, 28"h, mint 500-700 June 11, 1994 Sold for $700

Not Pictured:

2095. **RV Carnelian I** floor vase, blue drip over light blue, 18.5"h, mint 400-600 June 11, 1994 Sold for $400

2096. RV Lotus vase, peach and red hi-glaze, 10.5"h, mint 200-300   June 11, 1994 Sold for $90

2097. RV Velmoss Schroll compote, cream with red and green stylized roses, 9"dia., mint   100-200 June 11, 1994 Sold for $100

2098. RV Mostique bowl, cream ground, 8"dia., mint 100-200   June 11, 1994 Sold for $40

2099. RV Topeo vase, blue and green, 14"h, mint   400-600 June 11, 1994 Sold for $600

2100. RV Montacello vase, green and brown with black and white designs, paper label, 7"h, mint   150-250 June 11, 1994 Sold for $170

2101. RV Futura jardinere, brown and green, 12"dia. x 8"h, mint   400-600   June 11, 1994 Sold for $275

2102. RV Mostique vase, yellow and green designs on gray bisque, 10"h, mint   100-200 June 11, 1994 Sold for $55

2103. RV Donatello jardinere and pedestal, green and white with cherubs, 28"h, chips   500-700 June 11, 1994 Sold for $200

2104. RV Apple Blossom jardinere and pedestal, pink with brown branch handles and white flowers, 24.5"h, chip to base   500-700   June 11, 1994 Sold for $375

2105. RV Florentine jardinere and pedestal, dark to light brown with green, 27"h, mint   500-700   June 11, 1994 Sold for $400

Not Pictured:

2106. RV Donattello umbrella stand, green and cream, 20"h, mint   400-600   June 11, 1994 Sold for $600

131

2107. RV Pinecone hanging basket, green with two pine needle handles, 7.5"dia. x 5"h, mint 200-300 July 10, 1994 Sold for $200

2108. RV Pinecone jardinere, green, two handles, 9.5"dia. x 6.25"h, mint 200-300 July 10, 1994 Sold for $300

2109. RV Pinecone vase, green, footed with two handles, 7.5"h, mint 200-300 July 10, 1994 Sold for $210

2110. RV Pinecone plate, green, 8"dia., mint 150-250 July 10, 1994 Sold for $425

2111. RV Pinecone bowl, green, two handles, 7.5"dia. x 5"h, mint 150-250 July 10, 1994 Sold for $160

2112. RV Pinecone hanging basket, green, two handles, 7"dia. x 5.5"h, mint 200-300 July 10, 1994 Sold for $200

Not Pictured:

2113. RV Pinecone planter and underplate, green, marked, 6"dia. x 5.5"h, both mint 200-300 July 15, 1997 Sold for $210

2114. RV Pinecone vase, brown, 4"h, mint 100-200 July 13, 1994 Sold for $95

2115. RV Pinecone vase, brown, 8"h, mint 100-200 July 13, 1994 Sold for $155

2116. RV Pinecone vase, brown, 7"h, mint 100-200 July 13, 1994 Sold for $115

2117. RV Pinecone tray, green, 12"h, mint 150-250 July 13, 1994 Sold for $145

2118. RV Pinecone vase, green, paper label, 12"h, mint 250-350 July 13, 1994 Sold for $225

2119. RV Pinecone vase, brown, 7"h, small flake to top 100-200 July 13, 1994 Sold for $80

2120. RV Pinecone basket, green, 10"h, mint 250-350 July 13, 1994 Sold for $220

Not Pictured:

2121. RV Futura vase, Sailboat, brown and green dramatic flaring form on two feet with blue and green molded floral design, 3.5"h, mint 700-900 June 8, 1997 Sold for $425

2122. RV Futura vase, Sandtoy, flaring four-sided form in tan, green and blue with four open buttresses, 4.25"h, mint 350-550 June 8, 1997 Sold for $400

2123. RV Futura vase, Bomb, green hi-glaze with gunmetal at base, bulbous form, tiered neck, 12"h, repaired chip 500-700 June 8, 1997 Sold for $375

2124. RV Moderne vase, peach and white, 6.5"h, mint 100-150 June 11, 1994 Sold for $95

2125. RV Clemana bowl, green with white flowers, 6.5"h, mint 150-200 June 11, 1994 Sold for $325

2126. RV Thornapple vase, pink with white flowers, 4"h, mint 75-125 June 11, 1994 Sold for $65

2127. RV Morning Glory pedestal vase, white with lavender flowers, 10"h, chip repair to top 250-350 June 11, 1994 Sold for $150

2128. RV Fuschia bowl, blue and yellow, 4"h, mint 75-125 June 11, 1994 Sold for $105

2129. RV Luffa vase, green and brown, paper label, 8.5"h, mint 200-300 June 11, 1994 Sold for $325

2130. RV Windsor vase, blue and yellow with yellow design, 6"h, mint 150-250 June 11, 1994 Sold for $180

2131. RV Jonquil vase, brown and green with white flowers, 8.5"h, mint 200-300 June 11, 1994 Sold for $300

2132. RV Vista vase, green and gray with purple, 10"h, mint 200-300 June 11, 1994 Sold for $375

2133. RV Falline bowl, brown, 11"dia. x 3"h, mint 200-300 June 11, 1994 Sold for $170

2134. RV Luffa vase, brown and green with white flowers, 12"h, mint 250-350 June 11, 1994 Sold for $350

2135. RV Wisteria bowl, brown with dark blue and purple flowers, 7" x 3", mint 100-200 June 11, 1994 Sold for $200

2136. RV Wisteria vase, brown with purple flowers, 8.5"h, mint 300-400 June 11, 1994 Sold for $350

2137. RV Cherry Blossom vase, yellow and brown, 5"h, mint 200-300 June 11, 1994 Sold for $140

2138. RV Fuschia vase, brown with pink flowers, 6.5"h, mint 150-250   June 11, 1994 Sold for $75

2139. RV Cherry Blossom vase, brown and cream with white flowers, 8"h, small chip under foot   200-300 June 11, 1994 Sold for $190

2140. RV Iris vase, pink and green with white flower, 7.5"h, mint   100-200   June 11, 1994 Sold for $125

2141. RV Wisteria vase, dark blue to brown with purple floral design, 10"h, mint   400-600   June 11, 1994 Sold for $1300

2142. RV Dawn vase, aqua with white design, 6"h, mint 150-250   June 11, 1994 Sold for $115

2143. RV Laurel vase, orange and black, 10"h, mint 250-350   June 11, 1994 Sold for $275

2144. RV Cosmos bowl, green and yellow with white and lavender flowers, 4"h, mint   100-200   June 11, 1994 Sold for $70

Not Pictured:

2145. RV Moss vase, pink and green, 7.5"h, repaired base chip   150-250   June 11, 1994 Sold for $135

2146. RV Rozane vase, cream with red and yellow floral decoration, 9"dia., mint   100-200   June 11, 1994 Sold for $50

2147. RV Earlam vase, green exterior, brown interior, 7"h, mint   200-300   June 11, 1994 Sold for $325

2148. RV Persian bowl, cream with pink, yellow and green, 8"dia., mint   150-250   June 11, 1994 Sold for $130

2149. RV Windsor vase, orange and brown, 9"h, mint 300-500   June 11, 1994 Sold for $240

2150. RV Snowberry planter, green and brown with white flowers, 9"w, mint   100-200   June 11, 1994 Sold for $60

2151. RV Dogwood I jardinere, green with white flowers, brown branches, 6"h, mint   150-250   June 11, 1994 Sold for $160

2152. RV Corinthian bowl, green and cream, 9"dia., mint 100-150   June 11, 1994 Sold for $150

2153. **RV Jonquil** bowl, 8.5"dia. x 2"h, mint 100-150 July 10, 1994 Sold for $150

2154. **RV Jonquil** vase, two handles, unmarked, 8"dia. x 7"h, mint 250-350 July 10, 1994 Sold for $350

2155. **RV Topeo** bowl, deep red, 11.5"dia. x 3"h, mint 150-250 July 10, 1994 Sold for $110

2156. **RV Carnelian** vase, light green with brown drip, ornate handles, blue stamp mark, 10"h, mint 150-250 July 10, 1994 Sold for $160

2157. **RV Topeo** bowl, red high glaze, original label, 9"dia. x 2"h, mint 150-250 July 10, 1994 Sold for $100

2158. **RV Orian** vase, blue matt glaze with trial glaze numbers, 9"h, mint 300-500 July 10, 1994 Sold for $325

2159. **RV Mock Orange** bowl, yellow, mint 50-100 July 10, 1994 Sold for $40

Not Pictured:

2160. **RV Falline** vase, shades of brown and green, 8"h, mint 300-400 June 11, 1994 Sold for $400

2161. **RV Creamware** Nursery Plate, Higgeldy-Piggeldy, 7.5"h, mint 100-150 July 13, 1994 Sold for $110

2162. **RV Juvenile** bowl, banded design of five chicks, 8"dia., mint 100-150 July 13, 1994 Sold for $110

2163. **RV Juvenile** cup, duck with hat, RV mark, 3"h, mint 100-150 July 13, 1994 Sold for $120

2164. **RV Juvenile** plate, duck with hat, RV mark, 7.5"dia., mint 100-150 July 13, 1994 Sold for $100

2165. **RV Juvenile** cereal bowl, Sunbonnet Girl design, RV mark, 6"dia., mint 100-150 July 13, 1994 Sold for $140

2166. **RV Juvenile** egg cup, chick design, 4"h, mint 100-150 July 13, 1994 Sold for $150

2167. **RV Juvenile** bowl, decoration of three puppies, RV mark, 8"dia., mint 100-150 July 13, 1994 Sold for $160

2168. **RV Juvenile** bowl, duck with hat, RV mark, 8"dia., mint 100-150 July 13, 1994 Sold for $130

2169. **RV Donatello** bowl, footed, 12"dia. x 5"h, mint 100-150 July 13, 1994 Sold for $80

2170. **RV Donatello** wallpocket, RV mark, 10", mint 100-150 July 13, 1994 Sold for $110

2171. **RV Donatello** vase, 12"h, mint 200-250 July 13, 1994 Sold for $140

2172. **RV Donatello** candlestick, 6.5"h, mint 100-200 July 13, 1994 Sold for $120

2173. **RV Donatello** candlestick, two angular handles, 4.5"h, mint 100-150 July 13, 1994 Sold for $100

2174. **RV Donatello** jardinere, marked, 7"dia. x 5.5"h, mint 100-150 July 13, 1994 Sold for $80

2175. **RV Donatello** jardinere, marked, 5.5"dia. x 4"h, mint 75-125 July 13, 1994 Sold for $50

Not Pictured:

2176. **RV Donatello** jardinere and pedestal, 12"dia. jardinere, 28"h overall, minor flaws 500-700 July 10, 1994 Sold for $220

2177. **RV Rosecraft Vintage** jardinere and pedestal, dark brown with berries, vines and leaves around top, 14"dia. x 10"h, mint 200-300 June 11, 1994 Sold for $650

2178. **RV Donatello** jardinere and pedestal, 10"dia. jardinere, 23"h overall, minor chips 400-600 July 10, 1994 Sold for $210

2179. **RV Embossed** pitcher, tulip design, 7.5"h, flake to base 50-100 July 10, 1994 Sold for $40

2180. **RV Embossed** pitcher, bull with head down, 7.5"h, restoration to base 50-100 July 10, 1994 Sold for $120

2181. **RV Embossed** pitcher, iris decoration, 9"h, mint 50-100 July 10, 1994 Sold for $190

2182. **RV Dutch** scene pitcher, 9"h, lines in making 50-100 July 10, 1994 Sold for $130

2183. **RV Embossed** pitcher, cow decoration, 6.5"h, lines and chip repair to base 50-100 July 10, 1994 Sold for $150

2184. **RV Embossed** pitcher, golden rod, 9"h, mint 50-100 July 10, 1994 Sold for $150

2185. **RV Embossed** pitcher, wildrose, 9.5"h, mint 50-100 July 10, 1994 Sold for $190

2186. **RV Embossed** pitcher, landscape design, 7.5"h, mint 50-100 July 10, 1994 Sold for $120

2187. **RV Pinecone** hanging basket, green with two pine needle handles, 7.5"dia. x 5"h, mint   200-300   July 10, 1994 Sold for $200

2188. **RV Pinecone** jardinere, green, two handles, 9.5"dia. x 6.25"h, mint   200-300   July 10, 1994 Sold for $300

2189. **RV Pinecone** vase, green, footed with two handles, 7.5"h, mint   200-300   July 10, 1994 Sold for $210

2190. **RV Pinecone** plate, green, 8"dia., mint   150-250 July 10, 1994 Sold for $425

2191. **RV Pinecone** bowl, green, two handles, 7.5"dia. x 5"h, mint   150-250   July 10, 1994 Sold for $160

2192. **RV Pinecone** hanging basket, green, two handles, 7"dia. x 5.5"h, mint   200-300   July 10, 1994 Sold for $200

2193. **RV Pinecone** vase, brown, 4"h, mint   100-200 July 13, 1994 Sold for $95

2194. **RV Pinecone** vase, brown, 8"h, mint   100-200 July 13, 1994 Sold for $155

2195. **RV Pinecone** vase, brown, 7"h, mint   100-200 July 13, 1994 Sold for $115

2196. **RV Pinecone** tray, green, 12"h, mint   150-250 July 13, 1994 Sold for $145

2197. **RV Pinecone** vase, green, paper label, 12"h, mint 250-350   July 13, 1994 Sold for $225

2198. **RV Pinecone** vase, brown, 7"h, small flake to top 100-200   July 13, 1994 Sold for $80

2199. **RV Pinecone** basket, green, 10"h, mint 250-350 July 13, 1994 Sold for $220

Not Pictured:

2200. **RV Zephyr Lily** bookends, blue with yellow floral design, 5.25"w x 5.25"h, mint   250-350   July 16, 1997 Sold for $400

2201. **RV Mostique** bowl, gray, Arts & Crafts design, 6"dia., mint 50-100 July 10, 1994 Sold for $100

2202. **RV Mostique** vase, Arts & Crafts design, 8"h, mint 100-150 July 10, 1994 Sold for $100

2203. **RV Mostique** bowl, Arts & Crafts design on blue ground, 6"dia., mint 50-100 July 10, 1994 Sold for $70

2204. **RV Mostique** vase, gray, 15"h, mint 300-400 July 10, 1994 Sold for $350

2205. **RV Mostique** vase, Arts & Crafts design, 10"h, mint 100-200 July 10, 1994 Sold for $120

2206. **RV Mostique** vase, Arts & Crafts design in tan, 6"h, mint 50-100 July 10, 1994 Sold for $120

2207. **RV Mostique** wallpocket, Arts & Crafts design, 10"h, mint 100-150 July 10, 1994 Sold for $130

2208. **RV Pinecone** bowl, green, 9"w x 4"h, mint 200-250 July 10, 1994 Sold for $110

2209. **RV Pinecone** candle holders, green, 3.5"dia. x 2"h, mint 150-250 July 10, 1994 Sold for $250

2210. **RV Pinecone** vase, green, two handles, 5"dia. x 6.25"h, mint 200-250 Sold for $200

2211. **RV Pinecone** bowl, two handles, green, 9"dia. x 4"h, mint 100-200 July 10, 1994 Sold for $100

2212. **RV Pinecone** vase, green 9"w x 4.5"d x 8.5"h, mint 100-200 July 10, 1994 Sold for $120

2213. **RV Pinecone** match holder, green, 2.25"w x 2.75"h, mint 100-200 July 10, 1994 Sold for $130

2214. **RV Pinecone** bowl with flower frog, green, 16"w x 10"d x 8"h, mint 200-300 July 10, 1994 Sold for $300

2215. **RV Imperial** vase, brown and green, two-handled, 8"dia. x 8"h, mint 200-250 July 10, 1994 Sold for $260

2216. **RV Imperial** vase, brown and green, 12"h, small chip to bottom 200-250 July 10, 1994 Sold for $85

2217. **RV Imperial** umbrella stand, brown and green, 20"h, mint 500-700 July 10, 1994 Sold for $230

2218. **RV Dogwood** bowl, green with white dogwood decoration, 7"dia. x 3"h, mint 75-150 July 10, 1994 Sold for $70

2219. **RV Imperial** jardinere, green and brown, 10"dia. x 11"h, minor flakes 250-350 July 10, 1994 Sold for $90

2220. **RV Dogwood** vase, green with white dogwood decoration, 6"h, minor flakes to flowers 150-250 July 10, 1994 Sold for $30

2221. **RV Pinecone** planter, green, one handle, 9"w x 3.5"d x 3.5"h, mint 200-300 July 10, 1994 Sold for $160

2222. **RV Pinecone** bud vase, green with handle, 7"h, mint 150-250   July 10, 1994 Sold for $130

2223. **RV Pinecone** vase, green, two handles, 6"dia. x 4.5"h, mint 200-250 July 10, 1994 Sold for $150

2224. **RV Pinecone** vase, green, two handles, paper label, 7"dia. x 7"h, mint 200-300 July 10, 1994 Sold for $200

2225. **RV Pinecone** vase, green, one handle, 7.5"w x 3"h, mint 150-250 July 10, 1994 Sold for $100

2226. **RV Pinecone** vase, green, 8.5"h, 150-250 July 10, 1994 Sold for $150

2227. **RV Pinecone** planter, green, 10"w x 4"d x 4"h, mint 200-300 July 10, 1994 Sold for $160

Not Pictured:

2228. **RV Pinecone** candlesticks, blue with brown pinecone, green pine needles and handle, impressed Roseville, 3", both mint 200-300 July 16, 1997 Sold for $260

139

2229. **RV Pinecone** bowl, green, 11"w x 5"h, mint 150-250
July 10, 1994 Sold for $170

2230. **RV Pinecone** pitcher, green, 9"h, mint 250-350
July 10, 1994 Sold for $300

2231. **RV Pinecone** vase, green with one handle, 5.25"h, mint
100-200 July 10, 1994 Sold for $80

2232. **RV Pinecone** basket, handle, green, 8.5"dia. x 10"h,
mint 200-300 July 10, 1994 Sold for $260

2233. **RV Pinecone** vase, 7.5"w x 6.5"h, mint 100-150
July 10, 1994 Sold for $100

2234. **RV Pinecone** water jug, green, 8"h, mint 250-350
July 10, 1994 Sold for $325

2235. **RV Pinecone** planter, green with brown handle at
center, 13"w x 4.5"d x 4.5"h, mint 200-300
July 10, 1994 Sold for $260

2236. **RV Pinecone** vase, brown, 7"h, mint 150-250
July 10, 1994 Sold for $120

2237. **RV Pinecone** bowl, green, 6"d, mint 100-150
July 10, 1994 Sold for $120

2238. **RV Pinecone** bowl, brown, 15"w, mint 200-300
July 10, 1994 Sold for $270

2239. **RV Pinecone** vase, brown, 5"h, mint 100-200
July 10, 1994 Sold for $120

2240. **RV Pinecone** jardinere and pedestal, green, 8"h, mint
700-900 July 10, 1994 Sold for $750

2241. **RV Pinecone** bowl, brown, 15"l, mint 200-300
July 10, 1994 Sold for $170

2242. **RV Pinecone** vase, brown, 9"h, mint 100-200
July 10, 1994 Sold for $150

2243. **RV Pinecone** pitcher, brown, 10"h, mint 150-250
July 10, 1994 Sold for $270

2244. **RV Pinecone** basket, brown, 6"h, mint 150-250
July 10, 1994 Sold for $200

2245. **RV Pinecone** basket, green, 10", mint 200-300
July 10, 1994 Sold for $300

2246. RV Pinecone bowl, brown, 10"l, minor chip to foot
150-250 July 10, 1994 Sold for $150

2247. RV Pinecone vase, green, two handles, 7"h, mint
150-250 July 10, 1994 Sold for $100

2248. RV Pinecone vase, green, two handles, 5.5"dia. x
10.5"h, repair to foot   100-200 July 10, 1994
Sold for $120

2249. RV Pinecone bowl, green, two handles, 3"h, mint
75-150 July 10, 1994 Sold for $80

2250. RV Pinecone vase, brown, two handles, 7"h, mint
150-250 July 10, 1994 Sold for $110

2251. RV Pinecone vase, green, two handles, 12"h, mint
250-350 July 10, 1994 Sold for $180

2252. RV Pinecone vase, green two handles, 6.5"h, mint
150-250 July 10, 1994 Sold for $150

2253. RV Pinecone vase, brown, two handles, 6.5"h, mint
150-250 July 10, 1994 Sold for $160

2254. RV Pinecone vase, green two handles, 9"h, mint
100-200 July 10, 1994 Sold for $150

2255. RV Pinecone bowl, brown, 10"l, mint   200-300
July 10, 1994 Sold for $190

2256. RV Pinecone tray, green, 13.5"w x 5.75"d x 2.5"h,
mint 150-250 July 10, 1994 Sold for $130

2257. RV Pinecone ashtray, green, 4.5"dia., mint   100-200
July 10, 1994 Sold for $60

2258. RV Pinecone ashtray, green, 6"dia., mint   100-200
July 10, 1994 Sold for $90

2259. RV Pinecone vase, green with two handles, 7"dia. x
8.5"h, mint 150-250 July 10, 1994 Sold for $150

2260. RV Pinecone bowl, one handle, green, 7"dia. x 4"h,
mint 100-200 July 10, 1994 Sold for $100

2261. RV Pinecone ashtray, green, 5"dia. x 2.5"h, mint
100-200 July 10, 1994 Sold for $90

2262. RV Pinecone planter, green, 16"w x 2.75"d x 3.25"h,
mint 200-300 July 10, 1994 Sold for $170

Not Pictured:

2263. RV Snowberry teapot, creamer and sugar bowl, rose
to pink, teapot 10"dia. x 7"h, mint 250-350
June 11, 1994 Sold for $325

2264. RV Topeo console bowl, blue, 13", mint   150-250
July 10, 1994 Sold for $200

2265. RV Windsor vase, rust fern, 7"h, mint 250-300
July 10, 1994 Sold for $300

2266. RV Falline vase, brown, paper label, 12"h, mint
500-700 July 10, 1994 Sold for $650

2267. RV Ivory ginger jars, pair, paper labels, 10"h, mint
400-600 July 10, 1994 Sold for $270

2268. RV Futura jardinere, gray and pink, 8"h, glaze miss to
side and minor base chip 400-600 July 10, 1994
Sold for $250

2269. RV Windsor vase, rust leaves, 10"h, mint 300-500
July 10, 1994 Sold for $400

2270. RV Windsor vase, rust, 6"h, mint 200-300
July 10, 1994 Sold for $210

Not Pictured:

2271. RV Rozane pitcher, yellow daffodils, marked, 8"h,
mint 150-250 July 13, 1994 Sold for $210

2272. RV Aztec pitcher, blue with squeezebag decoration,
5"h, mint 300-400 June 11, 1994 Sold for $250

2273. RV Goodnight candlestick, handled form with green
ivy decoration, 7"h, mint 100-200 July 10, 1994
Sold for $375

2274. RV Futura vase, pink and green hi-glaze, star shape,
8"h, mint 300-400 July 10, 1994 Sold for $250

2275. RV Tuscany lamp, white matt, pottery section 10"h,
mint 150-250 July 10, 1994 Sold for $100

2276. RV Futura vase, pink and green hi-glaze, two handles,
8"h, mint 400-600 July 10, 1994 Sold for $1000

2277. RV Florane bowl, orange and brown, 9"dia. x 2"h,
mint 50-100 July 10, 1994 Sold for $20

2278. RV Wincraft vase, pinecone design in center, 12.5"h,
mint 200-300 July 10, 1994 Sold for $120

2279. RV Futura jardinere, 7"dia. x 11"h, mint 400-600
July 10, 1994 Sold for $400

2280. RV Tourmaline lamp, hi-glaze, pottery section 10"h,
mint 200-300 July 10, 1994 Sold for $325

Not Pictured:

2281. RV Sunflower vase, 6"dia. x 4"h, mint 200-300
July 13, 1994 Sold for $400

2282. RV Pinecone vase, brown, impressed mark, 6"h, mint
100-150   July 13, 1994   Sold for $80

2283. Roseville Pinecone tray, brown, 13.5"w x 2"d, mint
150-250   July 13, 1994   Sold for $140

2284. RV Pinecone vase, brown, impressed mark, 7"h, mint
100-150   July 13, 1994   Sold for $90

2285. RV Pinecone vase, blue, marked 12", mint   300-400
July 13, 1994   Sold for $280

2286. RV Pinecone vase, green, two handles, script mark, 6",
mint   100-200   July 13, 1994   Sold for $110

2287. RV Pinecone vase, brown, six candleholders, 11"w x
6"h, small nick on one candleholder   200-300
July 13, 1994   Sold for $300

Not Pictured:

2288. RV Luffa vase, green, 8"h, mint   125-175
July 13, 1994   Sold for $260

2289. RV Panel wallpocket, green with lavender and green
decoration, unmarked, 9", mint   100-200
July 13, 1994   Sold for $250

2290. RV Fuschia pedestal, blue, 6"dia. x 16"h, chip
200-300   July 10, 1994   Sold for $400

2291. RV Decorated Persian jardinere, design with
butterfly on a cream ground, 7", small chip to foot
150-250   July 10, 1994   Sold for $325

2292. RV Silhouette bowl, blue and green with nude in panel,
8.5"h, mint   250-350   June 11, 1994   Sold for $500

2293. RV Pinecone bookends pair, green, 5"h, mint
250-350   July 13, 1994   Sold for $230

2294. RV Pinecone vase, green, 6"h, mint   100-200
July 13, 1994   Sold for $80

2295. RV Pinecone vase, green, script signature, 8", mint
150-250   July 13, 1994   Sold for $190

2296. RV Pinecone tray, green, 13"w x 5"d x 7"h, mint
250-350   July 13, 1994   Sold for $250

2297. RV Pinecone vase, green, 7.5"w x 8.25"h, mint
250-350   July 13, 1994   Sold for $250

2298. RV Pinecone vase, green, script signature, 7", mint
100-200   July 13, 1994   Sold for $150

2299. RV Pinecone bowl, two handles, green, 7.5"dia. x 5"h,
mint   150-250   July 13, 1994   Sold for $140

Not Pictured:

2300. RV Peony basket, gold, 7"h, mint   100-150
July 13, 1994   Sold for $600

For more details please call:
(513) 321-6742

2301. **RV Dutch** creamware set, tankard and four mugs, decal, all in excellent condition, tankard 11.5"h and mugs 5"h; with **RV Dutch** creamware mug, decoration of boy, girl and cat on cream ground, 5"h; with a **RV Dutch** creamware mug, decoration of boy and girl on cream ground, 5"h, one has two small flakes and a hairline, others mint   300-500   July 13, 1994 Sold for $250

2302. **RV Elk** creamware set, tankard and seven mugs, decals on cream ground, tankard 11"h and mugs 5"h, one mug has hairline, others mint   300-500   July 13, 1994 Sold for $350

2303. **RV Donatello** wallpocket, white and green with raised cherubs, RV mark, 12", mint   100-200   July 13, 1994 Sold for $130

2304. **RV Donatello** candlestick, 8.5"h, mint   50-100 July 13, 1994   Sold for $70

2305. **RV Donatello** vase, 8"h; with a small flower frog not pictured, 3"h, both mint   50-100   July 13, 1994 Sold for $60

2306. **RV Donatello** jardinere, 7.5"dia. x 5"h, mint   50-100 July 13, 1994   Sold for $30

2307. **RV Donatello** wallpocket, no mark, 10", mint   100-200 July 13, 1994   Sold for $110

2308. **RV Donatello** vase, white and green with raised cherubs, marked, 10"h, mint   100-200   July 13, 1994 Sold for $250

2309. **RV Donatello** jardinere, 8"h, mint   75-150 July 13, 1994   Sold for $140

2310. **RV Donatello** candlestick, 8.5"h, mint   50-100 July 13, 1994   Sold for $65

Not Pictured:

2311. **RV Columbine** vase, blue with yellow and green floral decoration, 12"h, mint   150-250   June 11, 1994 Sold for $250

2312. **RV Iris** vase, orange and brown with white flowers, 10"h, mint   150-250   June 11, 1994   Sold for $250

2313. **RV Freesia** teapot with lid, white and pink on green matt ground, shape C, RV in relief, 7"h, mint   150-200 July 10, 1994   Sold for $220

2314. **RV Wisteria** vase, blue, 7"dia. x 5.5"h, mint   200-300 July 13, 1994   Sold for $300

2381. RV Futura vase, light and dark pink panels, geometric designs of green and dark blue in the lighter pink panels, 8"h, mint   300-500   July 13, 1994   Sold for $475

2382. RV Futura vase, ball-shaped base with tiered neck, green and pink hi-glaze, 8.5"h, mint   300-400   July 13, 1994   Sold for $425

2383. RV Futura vase, four leg base, blue to orange matt with green on columns, 8"h, mint   300-500   July 13, 1994   Sold for $400

2384. RV Futura vase, geometric design of pink and green on body and pink and green top, 8"h, mint   400-600   July 13, 1994   Sold for $500

2385. RV Futura vase, blue buds and green leaves, two Deco design buttresses, 5.5"h, mint   300-400   July 13, 1994   Sold for $400

2386. RV Futura vase, pink with green design on each side, raised arrow-shaped designs around base, 7"h, mint   400-600   July 13, 1994   Sold for $700

2387. RV Futura vase, covered in pink and green hi-glaze, 8"h, mint   250-350   July 13, 1994   Sold for $400

2388. RV Futura vase, blue/green leaf decoration on pale gray ground, 7.5"h, mint   600-800   July 13, 1994   Sold for $550

2389. RV Dogwood II basket, green with white and brown, 8"h, mint   150-250   July 13, 1994   Sold for $115

2390. RV Cremona vase, pink and green matt with lavender flowers and pale green leaves, unmarked, 8"h, mint   100-200   July 13, 1994   Sold for $170

2391. RV Cremona vase, light green with darker green drip over berries, leaves and vines, unmarked, 6.5"dia. x 4"h, small chip to bottom   50-100   July 13, 1994   Sold for $50

2392. RV Luffa vase, green and brown with white flowers, unmarked, 8.5"h, mint   200-250   July 13, 1994   Sold for $350

2393. RV Morning Glory vase, white, 4", chipped   100-200   July 13, 1994   Sold for $130

2394. RV Ferella vase, orange/brown with green pea pod design, unmarked, 7"h, chip to handle   150-250   July 13, 1994   Sold for $170

2395. RV Wincraft vase, lime with white tulip, script mark, 8", mint   100-150   July 13, 1994   Sold for $70

Not Pictured:

2396. RV Rozane ewer, dogwood, yellow and green leaves on brown ground, impressed signature, 11"h, mint   250-350   July 13, 1993   Sold for $475

149

2397. RV Freesia jardinere and pedestal, orange and brown with cream flowers, jardinere 12.5"dia. x 24"h overall, chip inside rim of jardinere   450-650   June 11, 1994 Sold for $125

2398. RV Clematis jardinere and pedestal, orange and green with yellow flowers, jardinere 12.5"dia. x 25"h overall, mint   500-700   June 11, 1994 Sold for $850

2399. RV Freesia jardinere and pedestal, dark brown and orange with cream flowers, jardinere 12.5"dia. x 24"h overall, mint   500-700   June 11, 1994 Sold for $550

Not Pictured:

2400. RV Clematis jardinere and pedestal, blue, jardinere 12"dia. x 8.5"h, pedestal 16"h, 24.5"h overall, chips and age line to jardinere   300-350   July 10, 1994 Sold for $475

2401. RV Baneda bowl, red, 9"dia., mint   150-250 July 13, 1994 Sold for $150

2402. RV Baneda vase, red, 7.5"h, mint   200-300 July 13, 1994 Sold for $350

2403. RV Baneda vase, red, 8.5"h, mint   250-350 July 13, 1994 Sold for $375

2404. RV Cherry Blossom vase, brown, 5.5"h, mint 150-250 July 13, 1994 Sold for $200

2405. RV Cherry Blossom vase, brown, 5.5"h, mint 200-300 July 13, 1994 Sold for $325

2406. RV Cherry Blossom vase, blue and pink, 5.5"h, mint 200-300 July 13, 1994 Sold for $450

2407. RV Donatello jardinere and pedestal, white and brown cherub figures with green and white stripes, 16"dia. x 30"h, minor chips   500-700   July 13, 1994 Sold for $475

2408. RV Pinecone jardinere and pedestal, green with bright orange pinecones, jardinere #3 is 11"dia. x 9"h, pedestal is 17"h, mint   900-1200   July 13, 1994 Sold for $900

2409. RV Mock Orange large jardinere and pedestal, green, 31"h, several small chips   600-800   July 13, 1994 Sold for $450

Not Pictured:

2410. RV Magnolia lamp, two-handled form with white flowers on tan and green ground, 21"h, mint   250-350 July 13, 1993   Sold for $425

2411. RV Ferella vase, brown, 10"h, mint   200-300 July 13, 1993   Sold for $375

2412. RV Orion vase, hi-glaze, tan with pale blue/green on handles, gray dripping from top, unmarked, 12.5"h, mint   75-150   July 13, 1993   Sold for $220

2413. RV Panel vase, brown with orange floral, RV stamp, 6.25"h, mint   100-150   July 13, 1994 Sold for $110

2414. RV Panel vase, brown with orange floral, RV stamp, 8"h, mint   100-150   July 13, 1994 Sold for $110

2415. RV Falline vase, green and blue, 6.5"h, mint 300-400   July 13, 1994 Sold for $475

2416. RV Falline vase, green and blue, 9"h, mint   300-400 July 13, 1994 Sold for $650

2417. RV Windsor vase, geometric yellow and green around rim, blue ground, 7"dia. x 6.5"h, mint   200-250 July 13, 1994 Sold for $250

2418. RV Windsor vase, geometric yellow, green, handles at neck, 6.5"h, mint   150-250   July 13, 1994 Sold for $270

151

2419. **RV Jonquil** bowl, 8.5"dia. x 2"h, mint 100-150
July 10, 1994 Sold for $150

2420. **RV Jonquil** vase, two handles, unmarked, 8"dia. x 7"h, mint 250-350 July 10, 1994 Sold for $350

2421. **RV Topeo** bowl, deep red, 11.5"dia. x 3"h, mint 150-250 July 10, 1994 Sold for $110

2422. **RV Carnelian** vase, light green with brown drip, ornate handles, blue stamp mark, 10"h, mint 150-250 July 10, 1994 Sold for $160

2423. **RV Topeo** bowl, red high glaze, original label, 9"dia. x 2"h, mint 150-250 July 10, 1994 Sold for $100

2424. **RV Orian** vase, blue matt glaze with trial glaze numbers, 9"h, mint 300-500 July 10, 1994 Sold for $325

2425. **RV Mock Orange** bowl, yellow, mint 50-100 July 10, 1994 Sold for $40

Not Pictured:

2426. **RV Rosecraft Vintage** jardinere and pedestal, dark brown with berries, vines and leaves around top, 14"dia. x 10"h, mint 200-300 June 11, 1994 Sold for $650

2427. **RV Wisteria** candleholders, brown and green, 4.5"h, mint 400-600 July 16, 1997 Sold for $425

2428. **RV Jonquil** vase, brown and green, 8"h, mint 300-400 July 16, 1997 Sold for $350

2429. **RV Sunflower** bowl, yellow, blue, green and brown, 6"h, mint 500-700 July 16, 1997 Sold for $750

2430. **RV Foxglove** jardinere, blue, 6"h, mint 100-150 July 16, 1997 Sold for $260

2431. **RV Fuschia** vase, blue, 8"h, mint 150-250 July 15, 1997 Sold for $290

2432. **RV Rozane** vase, yellow roses and bud, with olive green leaves and stems, impressed mark, artist L.M., 8"dia. x 10"h, small scratches, mint 500-700 July 13, 1993 Sold for $425

2433. **RV Tuscany** bowl, mottled pink with gray hi-glaze on oval two-handled shape, paper label, 4"dia., mint 75-150 July 10, 1994 Sold for $60

2434. **RV Freesia** teapot with lid, white and pink on green matt ground, shape C, RV in relief, 7"h, mint 150-200 July 10, 1994 Sold for $220

2435. **RV Tuscany** vase, gray with blue matt glaze, two handles, 7"dia., mint 100-150 July 10, 1994 Sold for $80

2436. **RV Tuscany** bowl, mottled pink with gray hi-glaze, 5"dia., mint 75-150 July 10, 1994 Sold for $120

2437. **RV Tourmaline** vase, mottled blue matt glaze on square shape, silver paper label, 7"h; with a **RV Burmese** planter not pictured, black semi-gloss rectangular piece, raised mark, 10"l, both mint 200-250 July 10, 1994 Sold for $80

2438. **RV Moderne** bowl, turquoise matt glaze, impressed RV, 11"w, mint 150-250 July 10, 1994 Sold for $170

2439. **RV Tuscany** bowl, mottled pink with gray hi-glaze, square shape, 7"dia., mint 100-150 July 10, 1994 Sold for $60

2440. RV Laurel vase, green, paper label, 6"h, mint   75-125
July 13, 1993 Sold for $80

2441. RV Sunflower vase, 5.5"h, mint   75-150
July 13, 1993 Sold for $280

2442. RV Velmoss vase, 10"h, mint   75-150   July 13, 1993
Sold for $90

2443. RV Russco vase, unmarked, 8.5"h, mint   100-200
July 13, 1993 Sold for $100

2444. RV Cherry Blossom vase, unmarked, 5"h, mint
100-200 July 13, 1993 Sold for $270

2445. RV Earlam vase, unmarked, 8"w x 7"h, mint   100-200
July 13, 1993   Sold for $160

2446. RV Topeo vase, unmarked, 7"h, mint   100-200
July 13, 1993 Sold for $200

2447. RV Orian vase, 8"w x 7"h, mint   150-250
July 13, 1993 Sold for $230

2448. RV Dogwood II double wallpocket, 8"h, mint
150-250 July 13, 1993 Sold for $325

2449. RV Dawn vase, 9"h, mint   100-200   July 13, 1993
Sold for $90

2450. RV Sunflower vase, 6"w x 4.5"h, mint   100-200
July 13, 1993 Sold for $300

2451. RV Pinecone hanging basket, blue, rounded bottom,
5.5" mint   150-250 July 13, 1993   Sold for $210

2452. RV Pinecone vase, blue, 6", mint   100-150
July 13, 1993   Sold for $140

2453. RV Pinecone bowl, blue, 10", mint   150-250
July 13, 1993 Sold for $130

2454. RV Pinecone candleholders, blue, 4.5", mint   150-250
July 13, 1993 Sold for $160

2455. RV Pinecone pitcher, blue, 9", mint   150-250
July 13, 1993   Sold for $260

2456. RV Pinecone vase, blue, 7", mint   150-200
July 13, 1993   Sold for $160

2457. RV Pinecone ashtray, blue, 1.5"h, mint, with a **RV
Pinecone** bowl, not shown, blue, 3", mint
50-100 July 13, 1993 Sold for $170

2458. RV Apple Blossom hanging basket, green, mint
100-200 July 13, 1993 Sold for $80

2459. RV Bittersweet hanging basket, green, 5", mint
100-200 July 13, 1993 Sold for $130

2460. RV Pinecone hanging basket, blue, 5.5", mint
150-250 July 13, 1993 Sold for $260

2461. **RV Pinecone** vase, brown, 10", underbase chip, tiny glaze flake at top, with a **RV Pinecone** vase, not shown, brown, 6", tiny ding on one handle   125-175   July 13, 1993   Sold for $200

2462. **RV Pinecone** bowl, blue, 6", mint   50-100   July 13, 1993   Sold for $115

2463. **RV Pinecone** vase, brown, 8", mint   100-150   July 13, 1993   Sold for $150

2464. **RV Pinecone** pedestal, brown, stem handles, 6"w x 16.5"h, mint   200-300   July 13, 1993   Sold for $300

2465. **RV Pinecone** bowl, blue, 9", mint 100-200   July 13, 1993   Sold for $270

2466. **RV Pinecone** tray, brown, 12", mint 100-200   July 13, 1993   Sold for $150

2467. **RV Pinecone** cider pitcher, blue, 9", three small rubs on stems, with a set of **Pinecone** tumblers, six, two shown, blue, 5.5", all mint   700-900   July 13, 1993   Sold for $850

2468. **RV Pinecone** match holder, blue, 2.5"h, mint   50-100   July 13, 1993   Sold for $130

2469. **RV Pinecone** triple bud vase, brown, paper label, 5"w x 8.5"h, small flaw on base, with a **RV Pinecone** bowl, not shown, green, 6", a couple of bubbles   125-175   July 13, 1993   Sold for $130

2470. **RV Pinecone** basket, brown, 6", mint   100-150   July 13, 1993   Sold for $170

2471. **RV Pinecone** vase, blue, 8", mint   100-200   July 13, 1993   Sold for $260

2472. **RV Wincraft** ewer, rust hi-glaze, 8", mint   100-150   July 13, 1993   Sold for $260

2473. **RV Pinecone** hanging basket, green, 8"w x 5"h, mint   100-200   July 13, 1993   Sold for $170

2474. **RV Foxglove** hanging basket, pink, 5"h, tiny glaze flake on one hole, with a **RV Foxglove** bowl, not shown, pink, 10"h, flake on one flower   150-250   July 13, 1993   Sold for $180

2475. **RV Apple Blossom** hanging basket, green, 6"h, mint   100-200   July 13, 1993   Sold for $50

2476. **RV Primrose** hanging basket, rust, 5.5", mint   100-200   July 13, 1993   Sold for $220

2477. **RV White Rose** hanging basket, rust and green, 8"w x 5"h, mint   100-200   July 13, 1993   Sold for $160

2478. **RV Foxglove** hanging basket, blue, 5.5"h, mint   100-200   July 13, 1993   Sold for $200

2479. **RV Mock Orange** hanging basket, pink, 5.5", tiny flake at top, with a **RV Mock Orange** planter, not shown, yellow, 8", mint   150-250   July 13, 1993   Sold for $165

2480. **RV Dogwood II** hanging basket, 8"w x 6"h, mint   200-300   July 13, 1993   Sold for $220

Not Pictured:

2481. **RV Primrose** jardinere, rust, 9", glaze rubs near bottom   200-300   July 13, 1993   Sold for $250

2482. **RV Freesia** jardinere and pedestal, brown, 24.5", mint   700-900   July 13, 1993   Sold for $550

2483. RV Windsor bowl, orange with green design, 10"w x 3"h, mint 100-200 July 13, 1993 Sold for $160

2484. RV Windsor bowl, orange with green geometric design, 7"w x 10.5"l x 3.5"h, mint 100-200 July 13, 1993 Sold for $60

2485. RV Baneda urn, red, 5", mint 150-200 July 13, 1993 Sold for $300

2486. RV Baneda vase, green, 6", mint 150-200 July 13, 1993 Sold for $290

2487. RV Peony jardinere, green, 8", mint 100-150 July 13, 1993 Sold for $120

2488. RV Carnelian II wallpocket, blue with green drip, 8"h, mint 100-150 July 13, 1993 Sold for $200

2489. RV Dogwood II bud vase, 9"h, mint 100-150 July 13, 1993 Sold for $80

2490. RV Jonquil jardinere, white floral on brown ground, 8.5"w x 6"h, mint 150-250 July 13, 1993 Sold for $130

2491. RV Tuscany vase, pink, 8"w x 5"h, mint 100-150 July 13, 1993 Sold for $110

2492. RV Rosecraft Hexagon vase, brown, 7.5"h, mint 100-150 July 13, 1993 Sold for $190

2493. RV Panel double bud vases, pair, one shown, brown, 5" x 7.5", both mint 100-150 July 13, 1993 Sold for $230

Not Pictured:

2494. RV Thornapple flower frog, rust, 5"h, ding, with a **RV Moss** flower frog, pink, 4.5"h, mint 75-125 July 13, 1993 Sold for $200

2495. RV Peony bookends, pink and green, tiny rub on one corner, with a **RV Peony** console bowl, not shown, green, 8", mint 150-250 July 13, 1993 Sold for $250

2496. RV Zephyr Lily basket, green, 8", mint 100-200 July 13, 1993 Sold for $160

2497. RV Bushberry hanging basket, green, 5"h, mint 100-200 July 13, 1993 Sold for $170

2498. RV Panel vase, brown with orange design, 6.5"w x 8"h, mint 100-200 July 13, 1993 Sold for $160

2499. RV Imperial II triple wallpocket, orange with green drip, 8.5"w x 6.5"h, mint 200-300 July 13, 1993 Sold for $280

2500. RV Pinecone hanging basket, blue, needles downside, 5", mint 150-250 July 13, 1993 Sold for $325

2501. RV Imperial I hanging basket, 8"w x 4"h, mint 200-300 July 13, 1993 Sold for $160

2502. RV Primrose pedestal, pink, 6"w at top x 16.5"h, mint 200-300 July 13, 1993 Sold for $210

2503. RV Iris wall shelf, pink, mint 100-150 July 13, 1993 Sold for $375

2504. RV Zephyr Lily basket, brown, 10", mint 100-200 July 13, 1993 Sold for $180

2505. RV Pinecone double tray, green, 13", mint 150-250 July 13, 1993 Sold for $180

2506. **RV Pinecone** basket, brown, 10", mint 150-200
July 13, 1993 Sold for $240

2507. **RV Luffa** vase, green, 8", mint 125-175 July 13, 1993
Sold for $150

2508. **RV Baneda** vase, red, 9", mint 150-200
July 13, 1993 Sold for $375

2509. **RV Primrose** flower frog, yellow, 5"h, mint 50-100
July 13, 1993 Sold for $120

2510. **RV Ferella** vase, red, 7.5"w x 7"h, mint 150-200
July 13, 1993 Sold for $350

2511. **RV Columbine** vase, rust, 14", mint 200-300
July 13, 1993 Sold for $240

2512. **RV Iris** vase, tan, 6", mint 50-100 July 13, 1993
Sold for $60

2513. **RV Dahlrose** jardinere, 7"h, mint 75-125
July 13, 1993 Sold for $110

2514. **RV Baneda** vase, red, 6", mint 150-250
July 13, 1993 Sold for $270

2515. **RV Morning Glory** vase, green, 9", mint 200-300
July 13, 1993 Sold for $260

2516. **RV Pinecone** vase, blue, 9", mint 100-200
July 13, 1993 Sold for $260

Not Pictured:

2517. **RV Pinecone** vase, brown, 12", mint 150-250
July 13, 1993 Sold for $250

2518. **RV Pinecone** bookends, brown, 4"h, mint 150-250
July 13, 1993 Sold for $245

2519. **RV Pinecone** vase, brown, 10", mint 150-250
July 13, 1993 Sold for $220

2520. **RV Pinecone** window box, brown, 15", mint 150-250
July 13, 1993 Sold for $110

2521. **RV Pinecone** candleholders, brown, 2", flake on one
tip, with a **RV Pinecone** ashtray, not shown, green, two
tiny popped bubbles 125-225 July 13, 1993
Sold for $120

2522. **RV Pinecone** vase, brown, 10", mint 150-250
July 13, 1993 Sold for $180

2523. **RV Pinecone** bud vase, brown, 7", mint 100-150
July 13, 1993 Sold for $140

2524. **RV Pinecone** planter, brown, 6", mint 100-150
July 13, 1993 Sold for $150

2525. **RV Pinecone** bowl, brown, 10", mint 150-250
July 13, 1993 Sold for $160

2526. **RV Pinecone** ewer, brown, 10", mint 150-250
July 13, 1993 Sold for $270

2527. **RV Pinecone** mugs, set of three, brown, 4", all mint
150-250 July 13, 1993 Sold for $325

2528. **RV Pinecone** pitcher, brown, 9", mint 150-250
July 13, 1993 Sold for $290

2529. **RV Burmese** bookends, turquoise, gold trim, 6"h, mint 200-300 July 13, 1993 Sold for $150

2530. **RV Florentine** hanging basket, brown, 5.5"h, mint 100-200 July 13, 1993 Sold for $135

2531. **RV Vista** basket, 6.5"w x 8"h, mint 150-250 July 13, 1993 Sold for $280

2532. **RV Florentine** wallpocket, brown, 12"h, hairline, with **RV Florentine** candleholders, not pictured, blonde, 3"h, mint 100-150 July 13, 1993 Sold for $100

2533. **RV Poppy** vase, green, 10", mint 100-200 July 13, 1993 Sold for $190

2534. **RV Futura** vase, yellow and rust, 6", mint 150-250 July 13, 1993 Sold for $300

2535. **RV Cherry Blossom** wallpocket, brown, 8"h, small flake on one corner 200-300 July 13, 1993 Sold for $450

2536. **RV Russco** vase, green, 7"h, mint 100-200 July 13, 1993 Sold for $90

2537. **RV Cherry Blossom** bowl, pink and blue, 11"h, small piece has been glued at base 100-200 July 13, 1993 Sold for $160

2538. **RV Cherry Blossom** jardinere, brown, 6", 8"w x 6"h, mint 200-300 July 13, 1993 Sold for $270

2539. **RV Ferella** vase, red, 6", mint 150-250 July 13, 1993 Sold for $375

2540. **RV Fuschia** ice-lip pitcher, blue, mint 100-200 July 13, 1993 Sold for $350

2541. **RV Peony** tray, gold, 11"l x 1.5"h, mint 50-100 July 13, 1993 Sold for $100

2542. **RV Bittersweet** vase, yellow, 16", mint 200-300 July 13, 1993 Sold for $325

2543. **RV Panel** wallpocket, brown, 9", mint 100-200 July 13, 1993 Sold for $300

2544. **RV Freesia** lamp base, brown, 13.5", mint 100-200 July 13, 1993 Sold for $275

2545. **RV Corinthian** wallpocket, 8"l, mint 75-125 July 13, 1993 Sold for $150

2546. **RV Pinecone** jardinere, green, 8", mint 200-250 July 13, 1993 Sold for $280

2547. **RV Primrose** vase, pink, 6", chip 50-100 July 13, 1993 Sold for $75

2548. **RV Snowberry** ashtray, green, 5.5"w x 1"h, mint 50-100 July 13, 1993 Sold for $40

2549. **RV Zephyr Lily** ewer, rust, 15", mint 150-250 July 13, 1993 Sold for $220

2550. **RV Dogwood II** basket, 8"w x 8"h, mint 150-250 July 13, 1993 Sold for $75

For more details please call:
(513) 321-6742

2551. RV Windsor vase, ferns, rust, 7", mint 150-250
July 13, 1993 Sold for $290

2552. RV Iris tiny jardinere, rust, flake on inside, with a **RV Iris** vase, not pictured, blue, 4", mint 100-150
July 13, 1993 Sold for $130

2553. RV Zephyr Lily floor vase, green, 15", mint 200-250
July 13, 1993 Sold for $260

2554. RV Dahlrose console bowl, 10"w x 4.5"h, mint 100-200 July 13, 1993 Sold for $80

2555. RV Donatello compote, 12"w x 6"h, mint 50-100
July 13, 1993 Sold for $190

2556. RV Iris vase, tan, 6", mint 50-100 July 13, 1993 Sold for $75

2557. RV Bushberry vase, rust, 14", mint 200-250
July 13, 1993 Sold for $240

2558. RV Cherry Blossom bowl, pink and blue, 11"l x 7"w x 3"h, factory flaw on side, mint 100-150 July 13, 1993 Sold for $240

2559. RV Mock Orange hanging basket, pink, 5.5", mint 100-150 July 13, 1993 Sold for $170

2560. RV Peony double cornucopia, gold, 5.5"h, mint 50-100 July 13, 1993 Sold for $90

Not Pictured:

2561. RV Gardenia jardinere and pedestal, gray, 30.5"h, chips 600-800 July 13, 1993 Sold for $550

2562. RV Carnelian I vase, green, 18"h, mint 400-600
July 13, 1993 Sold for $325

2563. RV Zephyr Lily jardinere and pedestal, rust, 8"dia. x 26"h, nick on pedestal 600-800 July 13, 1993 Sold for $400

2564. RV Silhouette bowl, brown, one handle, 12", mint 100-150 July 13, 1993 Sold for $55

2565. RV Silhouette vase, nude, white, 8", mint 200-300
July 13, 1993 Sold for $250

2566. RV Carnelian I bowl and frog, blue with darker drip, set, 10"w x 4"h, mint, with a **RV Carnelian I** flower frog, blue, 6.5"w x 2.5"h, mint 100-200 July 13, 1993 Sold for $130

2567. RV Carnelian I candleholders, pair, turquoise, 3"h, mint 50-100 July 13, 1993 Sold for $90

2568. RV Silhouette vase, nude in panel, white, 7", mint 150-250 July 13, 1993 Sold for $180

2569. RV Carnelian I oval bowl, green with curled handles, 11"l x 4"h, mint 100-150 July 13, 1993 Sold for $130

2570. RV Velmoss II vase, green, 6"h, mint 50-100
July 13, 1993 Sold for $110

2571. RV Nova planter, blue matt with orange interior, 6"w x 4"h, mint 50-100 July 13, 1993 Sold for $40

2572. RV Ivory II vase, Dawn pattern, 6"h, mint 100-150
July 13, 1993 Sold for $65

Not Pictured:

2573. RV Freesia vase, orange, 18"h, mint 300-400
July 13, 1993 Sold for $325

2574. RV Pinecone vase, blue, 4", mint 100-150
July 13, 1993 Sold for $170

2575. RV Pinecone bowl, brown, 10", underbase flake
100-150 July 13, 1993 Sold for $110

2576. RV Pinecone bowl, blue, 3", mint 75-125
July 13, 1993 Sold for $140

2577. RV Pinecone vase, brown, 10", mint 150-250
July 13, 1993 Sold for $170

2578. RV Pinecone window box, blue, 8", mint 100-200
July 13, 1993 Sold for $180

2579. RV Pinecone window box, brown, four nicks around
base, one on handle 150-250 July 13, 1993
Sold for $240

2580. RV Pinecone bowl, blue, 9", flake on top, two nicks on
leaves, with a **RV Pinecone** basket not pictured, deep
green, hairline inside, 6", mint 100-150 July 13, 1993
Sold for $120

2581. RV Pinecone vase, brown, 7", mint 100-150
July 13, 1993 Sold for $100

2582. RV Pinecone window box, blue, 12", mint 200-250
July 13, 1993 Sold for $260

2583. RV Apple Blossom jardinere and pedestal, green,
24.5"h, tiny flake inside edge of jardinere 500-700
July 13, 1993 Sold for $375

2584. RV Mock Orange pedestal, yellow, 10", mint
200-300 July 13, 1993 Sold for $50

2585. RV Cherry Blossom jardinere, orange, brown and
cream, 7"w x 9"h, mint 300-500 July 13, 1993
Sold for $350

2586. RV Donatello jardinere and pedestal, 27.5"h, hairline
and flake in jardinere 400-600 July 13, 1993
Sold for $300

2587. RV Florentine umbrella stand, cream and brown,
18.5", mint 300-500 July 13, 1993 Sold for $325

2588. RV Wisteria pedestal, brown, 6"w at top x 16.5"h, mint
300-500 July 13, 1993 Sold for $300

Not Pictured:

2589. RV Apple Blossom vase, green, 15", mint 250-350
July 13, 1993 Sold for $270

2590. RV Apple Blossom ewer, green, 15", mint 150-250
July 13, 1993 Sold for $230

159

2591. RV Pinecone hanging basket, brown, 5"h, mint 150-250   July 13, 1993   Sold for $190

2592. RV Pinecone vase, brown, 7", mint   150-200 July 13, 1993   Sold for $120

2593. RV Pinecone bud vase, brown, 7", mint   150-200 July 13, 1993   Sold for $100

2594. RV Pinecone vase, brown, 7", mint   150-200 July 13, 1993   Sold for $180

2595. RV Pinecone vase, brown, 4", mint   150-200 July 13, 1993   Sold for $110

2596. RV Pinecone window box, brown, 12", mint 150-200   July 13, 1993   Sold for $210

2597. RV Pinecone vase, brown, 7", mint   150-200 July 13, 1993   Sold for $120

2598. RV Pinecone hanging basket, brown, rounded bottom, 5.5", mint   150-250   July 13, 1993   Sold for $170

2599. RV Luffa vase, rust, 14", mint   300-500 July 13, 1993   Sold for $425

2600. RV Magnolia jardinere and pedestal, blue, 10", mint 700-900   July 13, 1993   Sold for $1600

2601. RV Poppy vase, blue/gray, 15", mint   250-350 July 13, 1993   Sold for $230

2602. RV Mock Orange jardinere and pedestal, green, 31", a couple of nicks on inside edge of jardinere   600-800 July 13, 1993   Sold for $400

2603. RV Decorated Creamware jardinere, cream with red roses, 13"w x 10"h, mint   200-300   July 13, 1993 Sold for $120

2604. RV Mostique jardinere and pedestal, gray, 28.5"h, mint 500-700   July 13, 1993   Sold for $750

Not Pictured:

2605. RV Donatello jardinere and pedestal, jardinere 11"dia., 27"h overall, pedestal has chip, jardinere mint   400-600 July 13, 1993   Sold for $300

2606. RV Pinecone cornucopia, brown, 6", glazed over mold mark under lip 100-150 July 13, 1993 Sold for $60

2607. RV Pinecone pitcher, brown, 9", mint, with a **RV Pinecone** tumblers, set of six, three pictured, brown, 5", all mint 700-900 July 13, 1993 Sold for $600

2608. RV Pinecone vase, brown, 10", mint 150-250 July 13, 1993 Sold for $180

2609. RV Pinecone bowl, brown, 12", mint 100-200 July 13, 1993 Sold for $130

2610. RV Pinecone bud vase, brown, 7", tiny flake 50-100 July 13, 1993 Sold for $100

2611. RV Pinecone vase, blue, 12", mint 200-300 July 13, 1993 Sold for $375

2612. RV Pinecone candleholders, pair, brown, 2", mint 75-150 July 13, 1993 Sold for $100

2613. RV Pinecone basket, brown, 10", mint 150-250 July 13, 1993 Sold for $250

2614. RV Pinecone vase, brown, paper label, 7", mint 150-250 July 13, 1993 Sold for $170

2615. RV Mock Orange jardinere and pedestal, pink, 8", 24.5" total height, mint 800-1100 July 13, 1993 Sold for $700

2616. RV Corinthian jardinere, 6"w x 9"h, mint 150-250 July 13, 1993 Sold for $160

2617. RV Clematis jardinere and pedestal, brown, 25"h, small flake on base of jardinere 600-800 July 13, 1993 Sold for $400

2618. RV Ixia jardinere, pink and green, 10", mint 250-350 July 13, 1993 Sold for $450

2619. RV Luffa jardinere and pedestal, orange and green, 24.5"h, small glaze flake 800-1100 July 13, 1993 Sold for $750

2620. RV Gardenia pedestal, gray, 5", mint 200-300 July 13, 1993 Sold for $120

161

2621. **RV Luffa** bowl, rust, 10"l x 4.5"h, mint   100-150 July 13, 1993 Sold for $140

2622. **RV Cherry Blossom** candleholders, brown, 4", mint 100-150   July 13, 1993 Sold for $200

2623. **RV Morning Glory** vase, white, 8", mint   200-300 July 13, 1993 Sold for $290

2624. **RV Pinecone** vase, blue, 10", mint   150-250 July 13, 1993 Sold for $325

2625. **RV Jonquil** basket, 8", mint, with a **RV Jonquil** basket, not shown, 8", mint   250-350   July 13, 1993 Sold for $450

2626. **RV Cherry Blossom** jardinere, brown, 6"w x 8"h, mint 150-250   July 13, 1993 Sold for $260

2627. **RV Baneda** vase, green, 7", mint   100-200 July 13, 1993 Sold for $220

2628. **RV Rosecraft Vintage** jardinere, brown, 8"w x 6"h, small flake on one grape, with a **RV Rosecraft** bowl/ vase blended not pictured, red/dark blue drip, 5.5"h, mint   50-100   July 13, 1993 Sold for $120

2629. **RV Pinecone** ashtray, brown, mint   50-100 July 13, 1993 Sold for $45

2630. **RV Dogwood I** vase, 6"h, tiny glaze chip at base 50-100   July 13, 1993 Sold for $65

2631. **RV Foxglove** pedestal, blue, 6"w x 16.5"h, mint 150-250   July 13, 1993 Sold for $160

2632. **RV Dogwood II** jardinere, 7"w x 9"h, mint   200-300 July 13, 1993 Sold for $140

2633. **RV Pinecone** jardinere and pedestal, green, 8", mint 800-1100   July 13, 1993 Sold for $700

2634. **RV Peony** jardinere and pedestal, green, 10", 30.5" total height, mint   700-900   July 13, 1993 Sold for $550

2635. **RV Peony** jardinere, gold, 10", mint   200-300 July 13, 1993 Sold for $140

2636. **RV Bushberry** jardinere and pedestal, orange, 8", mint 700-900   July 13, 1993 Sold for $550

2637. **RV Russco** vase, tan with crystals, 6", mint 100-200 July 13, 1993 Sold for $70

2638. **RV Carnelian I** candleholders, pair, blue, 3"h, mint 50-100 July 13, 1993 Sold for $50

2639. **RV Russco** bud vase, tan with gold crystals, 8"h, mint 75-125 July 13, 1993 Sold for $80

2640. **RV Orian** vase, turquoise, 9", mint 75-125 July 13, 1993 Sold for $170

2641. **RV Wisteria** vase, brown, 4", mint 150-200 July 13, 1993 Sold for $180

2642. **RV Moderne** vase, blue, 6", chip underneath 50-100 July 13, 1993 Sold for $40

2643. **RV Topeo** bowl, red, gold paper label, 9"w x 2.5"h, mint 100-200 July 13, 1993 Sold for $130

2644. **RV Pinecone** urn, brown, 15", mint 50-100 July 13, 1993 Sold for $800

2645. **RV Thornapple** vase, rust, 6"w x 4.5"h, mint 50-100 July 13, 1993 Sold for $60

2646. **RV Topeo** bowl, red, 10"l x 4"h, mint 150-250 July 13, 1993 Sold for $140

2647. **RV Carnelian II** wallpocket, blue with green drip, paper label, 8"h, with **RV Carnelian II** candleholders, pair, blue and tan, 2.5"h, both mint 150-200 July 13, 1993 Sold for $220

2648. **RV Carnelian I** vase, green with darker green drip, 8"h, mint 50-100 July 13, 1993 Sold for $25

2649. **RV Mayfair** flower pot and saucer, glossy brown, 5", mint 50-100 July 13, 1993 Sold for $75

2650. **RV Freesia** hanging basket, brown, 5", mint 100-200 July 13, 1993 Sold for $90

2651. **RV Florentine** hanging basket, brown, 5.5"h, mint 100-150 July 13, 1993 Sold for $100

2652. **RV Jonquil** bowl, 8.5"w x 2"l, mint 100-150 July 13, 1993 Sold for $50

2653. **RV Jonquil** vase, 7", glaze miss inside 125-175 July 13, 1993 Sold for $90

2654. **RV Jonquil** bowl, 12"l x 3.5"h, mint 150-200 July 13, 1993 Sold for $90

2655. **RV Jonquil** vase, 5.5"w x 4"h, mint 100-150 July 13, 1993 Sold for $65

2656. **RV Jonquil** pot and attached frog, 5.5"h, mint 125-175 July 13, 1993 Sold for $110

2657. **RV Zephyr Lily** hanging basket, rust, 5", tiny nick inside edge, with a **RV Zephyr Lily** pillow vase, brown, mint 150-200 July 13, 1993 Sold for $140

2658. **RV Jonquil** hanging basket, 7"w x 5"h, mint 150-200 July 13, 1993 Sold for $160

2659. **RV Florentine** hanging basket, 7"w x 4"h, mint 100-150 July 13, 1993 Sold for $60

2660. **RV Apple Blossom** ewer, pink, 15", mint   150-250
July 13, 1993 Sold for $270

2661. **RV Ixia** double candleholders, yellow, 4"w x 3.5"h,
mint   50-100   July 13, 1993 Sold for $65

2662. **RV White Rose** jardinere, pink, 10", mint   150-250
July 13, 1993 Sold for $150

2663. **RV Ixia** bowl, green, 14", with two **RV Ixia** flower
frogs, green, 3", all mint   100-200   July 13, 1993
Sold for $120

2664. **RV Apple Blossom** pedestal, green, 5.5"w at top x
16.5"h, mint   200-300   July 13, 1993 Sold for $60

2665. **RV Russco** factory lamp, rust, 11.5"h, mint   100-200
July 13, 1993 Sold for $150

2666. **RV Iris** vase, small jardinere shape, pink, 3", mint
50-100   July 13, 1993 Sold for $50

2667. **RV Donatello** jardinere, glossy, 5"w x 8"h, mint
100-150   July 13, 1993 Sold for $75

2668. **RV Zephyr Lily** bud vase, green, 7", with a **RV
Zephyr Lily** bud vase, not pictured, green, 7", mint
100-150   July 13, 1993 Sold for $45

Not Pictured:

2669. **RV Florentine** sand jar, blond, 16.5"h, mint   250-350
July 13, 1993 Sold for $375

2670. **RV Mock Orange** jardinere and pedestal, yellow, 8",
mint   700-900   July 13, 1993 Sold for $600

2671. **RV Futura** hanging basket, 5"d, mint   150-250
July 13, 1993 Sold for $250

2672. **RV Florentine** vase, brown matt glaze, 8"h, mint
50-100   July 13, 1993 Sold for $50

2673. **RV Falline** bowl, brown with green decoration, 11"d x
3"h, mint   200-250   July 13, 1993 Sold for $200

2674. **RV Windsor** lamp base, blue, 20"h, mint 200-300
July 13, 1993 Sold for $350

2675. **RV Rosecraft Panel** covered vase, green, 10"h, mint
250-350   July 13, 1993 Sold for $300

2676. **RV Lotus** bowl, green with yellow leaves, 9.5"d, mint
75-125   July 13, 1993 Sold for $120

2677. **RV Tuscany** lamp, brown, 20" total height, mint
200-300   July 13, 1993   Sold for $300

2678. **RV Florentine** vase, brown, 8"h, mint   50-100
July 13, 1993   Sold for $65

2679. **RV Velmoss** vase, blue, paper label, 5"h, mint   75-125
July 13, 1993   Sold for $90

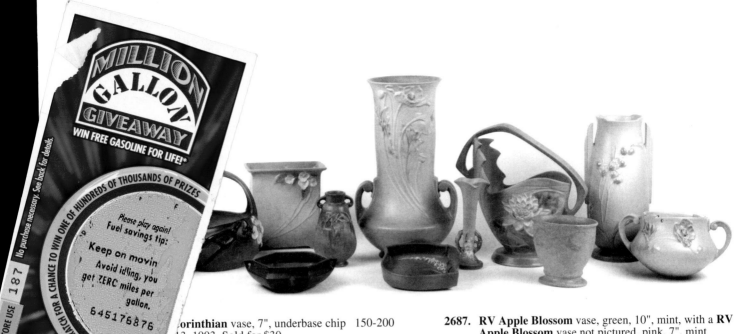

Corinthian vase, 7", underbase chip 150-200
13, 1993 Sold for $30

Dogwood II basket, 8", mint 150-200
y 13, 1993 Sold for $120

RV Mock Orange pillow vase, yellow, 7", mint
50-100 July 13, 1993 Sold for $90

2683. **RV Rosecraft Hexagon** bowl, 7.5"w x 2.5"h, mint
50-100 July 13, 1993 Sold for $130

2684. **RV Baneda** vase, green, 6", mint 100-200
July 13, 1993 Sold for $190

2685. **RV Poppy** vase, green, 15", mint 200-250
July 13, 1993 Sold for $400

2686. **RV Foxglove** tray, green, 8"w x 1.5"h, mint 50-100
July 13, 1993 Sold for $55

2687. **RV Apple Blossom** vase, green, 10", mint, with a **RV Apple Blossom** vase not pictured, pink, 7", mint
100-150 July 13, 1993 Sold for $75

2688. **RV Water lily** basket, blue, 12", tiny flake on handle, with a **RV Water lily** basket, not shown, turquoise, 12", tiny flake on one flower 150-200 July 13, 1993 Sold for $290

2689. **RV Cremona** vase, pink, 6"w x 5"h, mint 50-100
July 13, 1993 Sold for $55

2690. **RV Ixia** vase, yellow, 12", mint 75-125
July 13, 1993 Sold for $130

2691. **RV Poppy** hanging basket pink and yellow, 5.5"h, mint
100-200 July 13, 1993 Sold for $70

2692. **RV Dahlrose** vase, 7"w x 6"h, mint 100-150
July 13, 1993 Sold for $120

2693. **RV Pinecone** vase, blue, 8", mint 150-200
July 13, 1993 Sold for $300

2694. **RV Donatello** hanging basket, 7.5"w x 5"h, mint
50-100 July 13, 1993 Sold for $195

2695. **RV Columbine** hanging basket, rust, 8"w x 5"h, mint
100-150 July 13, 1993 Sold for $100

2696. **RV Pinecone** mug, blue, 4", mint 100-150
July 13, 1993 Sold for $250

2697. **RV Pinecone** vase, blue, 9", mint 200-250
July 13, 1993 Sold for $160

2698. **RV Ixia** hanging basket, pink, 5", mint 100-150
July 13, 1993 Sold for $150

2699. **RV Teasel** vase, rust, 6", couple of flakes on leaf, with a **RV Poppy** flower frog, not shown, pink, 3.5"h, chip on tip 75-125 July 13, 1993 Sold for $55

2700. **RV Pinecone** bowl, blue, 12", mint 200-250
July 13, 1993 Sold for $280

2701. **RV Pinecone** vase, blue, 7", mint 150-200
July 13, 1993 Sold for $190

165

2702. **RV Jonquil** vase, 7"w x 6"h, mint   100-200
July 13, 1993   Sold for $130

2703. **RV Imperial I** vase, unmarked, 7.5"w x 10"h, mint
150-250   July 13, 1993   Sold for $110

2704. **RV Imperial I** bowl, unmarked, 6.5"w x 3"h, chip
inside top   50-100   July 13, 1993   Sold for $30

2705. **RV Florentine** basket, unmarked, 9"h, mint   100-150
July 13, 1993   Sold for $140

2706. **RV Ivory II** vase, 14"h, small flake on base   100-150
July 13, 1993   Sold for $110

2707. **RV Dogwood II** basket, 8"h, mint   150-250
July 13, 1993   Sold for $100

2708. **RV Rozane** vase, red, purple and green glazed white
roses and leaves, 7"w x 10"h, mint   100-200
July 13, 1993   Sold for $150

2709. **RV White Rose** vases, pair, 4"h, both mint   100-150
July 13, 1993   Sold for $55

2710. **RV Tourmaline** vase, script mark 9"h, mint   100-150
July 13, 1993   Sold for $130

2711. **RV Freesia** vase, script mark, 8"h, mint   100-200
July 13, 1993   Sold for $85

2712. **RV Pinecone** vase, blue, 7"h, mint   100-200
July 13, 1993   Sold for $190

2713. **RV Pinecone** tumblers, six, one shown, blue, 5.5", all
mint   400-600   July 13, 1993   Sold for $450

2714. **RV Pinecone** bowl, green, 4"h, mint   100-150
July 13, 1993   Sold for $60

2715. **RV Freesia** vase, brown, 8"h, mint   75-125
July 13, 1993   Sold for $45

2716. **RV Velmoss Schroll** bowl, 8.5" x 2"h, mint, with a **RV
Velmoss Schroll** bowl, not shown, 7"w x 3"h, tiny nick
at tip   50-100   July 13, 1993   Sold for $70

2717. **RV Bittersweet** vase, green, 14"h, mint   150-250
July 13, 1993   Sold for $190

2718. **RV Pinecone** bowl, blue, 6"h, tiny ding on one needle
100-200   July 13, 1993   Sold for $55

2719. **RV Pinecone** pitcher, brown, 9"h, mint   100-200
July 13, 1993   Sold for $280

2720. **RV Freesia** ewer, blue, 6"h, mint   100-150
July 13, 1993   Sold for $120

2721. **RV Pinecone** vase, blue, 9"h, mint   100-150
July 13, 1993   Sold for $170

2722. **RV Bushberry** double bud vase, green, 4.5", mint
150-200   July 13, 1993   Sold for $45

2723. **RV Bushberry** bowl, green, 10FB, mint 100-150
July 13, 1993   Sold for $45

2724. **RV Baneda** vase, green, 5", mint   150-200
July 13, 1993   Sold for $220

2725. **RV Dahlrose** vase, 7"w x 6"h, mint   100-150
July 13, 1993   Sold for $110

2726. **RV Zephyr Lily** hanging basket, rust, 7"w, small flake,
with a **RV Zephyr Lily** bowl, rust, 6", mint   100-150
July 13, 1993   Sold for $85

2727. **RV Foxglove** vase, green, 9", tiny nick on one flower,
with a **RV Foxglove** bowl, turquoise and pink, mint
100-150   July 13, 1993   Sold for $60

2728. **RV Baneda** vase, green, 5", mint   150-200
July 13, 1993   Sold for $260

2729. **RV Velmoss II** vase, turquoise, 7"h, mint   50-100
July 13, 1993   Sold for $30

2730. **RV Bleeding Heart** bookends, green, 5"h, mint
150-200   July 13, 1993   Sold for $190

2731. **RV Moss** hanging basket, blue, 7"w x 4.5"h, mint
150-200   July 13, 1993   Sold for $170

Not Pictured:

2732. **RV Creamware** Knights of Pythias set, tankard and six
mugs, tankard 12"h, mint   500-700   July 13, 1993
Sold for $400

2733. **RV Magnolia** jardinere and pedestal, blue, 8", base
flake   600-800   July 13, 1993   Sold for $650

2734. **RV Poppy** jardinere and a 7"w top x 20.5" pedestal,
green, 10", flat flake on one flower and leaf of jardinere
600-800   July 13, 1993   Sold for $500

2735. **RV Water lily** jardinere, pink and green, 8", mint
200-250   July 13, 1993   Sold for $250

2736. **RV Baneda** bowl, green, 8", repair inside; with a **RV
Baneda** bowl, not shown, green, 6", mint   200-300
July 13, 1993   Sold for $250

2737. **RV Pinecone** hanging basket, deep green, needles
down sides, 8"w x 5"h, mint   150-200   July 13, 1993
Sold for $130

2738. **RV Silhouette** hanging basket, turquoise, 6"w x 4.5"h,
mint   100-150   July 13, 1993   Sold for $55

2739. **RV Gardenia** hanging basket, green, 5.5", mint
150-200   July 13, 1993   Sold for $100

2740. **RV Freesia** hanging basket, brown, 5", mint   100-150
July 13, 1993   Sold for $65

2741. **RV Juvenile** rolled edge plate, sun bonnet girl, 8", mint
100-150   July 13, 1993   Sold for $80

2742. **RV Juvenile** plate, 8", mint   100-150   July 13, 1993
Sold for $80

2743. **RV Dogwood II** hanging basket, 8"w x 6"h, mint
100-150   July 13, 1993   Sold for $120

2744. **RV Juvenile** plate, 8"h, glaze flake inside, with a **RV
Juvenile** plate, not shown, sun bonnet girl, 8", mint
150-200   July 13, 1993   Sold for $120

2745. **RV Gardenia** hanging basket, green, 5.5", mint
100-150   July 13, 1993   Sold for $100

2746. **RV Bittersweet** hanging basket, yellow, 5", mint
100-150   July 13, 1993   Sold for $190

2747. **RV Apple Blossom** hanging basket, blue, 5", mint
100-150   July 13, 1993   Sold for $120

2748. **RV Pinecone** hanging basket, green, rounded bottom,
5", mint   150-250   July 13, 1993   Sold for $130

2749. RV Mock Orange window box, yellow, 12", mint 100-200 July 13, 1993 Sold for $65

2750. RV Water lily conch shell, pink, 8", mint 100-200 July 13, 1993 Sold for $90

2751. RV Pinecone pitcher, brown, 10", tiny flake on inside, with a **RV Pinecone** ashtray, not shown, green, mint 100-150 July 13, 1993 Sold for $130

2752. RV Pinecone vase, brown, 6", mint 100-150 July 13, 1993 Sold for $80

2753. RV Pinecone vase, brown, 8", handle glued, three chips on base, with a **RV Pinecone** flower frog not pictured, blue, flake on tip 75-125 July 13, 1993 Sold for $180

2754. RV Pinecone vase, brown, 6", mint 100-150 July 13, 1993 Sold for $110

2755. RV Pinecone pitcher, brown, 10", mint 150-200 July 13, 1993 Sold for $280

2756. RV Pinecone bud vase, brown, 7", mint 100-200 July 13, 1993 Sold for $90

2757. RV Bittersweet vase, gray, 8", mint 50-100 July 13, 1993 Sold for $65

2758. RV Topeo bowl, red, 11.5"w x 3"h, mint 150-250 July 13, 1993 Sold for $90

Not Pictured:

2759. RV Freesia vase, green, 18", mint 300-400 July 13, 1993 Sold for $375

2760. RV Wisteria vase, paper label, 9"w x 6.5"h, mint 200-350 July 13, 1993 Sold for $400

2761. RV Fuschia vase, brown/orange to yellow, 18"h, mint 300-400 July 13, 1993 Sold for $475

2762. RV Cherry Blossom vase, brown, 7"h, mint 150-250 July 13, 1993 Sold for $240

2763. RV Pinecone basket, brown, 11", mint 150-250 July 13, 1993 Sold for $300

2764. RV Windsor vase, rust, green leaves, 10"h, mint 150-200 July 13, 1993 Sold for $275

2765. RV Primrose vase, blue, 6", tiny nick on handle, with a **RV Primrose** flower frog, not shown, yellow, 5"h, mint 75-125 July 13, 1993 Sold for $30

2766. RV Ixia hanging basket, green, 5"h, mint 100-150 July 13, 1993 Sold for $130

2767. RV Zephyr Lily urn, rust, 7", mint 75-125 July 13, 1993 Sold for $45

2768. RV Tuscany vase, pink, 4"h, mint 50-100 July 13, 1993 Sold for $105

2769. RV Magnolia urn, brown, 6", mint 75-125 July 13, 1993 Sold for $55

2770. RV Zephyr Lily basket, blue, 8", pinhead nick on one corner, with a **RV Zephyr Lily** vase, rust, 4", mint 100-150 July 13, 1993 Sold for $75

2771. RV Gardenia bowl, brown, 12", mint 100-150 July 13, 1993 Sold for $65

2772. RV Ixia hanging basket, green, 7"w x 5"h, two tiny nicks on inside, with a **RV Ixia** bowl, green, mint 100-150 July 13, 1993 Sold for $55

2773. RV Primrose jardinere, pink, 5", mint 75-125 July 13, 1993 Sold for $55

Not Pictured:

2774. RV Imperial II jardinere and pedestal, 11"dia. jardinere x 28"h overall, small chips to top of jardinere and pedestal 500-700 July 13, 1993 Sold for $300

2775. RV Mostique vase, gray textured surface with incised Arts & Crafts designs, 12"h, mint 100-200 July 13, 1993 Sold for $220

2776. RV Pinecone bookends, two sets, one shown, brown, mint   350-450   July 13, 1993 Sold for $325

2777. RV Pinecone cider pitcher, green, 9"h, mint   250-350   July 13, 1993 Sold for $300

2778. RV Pinecone tray, green, 12", mint   150-250   July 13, 1993 Sold for $50

2779. RV Pinecone basket, green, 10", mint   200-300   July 13, 1993 Sold for $180

2780. RV jardinere, green, 8", mint   250-350   July 13, 1993 Sold for $260

2781. RV Pinecone ashtray, green, mint   50-100   July 13, 1993 Sold for $40

2782. RV Pinecone vase, brown, 8", mint   150-200   July 13, 1993 Sold for $130

2783. RV Pinecone mug, green, 4", mint   100-150   July 13, 1993 Sold for $55

2784. RV Pinecone basket, green, 10", mint   100-150   July 13, 1993 Sold for $170

2785. RV Pinecone triple bud vase, brown, 8.5", mint 200-300   July 13, 1993 Sold for $170

2786. RV Pinecone bowl, brown, 10", mint   150-250 July 13, 1993 Sold for $120

2787. RV Pinecone candleholders, brown, 2", mint   50-100 July 13, 1993 Sold for $90

Not Pictured:

2788. RV Pinecone urn, brown, 15", mint   500-700 July 13, 1993 Sold for $750

2789. RV Apple Blossom ewer, pink, 15", mint   150-250 July 13, 1993   Sold for $255

2790. RV Foxglove ewer, blue, 15", mint   150-250 July 13, 1993   Sold for $300

2791. RV Snowberry hanging basket, green, 5"h, mint 100-200   July 13, 1993   Sold for $200

2792. RV Normandy jardinere, 7"w x 8.5"h, mint   100-200 July 13, 1993   Sold for $210

2793. RV Baneda vase, green, 7.5"w x 6.5"h, 6", mint 100-200   July 13, 1993   Sold for $210

2794. RV Apple Blossom vase, green, 15"h, three small glaze misses at top, mint   200-300   July 13, 1993 Sold for $300

2795. RV Imperial I bowl, 10"w x 3.5"h, mint   50-100 July 13, 1993 Sold for $35

2796. RV Vista basket, 6.5"h, mint   150-200   July 13, 1993 Sold for $180

2797. RV Jonquil vase, 6", base flake, with a **RV Jonquil** bowl/vase, not pictured, 6"w x 4"h, mint   100-150 July 13, 1993 Sold for $120

2798. RV Bushberry window box, rust, 8", mint   50-100 July 13, 1993 Sold for $45

2799. RV Bushberry vase, rust, 6", mint, with a **RV Bushberry** mug, not shown, blue, 3.5", glaze miss at top, mint 50-100   July 13, 1993   Sold for $75

2800. RV Bushberry vase, rust, 8", mint, with a **RV Bushberry** mug, not shown, blue, pinhead ding on handle 50-100   July 13, 1993   Sold for $145

2801. RV Baneda bowl, green, 6", mint   100-150 July 13, 1993 Sold for $160

2802. RV Bushberry basket, rust, 8", mint   100-150 July 13, 1993 Sold for $130

2803. RV Magnolia conch shell, brown, 6", mint   100-150 July 13, 1993 Sold for $70

2804. RV Baneda bowl, green, 10", mint   100-200 July 13, 1993 Sold for $140

169

2805. **RV Pinecone** planter, brown, 5", mint   100-150
July 13, 1993 Sold for $80

2806. **RV Pinecone** basket, brown, 6", mint   150-200
July 13, 1993 Sold for $130

2807. **RV Pinecone** vase, brown, 8", mint   150-200
July 13, 1993 Sold for $140

2808. **RV Pinecone** pitcher, green, 9", mint   200-250
July 13, 1993 Sold for $325

2809. **RV Pinecone** rose bowl, brown, 2", mint   100-150
July 13, 1993 Sold for $45

2810. **RV Pinecone** basket, brown, 8", mint   200-250
July 13, 1993 Sold for $300

2811. **RV Pinecone** ashtray, brown, mint   50-100
July 13, 1993 Sold for $45

2812. **RV Pinecone** vase, brown, flat flake at top has been
reglued, with a **RV Pinecone** planter, not shown, green,
5", tiny glaze flake at top   200-250   July 13, 1993
Sold for $60

2813. **RV Pinecone** flower pot and saucer, brown, 5", mint
150-200   July 13, 1993 Sold for $160

2814. **RV Pinecone** vase, brown, 6", mint   100-150
July 13, 1993 Sold for $65

2815. **RV Pinecone** vase, brown, 7", mint   150-200
July 13, 1993 Sold for $90

Not Pictured:

2816. **RV Monticello** bowl, blue, 13"l x 3"h, mint   100-200
July 13, 1993   Sold for $210

2817. **RV Florane** vase, rust and brown, 12.5"h, mint
100-200   July 13, 1993 Sold for $275

2818. **RV Russco** bud vase, tan with gold crystals, 8"h, mint
100-150   July 13, 1993 Sold for $110

2819. **RV Zephyr Lily** bookends, blue, 5"h, mint 100-200
July 13, 1993 Sold for $70

2820. **RV Moderne** vase, tan, 6", mint   50-150
July 13, 1993 Sold for $120

2821. **RV Pinecone** ewer, green, 15", mint   250-350
July 13, 1993 Sold for $450

2822. **RV Bushberry** basket, green, 6.5", mint   100-200
July 13, 1993 Sold for $50

2823. **RV Morning Glory** basket, white, 10"h, flake on top,
two on handle   150-250   July 13, 1993 Sold for $300

2824. **RV Cosmos** vase, tan, 4", mint, with a **RV Cosmos**
bowl, not shown, tan, 8", mint   100-150
July 13, 1993 Sold for $25

2825. **RV Apple Blossom** ewer, pink, 15"h, mint   150-250
July 13, 1993 Sold for $270

2826. **RV Primrose** vase, pink, 12", mint   150-250
July 13, 1993 Sold for $130

2827. **RV Clematis** ewer, brown, 15", mint   150-250
July 13, 1993 Sold for $160

2828. **RV Futura** bowl with flower frog, blue and green glaze over brown, molded floral design in yellow with green leaves, 12"l x 4"h, repaired top edge   100-150
July 13, 1993 Sold for $45

2829. **RV Tourmaline** vase, twisted shape with light pink mottled gloss glaze with mint blue over top edge, no marks, 8"h, mint   100-200   July 13, 1993
Sold for $70

2830. **RV Futura** vase, light brown with green drip around top with leaves in blue and green, 8.5"h, hairline
150-250   July 13, 1993 Sold for $170

2831. **RV Futura** vase, cone-shaped vase in orange/brown matt buttress arms supporting top from base, 12"h, mint
400-600   July 13, 1993 Sold for $650

2832. **RV Futura** vase, tiered design in orange and blue matt, 7"h, mint   200-300   July 13, 1993 Sold for $450

2833. **RV Futura** vase, blue glaze with green designs, 8"h, mint   300-500   July 13, 1993 Sold for $500

2834. **RV Futura** vase, blue and pink matt, green designs on top, 9"w x 6.5"h, small chip on two corners   150-250
July 13, 1993 Sold for $130

Not Pictured:

2835. **RV Futura** vase, cone-shaped vase in orange/brown matt on tiered round base in dark blue/gray with buttress arms supporting top from base, 12"h, mint
400-600   July 13, 1993 Sold for $550

2836. **RV Rozane** vase, portrait of a Native American in full headdress covering one side, artist signed A. Dunlavy, unmarked, 22"h, restored chip at top lip   4000-6000
July 13, 1993 Sold for $4750

Not Pictured:

2837. **RV Rozane** vase, portrait of Indian brave in caramel, yellow and dark brown against a caramel, green and dark brown hi-glaze ground, impressed mark, 14"h, mint
2000-2500   July 17, 1996   Sold for $1500

171

2838. RV Columbine vase, pink, 10"h, mint   100-200
July 17, 1991 Sold for $155

2839. RV Bleeding Heart vase, green, 15"h, mint   100-200
July 17, 1991 Sold for $290

2840. RV Jonquil vase, 8", mint   100-200   July 17, 1991
Sold for $110

2841. RV Ming floor vase, green hi-glaze, 15"h, mint
300-500   July 17, 1991 Sold for $650

2842. RV Pinecone basket, green, 10", mint   150-250
July 17, 1991 Sold for $160

2843. RV Orion vase, turquoise glaze, brown handles, 8",
mint   100-200   July 17, 1991 Sold for $100

2844. RV Zephyr Lily vase, orange, two handles, 15"h, mint
200-300   July 17, 1991 Sold for $220

Not Pictured:

2845. RV Apple Blossom jardinere and pedestal, green,
jardinere is 11.5"dia. x 9"h, pedestal 24.5"h, mint
600-800   July 10, 1994 Sold for $475

2846. RV Water lily hanging baskets, pair, blue with white
and green, complete with original liner and chains, 5"h,
mint   300-500   June 12, 1995 Sold for $400

2847. RV Morning Glory planter, green with purple and
yellow flowers, 13.5"w, mint   300-500   June 11, 1994
Sold for $290

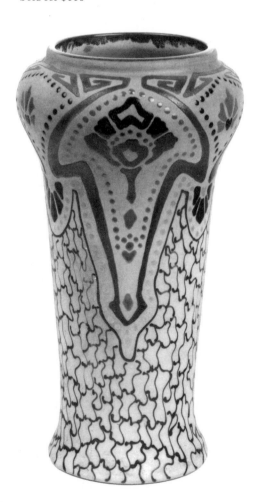

2848. RV Rozane Fudji vase, dark blue and rusty-orange
stylized floral design at top above a web-like pattern in
dark turquoise, rust, dark blue and pale green beading
accent design, 10", no mark, mint   1250-1750
July 17, 1991 Sold for $1500

Not Pictured:

2849. RV Futura vase, green and pink Deco design, hi-glaze,
8"h x 6", mint   350-550   July 17, 1991 Sold for $700

2850. RV brown Ferella vase, 9", mint 300-400
July 17, 1991 Sold for $350

2851. RV Rosecraft Vintage vase, dark brown with purple
and yellow grape and vine, 5", mint, with an **RV
Donatello** bowl, not pictured, 8"dia., hairline 50-100
July 17, 1991 Sold for $105

2852. RV Pinecone brown vase, 8", mint 200-300
July 17, 1991 Sold for $180

2853. RV blue Pinecone vase, blue, silver paper label, 5" x
8", mint 100-200 July 17, 1991 Sold for $150

2854. RV Falline vase, brown, 9", mint 300-500
July 17, 1991 Sold for $375

2855. RV Luffa vase, gold paper label, 8", mint 100-200
July 17, 1991 Sold for $140

2856. RV Blackberry vase, 5" x 6", mint 100-200
July 17, 1991 Sold for $160

2857. RV orange Windsor vase, deep orange matt glaze, 7",
mint 100-200 July 17, 1991 Sold for $325

Not Pictured:

2858. RV Iris basket, tan, 10"h, mint 200-300 July 10, 1994
Sold for $260

2859. RV Magnolia vase, green, 18"h, small nick to handle
400-600 July 10, 1994 Sold for $325

2860. RV Pinecone tumblers, eight, green, 5"h, all mint
400-600 July 13, 1993 Sold for $275

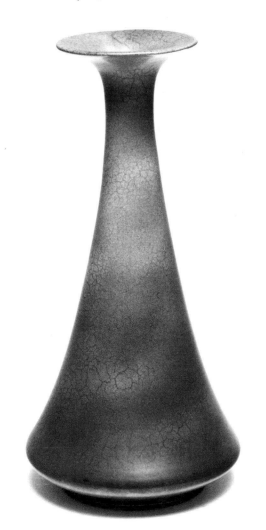

2861. RV Pauleo vase, matt glaze shading from purple,
lavender to pink with gold highlights, no mark, 15",
mint 1000-2000 July 17, 1991 Sold for $1300

Not Pictured:

2862. RV Futura wallpockets, pair, pink triangular form with
yellow, green and blue, 8" high, one mint, one with
small flake 250-300 June 15, 1990 Sold for $325

2863. RV Rozane Mongol vase, deep burgundy red glaze,
footed, wafer mark, 7.5"h, mint 1000-2000
July 17, 1991 Sold for $2100

173

2864. RV Rozane vase, decoration of three boats on gray to blue ocean, impressed, 10"h, mint 800-1100 July 15, 1992 Sold for $700

2865. Weller Jap Birdimal vase, green with squeezebag decoration of nine cream and black fish surrounded by cream bubbles and waves, impressed mark artist's initial F, 8"h, hairline 400-600 July 15, 1992 Sold for $550

2866. RV Rozane Mongol vase, burgundy to black, wafer mark, 15"h, some minor scratches, mint 600-800 July 15, 1992 Sold for $550

2867. RV Rozane Della Robbia bowl, green hi-glaze with incised floral decoration, incised spade decoration around base, wafer mark, 10"dia. x 4"h, glaze flakes 400-600 July 15, 1992 Sold for $400

2868. RV Rozane Della Robbia teapot, green with rooster on one side, owl on other in circular panels with brown ground, wafer mark, 7"dia. x 6"h, repaired 600-900 July 15, 1992 Sold for $450

2869. RV Creamware vase, portrait of woman in floor length gown, cream ground, 13"h, repaired foot 200-300 July 15, 1992 Sold for $265

2870. RV Pauleo vase, purple and blue matt glaze, wafer mark, 9"h, mint 500-700 July 15, 1992 Sold for $475

2871. RV Rozane Woodland vase, orange flowers and green leaves against tan to pale blue ground, wafer mark, 10"h, mint 700-900 July 15, 1992 Sold for $550

2872. RV Mongol vase, dark maroon to brown and tan hi-glaze, 7"h, mint 600-800 July 15, 1992 Sold for $475

2873. RV Rozane Woodland vase, orange and brown floral against tan bisque finish, wafer mark, 17"h, hairline at top 1500-2500 July 15, 1992 Sold for $2000

Not Pictured:

2874. RV Rozane Woodland vase, cream bisque finish with incised and hi-glaze floral decoration in mustard and brown, wafer mark, 10.5"h, mint 800-1100 June 10, 1995 Sold for $550

2875. RV Jonquil vase, 8"h, mint   150-250   July 17, 1991
Sold for $180

2876. RV Carnelian I vase, handles, two tone blue, 8"h, mint
100-200   July 17, 1991   Sold for $75

2877. RV Falline vase, brown, 8"h, mint   200-300
July 17, 1991   Sold for $260

2878. RV Magnolia cider pitcher, blue, 7"h, mint   100-200
July 17, 1991   Sold for $215

2879. RV Magnolia vase, blue, 12"h, mint   150-250
July 17, 1991   Sold for $130

2880. RV Pinecone vase, blue, 8"h, chipped   100-200
July 17, 1991   Sold for $125

2881. RV Dogwood II vase, dark green, 8", mint   150-250
July 17, 1991   Sold for $100

2882. RV Pinecone handled jug, green, 9"h, mint   200-300
July 17, 1991   Sold for $280

Not Pictured:

2883. RV Carnelian II vase, blue experimental gloss glaze
with pale green streaks, 10"h, mint   150-250
July 17, 1991   Sold for $250

2884. RV Crystalis urn, orange crystalline glaze, 8"h, wafer
mark, mint   1500-2000   July 17, 1991   Sold for $700

For more details please call:
(513) 321-6742

2885. RV Aztec vase, blue glaze with squeezebag decoration in white, orange and green, unmarked, 10"h, minute chip on bottom, unchipped chip on side   150-250
July 15, 1992   Sold for $120

2886. RV Pauleo vase, lavender and beige top to blue and lavender bottom, unmarked, 15"h, mint   500-700
July 15, 1992   Sold for $600

2887. RV Rozane Egypto jug, green matt with gray, wafer mark, 12", stilt pull   250-350   July 15, 1992
Sold for $280

2888. RV Woodland vase, yellow and orange floral with trailing green leaves on brown, tan to pale blue ground, wafer mark, 11"h, mint   1000-1500   July 15, 1992
Sold for $1000

2889. RV Rozane Royal vase, white to dark blue ground with pink and green thistle decoration, artist signed, water mark, 17"h, glaze flakes around top   300-500
July 15, 1992   Sold for $1200

2890. RV Woodland vase, orange and green daisies, wafer mark, 7"h, several chips   200-300   July 15, 1992
Sold for $70

2891. RV Rozane Egypto vase, molded floral and vine decoration, green man glaze, wafer mark, 13"h, repaired chip on bottom 100-200   July 15, 1992
Sold for $250

2892. Weller Matt Louwelsa vase, pink and tan grapes, on tan to pale pink shading to green ground, artist signed M. Lybarger, impressed mark, 14"h, mint   700-900
July 15, 1992   Sold for $800

Not Pictured:

2893. RV Pinecone brown vase, 4"h, mint   100-200
June 15, 1991   Sold for $225

2894. RV Imperial II vase, mottled red glaze, 7.5", mint
200-300   June 15, 1991   Sold for $275

2895. RV Pauleo vase, blue and pink irises and buds, green leaves, gold and silver banding and black outlines against pale blue ground, impressed mark, 18"h, mint
1500-2500   July 15, 1992   Sold for $2500

2896. RV Rozane light vase, green to cream with beautiful decoration of flowers in raspberry and deep pink, green leaves, initialed on bottom, 18"h, cracked   250-350 July 18, 1990 Sold for $125

2897. RV Rozane Azurean vase with large dec. of white and blue mums, RP Co. mark, 18"h, repaired   300-400 July 18, 1990 Sold for $200

2898. Weller Eocean Rose vase, slender handles close to body, green to pale peach with peach color dogwood decoration, 16"h, chipped   250-350   July 18, 1990 Sold for $125

2899. RV Rozane light vase, grey to white, decoration of white & yellow roses, green leaves, Myers signed on side, 18"h, chipped top   250-350   July 18, 1990 Sold for $325

Not Pictured:

2900. RV Futura vase, triangular shape narrows to round base, dark blue Deco line design on lighter blue ground, 9", some pitting around top   300-500 June 15, 1991 Sold for $475

2901. RV Futura vase, orange-brown to green, green leaf design around neck, square handles, 6", black label, mint   250-350   June 15, 1991 Sold for $300

2902. RV Futura pair of bud vases or candleholders, deep orange-brown with colorful Deco designs, 10", both mint   300-500   June 15, 1991 Sold for $750

2903. RV Futura vase, shades of pink with green design, 7", mint   250-350   June 15, 1991 Sold for $375

2904. RV Futura candlesticks, brown and green Deco design, paper labels, 4", mint   250-350   June 15, 1991 Sold for $425

2905. RV Bushberry cider set, orange and brown, ice-lip pitcher and six mugs, three pictured, all mint   400-600 July 13, 1993 Sold for $275

2906. RV Moss hanging basket, pink, 4.5"h, small glaze miss on handle   150-250   July 13, 1993 Sold for $210

2907. RV Cosmos ewer, blue, 15", mint   150-250 July 13, 1993 Sold for $370

2908. RV Pinecone double wallpocket, brown, 9"h, mint 150-250   July 13, 1993 Sold for $300

2909. RV Rozane Crystalis vase, light and dark green crystalline glaze, Rozane wafer mark, 8"w x 6"h, mint 1200-1700   July 15, 1992 Sold for $1100

177

2910. **RV Mostique** jardinere and pedestal, dark gray, 28" set, flaws to top of pedestal   400-600   July 17, 1991   Sold for $325

2911. **RV Florentine** umbrella stand, 20"h, mint   400-600   July 17, 1991   Sold for $225

2912. **RV Magnolia** jardinere and pedestal, brown, 24"h, mint   500-700   July 17, 1991   Sold for $350

Not Pictured:

2913. **RV Moss** green vase, 12"h, mint   150-250   July 17, 1991   Sold for $230

2914. **RV Zephyr Lily** blue jardinere and pedestal, 24"h, small chip on jardinere   400-600   July 17, 1991   Sold for $280

2915. **RV Columbine** vase, green with pink and white flowers, 17"h, mint   200-300   July 17, 1991   Sold for $280

2916. **RV Futura** vase, bulbous body atop trapezoidal base, stylized decoration of grasses in blue and green on gray ground, 7"h, mint   600-800   July 15, 1992   Sold for $425

2917. **RV Imperial ll** vase, blue with yellow design around neck, 10"h, mint   100-200   July 15, 1992   Sold for $250

2918. **RV Ferella** bowl, red, unmarked, 13"w x 6"h, mint   200-300   July 15, 1992   Sold for $350

2919. **RV Blackberry** vase, 8"h, unchipped chip on handle   100-150   July 15, 1992   Sold for $240

2920. **RV Blackberry** vase, unmarked, 6"h, mint   100-200   July 15, 1992   Sold for $325

2921. **RV Wincraft** vase, black panther against yellow to brown ground with pink highlights, 11", mint   150-250   July 15, 1992   Sold for $325

2922. **RV Wisteria** vase, sharp mold, 8"w x 7"h, mint   150-250   July 15, 1992   Sold for $375

2923. **RV Cherry Blossom** jardinere and pedestal, pink and green, jardinere 9"w x 8"h, pedestal 17"h, both mint   700-900   July 15, 1992   Sold for $1900

2924. **RV Mostique** vase, matt cream with glossy flower and brown line design, 10"h, mint   150-250   July 15, 1992   Sold for $260

2925. **RV Mostique** vase, 13"h, mint   200-350   July 15, 1992   Sold for $290

2926. **RV Pinecone** bowl, blue, 11"w x 4"h, mint   150-250   July 15, 1992   Sold for $230

2927. **RV Apple Blossom** vase, green, 15"h, mint   150-250   July 15, 1992   Sold for $235

2928. **RV Vista** lamp base, green and purple, 10"h, mint   200-350   July 15, 1992   Sold for $300

2929. **RV Baneda** vase, red, 6", mint   150-250   July 13, 1993   Sold for $210

2930. **RV Futura** vase, gray base, orange and green bands and sides, 8", mint   250-350   July 13, 1993   Sold for $325

2931. **RV Panel** vase, brown, 12.5", mint   150-250   July 13, 1993   Sold for $260

2932. **RV Water lily** ewer, brown, 15", mint   150-200   July 13, 1993   Sold for $250

2933. RV Donatello jardinere and pedestal, 29"h, chips 500-700   July 17, 1991   Sold for $290

2934. RV Magnolia jardinere and pedestal, green, 30"h, pedestal restored   400-600   July 17, 1991 Sold for $230

2935. RV Rozane jardinere and pedestal, white, 28"h, mismatched set   350-500   July 17, 1991   Sold for $200

Not Pictured:

2936. RV Snowberry jardinere and pedestal, blue, 9"w top, 25"h, hairlines in base of jardinere   200-300 July 17, 1991   Sold for $240

2937. RV Jonquil jardinere, 8"h, mint   200-300 June 15, 1991   Sold for $220

2938. RV Futura vase, orange and brown, bulbous shapes around square base, 12", mint   500-700   June 15, 1991 Sold for $650

2939. RV Futura vase, pink and green hi-glaze, 8", mint 300-500   June 15, 1991   Sold for $400

2940. RV Futura vase, stacked neck, square handles, orange-brown to deep green, 7", mint   250-350   June 15, 1991 Sold for $275

2941. RV Pinecone umbrella stand, brown, 21"h, mint 900-1200   July 18, 1990   Sold for $700

2942. RV Pinecone jardinere and pedestal, green, 29"h overall, mint   900-1200   July 18, 1990 Sold for $700

2943. RV Columbine vase, blue, 17"h, mint   200-300 July 15, 1992   Sold for $375

2944. RV Donatello basket, impressed RP Co. mark, 8"h, two glaze flakes, with a **RV Jonquil** hanging basket with chains, 6"w x 5"h, mint   100-150   July 15, 1992 Sold for $220

2945. RV Water lily vase, blue and green with white flower, 19"h, mint   200-300   July 15, 1992 Sold for $350

2946. RV Ferella candlestick, brown, paper label, 6"w x 4"h, mint   200-300   July 13, 1993   Sold for $300

2947. RV Rozane ewer, brown, signed, 16"h, repair on lip 100-200   July 13, 1993   Sold for $200

2948. RV Vista vase, two-handles, molded landscape, 21"h, mint   700-900   June 7, 1998   Sold for $1200

2949. RV Imperial vase, yellow matt with white and pink highlights, blue, green and brown squares at top, 8.5"h, mint   250-350   July 13, 1993   Sold for $450

2950. RV Rozane ewer, grapes in purple, green, yellow and orange with orange and green stems and green leaves, ground shading from green, orange to dark brown, artist signed W. Myers, 16.5"h, mint   400-600   July 13, 1993 Sold for $500

2951. RV Vintage jardinere and pedestal, brown ground with yellow and orange design, jardinere 13.5"dia., 30.5" overall height, both with minute flakes   700-900 June 7, 1998   Sold for $1100

2952. RV Burmese bookends, bust of woman, green matt with brown highlights, 7"h, mint; with a **RV Futura** vase (pictured next), cone shape with green stacked design on blue round base, 8"h, tight hairline   200-250
July 15, 1992   Sold for $285

2953. RV Futura vase, pink to purple with pink and green thistle decoration, 8"h, mint   300-500   July 15, 1992
Sold for $625

2954. RV Wincraft vase, brown and yellow hi-glaze with cloud design in four panels, mint   100-150
July 15, 1992   Sold for $45

2955. RV Futura jardinere, orange to green ground with leaf and triangle decoration, 14"dia. x 10"h, small glaze flake   250-350   July 15, 1992   Sold for $425

2956. RV Wincraft vase, square shape on round base, blue hi-glaze with cloud design in four panels, 7",mint 100-150
July 15, 1992   Sold for $65

2957. RV Imperial II vase, mottled green and pink crystal line drip glaze over green matt, impressed geometric design around top, 6"w x 5"h, mint   50-100
July 15, 1992   Sold for $130

2958. RV Earlam vase, yellow, orange and blue matt glaze with cream highlights, unmarked, 8"w x 7"h, mint
100-200   July 15, 1992   Sold for $160

2959. RV Futura vase, beehive shape, yellow to brown with painted blue and green floral decoration, 8"h, mint
250-350   July 15, 1992   Sold for $300

2960. RV Wisteria vase, pale purple and green decoration on brown to yellow to green ground, 8"w x 7"h, mint
200-300   July 15, 1992   Sold for $350

2961. RV Futura vase, brown to orange ground with green Deco design in triangular shape, stacked neck with handles on either side, unmarked, 9"w x 9"h, mint
500-700   July 15, 1992   Sold for $850

2962. RV Futura vase, bulbous body on trapezoidal base stylized decoration of grasses in shades of blue and green on pale blue ground, 7"h, mint   600-800
July 15, 1992   Sold for $450

2963. RV Futura jardinere, orange and green with leaf decoration, 11"w x 8"h, repaired top   200-300
July 15, 1992   Sold for $270

2964. RV Futura vase, four connecting columns, overlap ping circle motif in violet, blue, yellow and white on green drip ground, 7"w x 8"h, mint   700-900   July 15, 1992
Sold for $900

2965. RV Victorian Art Pottery vase, dark brown with blue and yellow decoration, 10"h, mint   100-200
July 15, 1992   Sold for $220

2966. RV Ferella bowl, brown with green and yellow design, original paper label, 9"w x 5"h, mint   150-250
July 15, 1992   Sold for $300

2967. Weller tiles, set of six, scene of barns where pottery is being produced, tile at bottom reads "Weller Pottery 1872", we assume this scene depicts the pottery's first production facility, mounted in an oak frame, signed by Timberlake, 9"h x 14"w, mint   6000-8000   July 17, 1996 Sold for $20,000

2968. Weller Louwelsa chamberstick, pansy decoration, 5"h, mint 100-200 July 11, 2000 Sold for $210

2969. Weller Dickensware tobacco humidor, Pilgrim scene, 7"h, mint 500-700 July 11, 2000 Sold for $700

2970. Weller Hudson vase, floral decoration, 12"h, hairline 250-350 July 11, 2000 Sold for $170

2971. Weller Coppertone planter, 5"h, minor chip to base 200-250 July 11, 2000 Sold for $250

2972. Weller Dickensware vase, drip hi-glaze, 8"h, mint 200-300 July 11, 2000 Sold for $160

2973. Weller Art Nouveau tankard, green, grape design, 12"h, mint 450-650 July 11, 2000 Sold for $375

2974. Weller Dickensware mug, fruit decoration, 6"h, mint 150-250 July 11, 2000 Sold for $90

2975. Owens jug, leaf decoration, pearlized grey ground, 7"h, mint 200-300 July 11, 2000 Sold for $240

2976. Weller Hudson vase, floral decoration, signed, 7"h, mint 300-400 July 11, 2000 Sold for $475

2977. Weller Athens vase, 9.5"h, mint 350-550 July 11, 2000 Sold for $350

2978. Weller Dickensware mug, Native American, 3"h, mint 350-550 July 11, 2000 Sold for $475

2979. Weller Dickensware vase, impressed mark, 11"h, mint 500-700 July 11, 2000 Sold for $600

2980. Weller Lasa bud vase, palm tree, label, 7.5"h, minor scratches 200-300 July 11, 2000 Sold for $100

2981. Weller Hudson vase, daisies, signed Kennedy, 11"h, mint 500-700 July 11, 2000 Sold for $800

2982. Owens Henri Deux vase, incised female, 6.5"h, scratches 400-500 July 11, 2000 Sold for $260

2984. Weller vase, incised and painted birds soaring through trees, stamped Weller mark, 14.5"h, minor repair to top 1500-2000 July 11, 2000 Sold for $2300

2983. RV Light mug, grape decoration, 5.5"h, minor glaze loss to handle, burst bubble 100-200 July 11, 2000 Sold for $70

2985. **Weller Hudson** vase, daisies, signed Timberlake, 6"h, mint 350-450 July 11, 2000 Sold for $350

2986. **Weller Jap Birdimal** vase, blue, bird decoration, 11"h, mint 450-650 July 11, 2000 Sold for $550

2987. **Weller Hudson** vase, blue floral, 10"h, factory flaw, mint 150-250 July 11, 2000 Sold for $270

2988. **Weller Hudson** vase, geometric decoration, impressed mark, 9.25"h, mint 250-350 July 11, 2000 Sold for $325

2989. **Weller Hudson** vase, floral decoration, signed H. Pillsbury, impressed mark, 10.5"h, mint 400-600 July 11, 2000 Sold for $900

2990. **Weller Dresden** vase, windmill decoration, 10.5"h, mint 550-750 July 11, 2000 Sold for $600

2991. **Weller Hudson** vase, floral decoration, 7.5"h, mint 200-300 July 11, 2000 Sold for $210

2992. **Weller Hudson** vase, blue and cream, iris decoration, 8.5"h, mint 350-450 July 11, 2000 Sold for $500

2993. **Weller Hudson** vase, blue, floral decoration, 10.5"h, mint 550-750 July 11, 2000 Sold for $475

2994. **Weller Hudson** vase, blue, floral decoration, 9"h, mint 200-250 July 11, 2000 Sold for $375

2995. **Rozane Royal** vase, cream and green, daisy decoration, water mark, 8.5"h, mint 400-600 July 11, 2000 Sold for $425

2996. **Weller Hudson** vase, blue floral decoration, 10.5"h, mint 150-250 July 11, 2000 Sold for $325

2997. **Weller Dickensware** tankard, monk portrait, 11"h, mint 300-400 July 11, 2000 Sold for $600

2998. **Weller Besline** vase, blue, floral decoration, 12.5"h, minor wear 250-350 July 11, 2000 Sold for $160

2999. **Weller Louwelsa** vase, painted owl on an evergreen branch, signed Ed Abel, impressed mark, 20"h, mint 2500-3500 July 11, 2000 Sold for $4500

3000. Weller Dickensware vase, etched matt silhouette of lady, artist signed E.L. Pickens, 20"h, mint 1200-1700 July 11, 2000 Sold for $1300

3001. Weller Dickensware vase, tavern scene, artist signed John Harold, impressed mark, 14.25"h, mint 1000-1500 July 11, 2000 Sold for $1500

Not Pictured:

3002. Weller Dickensware vase, gray-haired man in blue suit and hat and brown and white shirt smokes pipe against a tan and blue matt ground, green vine with brown and yellow flowers on reverse, impressed mark, 10.5"h, two glaze scratches to rim, mint 450-650 July 15, 1997 Sold for $400

3003. Weller Sicard vase, double handle form, metallic floral decoration, #55, 6"h, wear to upper body 700-900 July 11, 2000 Sold for $650

3004. Weller Sicard vase, metallic floral decoration, unmarked, 7"h, mint 700-900 July 11, 2000 Sold for $1300

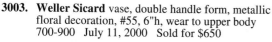

3005. Weller Hudson vase, delicate floral decoration, painted and signed by E. Roberts, ink mark, 12"h, mint 1200-1700 July 11, 2000 Sold for $1500

3006. Weller Hudson vase, beautifully painted floral decoration, impressed mark, 8.5"h, restored 200-300 July 11, 2000 Sold for $215

3007. Weller Glendale vase, detailed birds and nest, magnificent color, 9"h, impressed mark, mint   1000-1500 July 11, 2000   Sold for $1300

3008. Weller Hudson vase, floral and leaf design, 9"h, impressed mark, mint 1500-2000   July 11, 2000 Sold for $2000

3009. RV Magnolia vase, experimental example covered with an unusual green and yellow glaze, trial numbers written on bottom, 8"h, mint   650-850   July 11, 2000 Sold for $600

3010. Weller Matt vase, twisted form with pronounced panels under an unusual burgundy, green and light gray matt glaze, impressed mark, 7.5"h, mint   800-1100 July 11, 2000   Sold for $600

3011. Weller vase, raised and incised design of boat at sea with sun rising in background, impressed mark, 8"h, minor line in top   500-700   July 11, 2000 Sold for $4000

3012. Weller Matt vase, raised colorful design of fruit and flowers in four panels, matt glaze, incised mark, 13"h, mint   900-1200   July 11, 2000 Sold for $1400

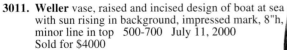

3013. Weller Blue Louwelsa vase, holly decoration, impressed mark, 8"h, minor flaws in making, mint 700-900   July 11, 2000   Sold for $750

3014. Weller Blue Louwelsa vase, flattened form, floral decoration, impressed mark, 5"h, mint   600-800 July 11, 2000   Sold for $850

Not Pictured:

3015. Weller Blue Louwelsa vase, decoration of leaves and berries, impressed mark, 9"h, mint   1000-1500 June 6, 1999   Sold for $1600

3016. Weller Red Louwelsa vase, decorated with wild roses in tones of pink and red, 10.5"h, mint   1500-2000 June 6, 1999   Sold for $3250

3017. Weller Hudson vase, beautifully painted iris decoration, executed by Pillsbury, ink mark, 15"h, minor restoration to base   1500-2500 July 11, 2000   Sold for $1900

Not Pictured:

3018. Weller Hudson vase, pink and yellow wild roses with green leaves on a blue ground, decorated and signed by Sara Timberlake, ink mark, 8"h, mint 350-450   July 13, 1998 Sold for $475

3019. Weller Coppertone fan vase, with two frogs one on each side, impressed mark, 8"h, mint with minor factory hole to side   700-900 July 11, 2000   Sold for $750

3020. Weller Coppertone bowl, frog resting on lilypad edge, incised mark, 15"l, mint 900-1100   July 11, 2000   Sold for $1100

3021. Weller Coppertone bowl, frog resting on lilypad edge, good detail, ink mark, 10.5"l, mint 600-800   July 11, 2000   Sold for $600

Not Pictured:

3022. Weller Coppertone bowl with frog and lily pad on side, marked, 10.5"l x 3.5"h, mint   500-700 June 6, 1999   Sold for $600

3023. Weller Eocean vase, five nicely painted mushrooms, impressed mark, 6"h, mint 450-650   July 11, 2000   Sold for $550

3024. Weller Eocean vase, underwater scene with fish, painted by L.J. Burgess, incised mark, 6"h, minor scratches   450-650
July 11, 2000   Sold for $750

3025. Weller Hudson vase, beautifully painted floral decoration, executed by Hood, ink mark, 15"h, mint   2500-3500   July 11, 2000
Sold for $2900

Not Pictured:

3026. Weller Hudson jardiniere, blue and pink iris with gray highlights and green leaves against a gray and white ground, impressed mark, 10"dia. x 7"h, mint   400-600   July 15, 1997 Sold for $375

3027. Weller Glossy Hudson vase, gray with good floral decoration and pink leaves, 7.5"h, mint   200-300   July 15, 1998 Sold for $325

3028. Weller Hudson vase, double handled form, floral decoration, signed by McLaughlin, impressed mark, ink mark, 8"h, mint 1000-1500   July 11, 2000
Sold for $1600

3029. Weller Hudson vase, tapered square form with nicely painted bird decoration, impressed mark, 9.5"h, mint   900-1200   July 11, 2000
Sold for $1200

187

3030. **Weller Hudson** vase, painted decoration of flowers, signed McLaughlin, stamp mark, 7.75"h, chip to foot 300-350   June 6, 1999   Sold for $300

3031. **Weller White and Decorated** Hudson jardinere, daffodils, 11"dia. x 9"h, repaired chip   350-550 June 6, 1999   Sold for $300

3032. **Weller Hudson** vase, painted decoration of flowers, signed Timberlake, 8.75"h, mint   350-550 June 6, 1999   Sold for $550

Not Pictured:

3033. **Weller Baldin** vase, molded decoration, 9.5"h, mint 250-350   June 6, 1999   Sold for $230

3034. **Weller Baldin** vase, molded decoration, 13"h, mint 400-600   June 6, 1999   Sold for $450

3035. **Weller Hudson** blue with pink & white rose decoration by Pillsbury, 8", mint   250-350   June 15, 1990 Sold for $200

3036. **Weller Hudson** vase, blue with blue & yellow iris decoration by D. England, cylindrical form, 9", mint 350-450   June 15, 1990 Sold for $400

3037. **Weller Hudson** vase, roses in matt glaze, 10"dia. x 12"h, repaired drill hole   350-550   July 10, 1994 Sold for $350

3038. **Weller Blue and Decorated Hudson** vase, pink and white roses cover full length of vase on a dark blue ground, 13.5"h, mint   200-300   July 10, 1994 Sold for $270

3039. **Weller Hudson** vase, painted decoration of robin in tree, two-handles, artist signed LBM, stamp mark, 8"h, flake to foot in making, mint   550-750   June 6, 1999 Sold for $1600

3040. **Weller Hudson** vase, decoration of Lily of the Valley, artist signed L. Morris, stamp mark, 9"h, mint   400-600 June 6, 1999   Sold for $800

3041. Weller Glendale vase, molded design of birds, 13"h, mint   1200-1700   June 6, 1999
Sold for $1200

3042. Weller Glendale double bud vase, 7"h, hairline
200-300   June 6, 1999   Sold for $130

Not Pictured:

3043. Weller Glendale bowl, molded design of seagulls with flower frog with molded eggs, 15"dia. x 3"h, signed, frog with tiny flake, bowl mint   350-450
June 7, 1998   Sold for $700

3044. Weller Silvertone bowl with flower frog, 12"dia., frog 4"dia., both marked and mint   150-250
June 6, 1999   Sold for $300

3045. Weller wallpocket, figural with dress covered in a blue matt glaze, impressed mark, 8"l, mint
200-300   July 13, 1998   Sold for $325

3046. Weller Hudson White and Decorated vase, painted decoration with pair of yellow birds in tree, pair, 10"h, mint   1200-1700
June 6, 1999   Sold for $1400

3047. Weller Hudson vase, two-handled form with painted iris decoration, signed by McLaughlin, 9"h, repair to top and bottom   600-800
June 6, 1999   Sold for $400

Not Pictured:

3048. Weller Blue and Decorated bud vase, pink, cream and black flowers on blue ground, impressed mark, 10"h, mint   150-250
July 15, 1997   Sold for $210

3049. Weller Hudson vase, pink and cream dogwood blossoms with green leaves, all outlined in gray, against a gray to lavender ground, signed by S.R. McLaughlin, ink mark, 7"h, chip to base
250-300   July 15, 1997   Sold for $210

3050. Weller Blue and Decorated bud vase, pink, green and cream flowers on blue ground, impressed mark, 10.5"h, mint   150-250
July 15, 1997   Sold for $210

3051. Weller Brighton kingfisher, 6.5"h, mint   300-500
June 6, 1999   Sold for $425

3052. Weller Muskota flower frog of dragonfly, 4.5"w, minor
flake   200-300   June 6, 1999   Sold for $270

3053. Weller Muskota kneeling nude figural, 4.5"l, mint
250-350   June 6, 1999   Sold for $450

3054. Weller Muskota Owl on book, 6.5"h, repair to ear
250-350   June 6, 1999   Sold for $375

3055. Weller Woodcraft bud vase with crow, molded
decoration, 9"h, mint   550-750   June 6, 1999
Sold for $300

3056. Weller Knifewood tobacco jar, molded hunting dogs
and ducks, black glass pedestal base (not shown), 7"h,
chip to foot on base, pottery mint   450-650
June 6, 1999   Sold for $700

3057. Weller Brighton kingfisher figural, 9"h, mint   350-550
June 6, 1999   Sold for $375

3058. Weller Flemish wallpocket, 9.5"l, minor flake   200-250
June 6, 1999   Sold for $120

3059. Weller Brighton figural with canaries, 4"h, minor flake
to beak and repair to tail   200-300   June 6, 1999
Sold for $170

3060. Weller Woodcraft wallpocket, 8"l, minor flakes
150-250   June 6, 1999   Sold for $160

3061. Weller Hobart candy dish, boy with grapes, 9.5"h, mint
400-600   June 6, 1999   Sold for $200

3062. Weller Experimental double bud vase, woodcraft mold
with Brighton glaze, bird of paradise and parrot in
branches, 7.5"h, mint   600-800   June 6, 1999
Sold for $700

3063. Weller Muskota flower frog, pagoda, 6.5"h, mint
250-350   June 6, 1999   Sold for $230

3064. Weller Woodcraft squirrel, molded decoration, 4"h,
mint   250-350   June 6, 1999   Sold for $450

3065. Weller Muskota frog on toadstool, 4"w, minute flake
150-250   June 6, 1999   Sold for $210

3066. Weller Brighton bird figural, excellent color, 6"h, mint
200-300   June 6, 1999   Sold for $270

Not Pictured:

3067. Weller Muskota flower frog, figural, 4.5"h, mint
150-250   June 6, 1999   Sold for $250

3068. Weller Butterflies, pair, small, one edged in green, the
other pink, 1.25"w x 1"h, tail chipped on pink one
150-250   June 6, 1999   Sold for $300

3069. Weller Butterfly, edged in dark pink, 3"w, mint; with a
Weller Butterfly, edged in green, 3"w, tiny chip to edge
150-250   June 6, 1999   Sold for $350

3070. Weller Muskota starfish, 6"dia., mint   150-250
June 6, 1999   Sold for $210

3071. Weller Brighton bluebird figural, attribution, 5.5"h,
flake to beak   100-200   June 6, 1999   Sold for $150

3072. Weller Muskota woman with swan, 7"h, mint
350-450   June 6, 1999   Sold for $450

3073. Weller Muskota frog on lily pad, 4.5"l, mint   150-250
June 6, 1999   Sold for $230

3074. Weller Brighton bluebird figural, 9"h, restoration
300-400   June 6, 1999   Sold for $160

3075. Weller Brighton parrot figural, 8"h, mint
400-600   June 6, 1999   Sold for $600

3076. Weller Muskota turtle on rock, 5"dia., mint
150-250   June 6, 1999   Sold for $350

3077. Weller Muskota turtle inkwell with frog on lid, 6"l x
3.5"h, mint   450-650   June 6, 1999   Sold for $1000

3078. Weller Muskota robin with wings spread, 5", minor
flakes   250-350   June 6, 1999   Sold for $400

3079. Weller Muskota fly on toadstool, 4", mint   250-350
June 6, 1999   Sold for $240

3080. Weller Muskota fisher boy figural, 7.5"h, mint
300-400   June 6, 1999   Sold for $160

3081. Weller Muskota boat figural, 9.5"l, minor flake
300-400   June 6, 1999   Sold for $375

3082. Weller Brighton crow figural, 9.5"h, mint
450-650   June 6, 1999   Sold for $250

3083. Weller Muskota fish and stump figural, 5"h, mint
200-300   June 6, 1999   Sold for $400

3084. Weller Muskota frog and water lily, 5"h, minor flakes
150-250   June 6, 1999   Sold for $80

Not Pictured:

3085. Weller Bonito candlesticks, pair, script mark, 4"dia. x
1.5"h, mint   50-100   June 6, 1999   Sold for $200

3086. Weller Coppertone bowl with frog, stamp mark,
15.25"l x 1.5"h, two lines in making, mint   600-800
June 6, 1999   Sold for $450

3087. Weller Voile jardinere, 8"dia. x 7.25"h, mint   250-350
June 6, 1999   Sold for $260

191

3088. **Weller Pumila** bowl, molded floral, 4.5"h, firing flaw, mint 100-150 June 6, 1999 Sold for $50

3089. **Weller Brighton** bird figural, 5.5"h, mint 250-350 June 6, 1999 Sold for $160

3103. **Weller Duck** garden or lawn ornament, 12"h, mint 3000-4000 July 13, 1999 Sold for $3250

3090. **Weller** jardinere, purple with white gladiators, stamped, 7.5"h, hairlines and minor flaking 300-500 June 6, 1999 Sold for $170

3091. **Weller Zona** coffee cups and saucers, four of each, molded decoration, saucers 6"dia., one cup with bruise, saucers mint 200-300 June 6, 1999 Sold for $100

3092. **Weller Woodcraft** jardinere, two woodpeckers, 8"h, mint 800-1100 June 6, 1999 Sold for $1100

3093. **Weller Rosemont** jardinere, 5"h, insignificant line to top 150-200 June 6, 1999 Sold for $60

3094. **Weller Voile** hanging basket, yellow, with chains, 6"l, mint 200-300 June 6, 1999 Sold for $110

3095. **Weller Zona** platters, two, molded decoration, largest 12.5"dia., tight line to one 100-200 June 6, 1999 Sold for $70

3096. **Weller Zona** plates, five, molded decoration, 9"dia., all mint 200-300 June 6, 1999 Sold for $110

3097. **Weller Zona** coffee pot, creamer and sugar, molded decoration, pot is 6"h, mint 300-400 June 6, 1999 Sold for $170

3098. **Weller Knifewood** vase, molded design of peacock, 11"h, mint 400-600 June 6, 1999 Sold for $650

3099. **Weller Zona** tea set, teapot, creamer and sugar, molded decoration, teapot 5"h, mint 250-350 June 6, 1999 Sold for $180

3100. **Weller Zona** salad plates, four, molded decoration, 7.5"dia., mint 150-250 June 6, 1999 Sold for $80

3101. **Weller Blue Ware** vase, classical figures, 7"h, mint 300-400 June 6, 1999 Sold for $250

3102. **Weller Selma** lamp base with shade, 11"h, mint 300-400 June 6, 1999 Sold for $550

3104. Weller Greora strawberry jar, impressed mark, 5"h, mint   200-220   June 6, 1999   Sold for $110

3105. Weller Dickensware humidor, monk decoration, impressed mark, 6"h, hidden chips to lid   400-500 June 6, 1999   Sold for $250

3106. Weller Baldin vase, impressed mark, 6.5"h x 10"dia., minor glaze flakes hidden at base   250-350 June 6, 1999   Sold for $230

3107. Weller Bonito bowl, impressed mark, 5.25"h, mint 50-100   June 6, 1999   Sold for $170

3108. Weller Woodcraft wallpocket, impressed mark, 9"h, mint   150-250   June 6, 1999   Sold for $120

3109. Weller Floretta vase, impressed mark, 7.5"h, repair to rim   100-200   June 6, 1999   Sold for $30

3110. Weller Forest jardinere, ink mark, 11"h x 12"dia., mint 400-600   June 6, 1999   Sold for $950

3111. Weller Floretta ewer, impressed mark, floral decoration, 4.25"h, mint   100-200   June 6, 1999 Sold for $50

3112. Weller Hudson bowl, floral decoration, impressed mark, 11.5"dia., minor glaze loss to foot   100-200 June 6, 1999   Sold for $50

3113. Weller Woodcraft smokers set, 8"dia. x 5"h, mint 200-300   June 6, 1999   Sold for $200

3114. Weller Forest jardinere, 4.5"h, mint   150-250 June 6, 1999   Sold for $110

3115. Weller Baldin vase, 5.75"h, mint   100-150 June 6, 1999   Sold for $70

3116. Weller Louwelsa ewer, daffodil, impressed mark, signed M. Mitchell, 14"h, flake to base and glaze loss to handle   200-300   June 6, 1999   Sold for $260

3117. Weller Louwelsa vase, floral, impressed mark, 4"h, glaze loss to lip   50-100   June 6, 1999   Sold for $30

3118. Weller Dickensware vase, portrait of a monk, impressed mark, 6"h, mint   400-600   June 6, 1999 Sold for $260

3119. Weller Louwelsa ewer, floral, impressed mark, chip on rim   100-150   June 6, 1999   Sold for $40

3120. Weller Aurelian vase, grapes against brown, yellow, and orange ground, decorated by E. Roberts, 20"h, minor chip repair at base   2500-3500   June 6, 1999 Sold for $1500

193

3121. **Weller Ivory** umbrella stand, molded design, 20"h, mint 550-750 June 6, 1999 Sold for $220

3122. **Weller Woodcraft** jardinere and pedestal, molded design of squirrels, 29"h, both mint 2000-3000 June 6, 1999 Sold for $4250

3123. **Weller Ivory** umbrella stand, ornate molded design, 20"h, minor exterior chips 450-650 June 6, 1999 Sold for $210

Not Pictured:

3124. **Weller Woodcraft** vase, molded decoration, 12"h, mint 250-350 June 6, 1999 Sold for $400

3125. **Weller Blueware** jardinere and pedestal, molded heads and flowers, impressed mark, 32", minor flaws 500-700 July 13, 1999 Sold for $700

3126. **Weller Aurelian** umbrella stand, molded Art Nouveau body, decoration of grapes, leaves and vines, marked, 24"h, chips 1000-2000 June 6, 1999 Sold for $500

3127. **Weller Aurelian** pedestal, twisted shape with roses, 27"h, surface scratches 500-1000 June 6, 1999 Sold for $280

3128. **Weller Louwelsa** umbrella stand, mums with leaves, signed Ferrell, 22"h, flakes to top 1000-2000 June 6, 1999 Sold for $1400

Not Pictured:

3129. **Weller Aurelian** jardiniere and pedestal, dark brown, yellow, green and orange ground with blue grapes, M. Lybarger signature, incised mark, 38"h, minor scratches to pedestal, repair to jardiniere 2000-3000 June 7, 1998 Sold for $1500

3130. Weller Eocean jardinere, iris decoration, 12"dia. x 8.5"h, mint 600-800 July 13, 1999 Sold for $475

3131. Cambridge jardinere and pedestal, attribution, brown glaze with yellow iris, fluted, 27.5"h, repaired chips to jar, pedestal mint 1000-1500 July 13, 1999 Sold for $475

3132. Weller Louwelsa jardinere, attribution, brown glaze with fern and palm leaves, 11"h x 13"dia., mint 600-800 July 13, 1999 Sold for $250

Not Pictured:

3133. Weller Louwelsa jardinere and pedestal, attribution, brown glaze with roses and thorns, fluted rim, 32"h, minor flaws to jar 1250-1700 July 13, 1999 Sold for $650

3134. Weller Jewel Cameo jardiniere and pedestal, 26"h, repair to jardiniere, hairline to pedestal 500-700 July 15, 1998 Sold for $425

3135. Weller Flemish jardinere, apple and grape panels, 11"h, minor flakes 450-650 July 13, 1999 Sold for $550

3136. Weller Flemish jardinere and pedestal, parrots, great set, 32"h, insignificant tight line to jar, line in pedestal does not go through and minor chip repairs 1200-1700 July 13, 1999 Sold for $950

3137. Weller Roma jardinere, green, four lion heads with laurel, 13"dia. x 10"h, mint 500-700 July 13, 1999 Sold for $600

3138. Weller Woodcraft jardinere, molded decoration of squirrel, 9.5"h, minute rough spot to ear 600-800 July 13, 1999 Sold for $650

3139. Weller Woodcraft umbrella stand, molded design, 23"h, mint 1000-1500 July 13, 1999 Sold for $3750

3140. Weller Woodcraft jardinere, molded decoration of squirrel , 9.5"h, minute rough spot to ear 600-800 July 13, 1999 Sold for $650

3141. Weller Woodcraft bowl, branches across top, marked, 7.5"dia., minor glaze flakes   200-300   July 13, 1999   Sold for $300

3142. Weller Woodcraft vase, stamp mark, 9"h, chip to base 150-200   July 13, 1999   Sold for $160

3143. Weller Woodrose bowl, marked, 6"dia., flake to handle 50-100   July 13, 1999   Sold for $60

3144. Weller Silvertone vase, stamp mark, 10"h, mint 250-350   July 13, 1999   Sold for $240

3145. RV Donatello vase, impressed mark, 10"h, mint 100-200   July 13, 1999   Sold for $120

3146. Weller Claywood vase, pinecone, marked, 6.5"h, mint 100-150   July 13, 1999   Sold for $120

3147. Weller Woodcraft bowl with squirrel, marked, 5.5", mint   150-250   July 13, 1999   Sold for $400

3148. Weller Art Nouveau vase, panels with flowers and female, marked, 10"h, mint   250-350   July 13, 1999 Sold for $325

3149. Weller Iris bowl, with flower frog, marked, bowl 14.5"l frog 6"h, mint   250-350   July 13, 1999   Sold for $450

3150. Weller Woodcraft wallpocket, marked, 9"h, minute chips   150-250   July 13, 1999   Sold for $110

3151. Weller Marbleized vase, marked, 7"h, mint 100-200   July 13, 1999   Sold for $110

3152. Weller Woodcraft vase, 10"h, mint   200-300 July 13, 1999   Sold for $170

3153. Weller Woodrose wallpocket, marked, 6"h, mint 200-300   July 13, 1999   Sold for $350

3154. Weller Glendale vase, marked, 7"h, crack to top 150-250   July 13, 1999   Sold for $375

3155. Weller Claywood vase, pinecone design, marked, 6.5"h, mint   100-200   July 13, 1999   Sold for $80

3156. Weller Klyro vase, marked, 7.5"h, mint   100-200 July 13, 1999   Sold for $150

3157. Weller Knifewood bowl, squirrels, marked, 6"dia., mint 100-200   July 13, 1999   Sold for $140

3158. Weller Dog garden or lawn ornament, 12"h, minute flakes   2500-3500   July 13, 1999   Sold for $1300

3159. Weller Forest basket, two-handled form, 3.5"h, hairline; with a **Weller Forest** basket, handles, molded landscape design, 5.5"dia. x 2.75"h, minute chips and repair to handle   200-250   July 13, 1999   Sold for $130

3160. Weller Forest pitcher, molded landscape design, 6.25"h, mint   150-250   July 13, 1999   Sold for $325

3161. Weller Etna jardinere, molded roses, mint   350-450 July 13, 1999   Sold for $200

3162. Weller Hobart bowl, kingfisher frog, 11"dia., line to bowl, repair to bird's beak   150-250   July 13, 1999 Sold for $170

3163. Weller wallpocket, molded lady in garden, 7.5", mint 150-250   July 13, 1999   Sold for $180

3164. Weller Blue Ware vase, classical figures, 10"h, mint 250-350   July 13, 1999   Sold for $210

3165. Weller Forest teapot, hi-glaze, molded landscape, 6"h, mint   250-350   July 13, 1999   Sold for $300

3166. Weller Forest vase, molded landscape design, 8"h, mint 200-300   July 13, 1999   Sold for $200

3167. Weller Baldin vase, blue, molded decoration, 9.5"h, harmless line to bottom   400-600   July 13, 1999 Sold for $325

3168. Weller Blue Ware wallpocket, 10.5"l, minor flakes 200-300   July 13, 1999   Sold for $220

3169. Weller Hobart bowl, boy holding grapes and frog, 11"dia., mint   300-400   July 13, 1999   Sold for $230

3170. Weller Etna jardinere, molded iris decoration, 10"dia., minor flakes   250-350   July 13, 1999   Sold for $190

3171. Weller Blue Ware vase, classical figures, 7.5"h, mint 150-250   July 13, 1999   Sold for $220

3172. Weller Pelican garden or lawn ornament, marked, 20"h, minute flake to foot   5500-7500   July 13, 1999 Sold for $5000

Not Pictured:

3173. Weller Pelican garden or lawn ornament, unmarked, 20"h, some lines in making, mint   4500-6500 July 16, 1997   Sold for $5000

For more details please call:
(513) 321-6742

3174. Weller Sabrinian vase, molded seahorses, 6"w, mint
100-200   July 13, 1999   Sold for $230

3175. Weller Forest bowl, molded landscape, 8"w, cracked;
with a **Weller Forest** vase, molded landscape, 5.5"h,
mint 200-250   July 13, 1999   Sold for $220

3176. Weller Patricia bowl, marked, 10.5"l, mint   100-150
July 13, 1999   Sold for $170

3177. Weller Woodrose wallpocket, impressed mark, 6"h;
with a **Weller Woodrose** vase, 4.5"h, both mint
250-350   July 13, 1999   Sold for $190

3178. Weller Roma window box, molded grapes, incised
mark, 15"dia., mint   300-400   July 13, 1999
Sold for $450

3179. Weller Roma double bud vase, impressed mark, 8"h,
mint; with a **Weller Louella** vase painted floral design,
impressed mark, 6"h, minor flake   200-250
July 13, 1999   Sold for $110

3180. Weller Woodcraft vase, molded blossoms, impressed
mark, 10"h, mint   200-300   July 13, 1999
Sold for $200

3181. Weller TuTone vase, molded flowers, stamp mark, 5"h;
with a **Weller Noval** compote, impressed mark, 5.5"h,
both mint   200-250   July 13, 1999   Sold for $250

3182. Weller Ivory wallpocket, molded floral design, 8"l;
with a **Weller Klyro** wallpocket, original label,
impressed mark, 7"l, both mint   200-300
July 13, 1999   Sold for $190

3183. Weller Blue Drapery vase, molded floral design, 8"h,
mint; with a **Weller Florala** double bud vase, 8.5"w,
minor flaws   200-300   July 13, 1999
Sold for $200

3184. Weller Woodcraft bowl, molded cherries, 7"w, mint
100-150   July 13, 1999   Sold for $100

3185. Weller Hudson floor vase, painting of two birds on limb
with fruit, leaves and branches, marked, 19"h, repaired
top   1200-1700   July 13, 1999   Sold for $1300

3186. Weller Hudson vase, painted grapes, leaves and vines,
marked and artist initial, 15.5"h, mint   1000-1500
July 13, 1999   Sold for $900

3187. Weller Roma planter, molded floral design, round with handles, 3.5"h x 8.25"dia., tight line to top   100-200 July 13, 1999   Sold for $60

3188. Weller Roma vase, molded floral design, 5.75"h, mint   150-250   July 13, 1999   Sold for $80

3189. Weller Roma console bowl with liner, molded grapevines, 4.5"h x 13"dia., mint   200-300   July 13, 1999 Sold for $200

3190. Weller Roma compote, molded floral design, 6"h, mint flake to bottom   50-100   July 13, 1999   Sold for $40

3191. Weller Roma wall vase, 10"l, mint   150-250 July 13, 1999   Sold for $230

3192. Weller Roma planter, molded floral design, cameos, 4"h x 4"l x 4"w, mint   100-200   July 13, 1999 Sold for $40

3193. Weller Roma tobacco jar, molded design, 7"h, minor repair   250-350   July 13, 1999   Sold for $230

3194. Weller Roma wall vase, 10"l, mint   150-250 July 13, 1999   Sold for $220

3195. Weller Roma vase, molded floral design, handles, 6"h, mint   100-150   July 13, 1999   Sold for $120

3196. Weller Dupont planter, molded floral design, 3.5"h, mint   100-200   July 13, 1999   Sold for $50

3197. Weller Ivory vase, molded design, 10"h, mint 150-200 July 13, 1999   Sold for $90

3198. Weller Pearl wallpocket, 7"l, minor flake   100-200 July 13, 1999   Sold for $120

3199. Weller Roma wall vase, 10"l, mint   150-250 July 13, 1999   Sold for $280

3200. Weller Roma compote, molded floral design, 11"w, mint   250-350   July 13, 1999   Sold for $240

3201. Weller Roma planter, floral design, octagonal, 4.75"h, mint   100-150   July 13, 1999   Sold for $120

3202. Weller Pearl bowl, 3"h, minor flakes   100-150 July 13, 1999   Sold for $50

3203. Weller Matt vase, molded serpent, green, purple and gray matt glaze, impressed mark, 9.5"h, mint 1500-2500   July 13, 1999   Sold for $3000

3204. Weller Matt vase, seahorses, raised seaweed covered in a green, gray and blue glaze, impressed mark, 5.5"h, mint   800-1100   July 13, 1999   Sold for $1000

199

3205. Weller Woodcraft ashtray, molded decoration, 7"dia., mint   100-200   July 13, 1999   Sold for $110

3206. Weller Woodcraft bowl, molded decoration of squirrel, 3.5"dia., mint   100-200   July 13, 1999   Sold for $110

3207. Weller Woodcraft planter, molded decoration of three foxes, 6"h, mint   400-600   July 13, 1999
Sold for $375

3208. Weller Knifewood vase, molded design of, 7.5"h, mint 100-150   July 13, 1999   Sold for $80

3209. Weller Greenaways jardinere, painted design of windmill and house, 10"h, insignificant line to base 550-750   July 13, 1999   Sold for $450

3210. Weller Elberta vase, orange and green, 5.25"h, flake to foot   50-100   July 13, 1999   Sold for $40

3211. Weller Woodcraft owl lamp, molded decoration, 13.5"h, mint   650-850   July 13, 1999   Sold for $550

3212. Weller Baldin vase, molded decoration, 7.5"h, mint 70-120   July 13, 1999   Sold for $70

3213. Weller Woodrose vase, molded decoration, 4"h, mint 100-150   July 13, 1999   Sold for $50

3214. Weller Woodcraft bud vase, molded decoration, 9"h, mint   100-150   July 13, 1999   Sold for $80

3215. Weller Baldin vase, molded decoration, 6"h, mint 70-120   July 13, 1999   Sold for $60

3216. Weller Flemish vase, molded floral decoration, 8.25"h, mint   100-150   July 13, 1999   Sold for $140

3217. Weller Woodcraft planter, molded decoration, 10"l, minor flaws to foot   100-150   July 13, 1999
Sold for $40

3218. Weller Woodcraft bowl, molded decoration of squirrel, 3.5"dia., minor repair to ear   100-200   July 13, 1999
Sold for $210

Not Pictured:

3219. Weller Experimental vine design, yellow and brown with green and yellow leaves, 16.5"h, minor flaws 600-800   July 14, 1998   Sold for $600

3220. Weller Woodcraft wallpocket, tree branch with owl looking out, 10.5"h, chip on back   150-250 July 14, 1998   Sold for $350

3221. Weller Lorber vase, women picking fruit, 11.5"h, minor staining and chips   250-350   July 15, 1998 Sold for $290

3222. Weller Woodcraft compote, earth tones with red berries, impressed mark, 10"h, mint   350-450 July 15, 1998   Sold for $425

3223. Weller Woodcraft jardiniere, green and brown, impressed mark, 11"dia. x 9.5"h, flakes to side 150-250   July 16, 1997   Sold for $425

3224. Weller Coppertone candlesticks, pair, frog on lily pad with flower on his back, stamp mark, 3.5"h, discoloration in flower   400-600   July 15, 1997   Sold for $250

3225. Weller Muskota cats on gate, marked, 7.5", mint 800-1100   July 13, 1999   Sold for $850

3226. Weller Woodcraft tankard, molded decoration of three foxes, 12.5"h, minor flakes   450-650 July 13, 1999   Sold for $600

3227. Weller Baldin vase, molded decoration, 6"h, mint 80-120   July 13, 1999   Sold for $70

3228. Weller Knifewood vase, molded design of four owls and crescent moon, 8.5"h, mint   650-850 July 13, 1999   Sold for $1100

3229. Weller Woodrose wallpocket, molded decoration, 10"h, minor flake   150-250   July 13, 1999   Sold for $150

3230. Weller Ardsley bowl with kingfisher frog, bowl 17"dia., frog 9"h, repair to bill on frog   350-550 July 13, 1999   Sold for $550

3231. Weller Flemish vase, floral decoration, 9"h, chips under foot   100-200   July 13, 1999   Sold for $50

3232. Weller Woodcraft bowl, molded decoration of squirrel, 3.5"dia., mint   100-200   July 13, 1999 Sold for $140

3233. Weller Woodcraft wallpocket, molded floral decoration, 9"l, chip to back   100-150   July 13, 1999 Sold for $120

3234. Weller Muskota frog and fly, 5"w, minor flaws 100-200   July 13, 1999   Sold for $160

3235. Weller Baldin vase, molded decoration, 7"h, minor flake to base   50-100   July 13, 1999   Sold for $60

3236. Weller Woodcraft candleholder, molded decoration of four owls, 14"h, mint   650-850   July 13, 1999 Sold for $950

3237. Weller Woodcraft double bud vase, molded decoration, 8"h, minor flaking   100-150   July 13, 1999 Sold for $100

Not Pictured:

3238. Weller figural, owl, blue matt glaze, incised mark, 8.5"h, repaired hairline   300-400   July 13, 1998 Sold for $500

3239. Weller Copra vase, two-handled form with yellow and red roses against a multicolored ground, impressed mark, 8"h, mint   200-300   July 13, 1998 Sold for $280

3240. Weller garden ornament, Fisher Boy, multicolored figure on Coppertone base, 20"h, some restoration and paint   800-1100   July 13, 1998   Sold for $500

3241. Weller Marengo vase, six-sided shape, landscape with trees in front of river and hills, tones of orange and white, 8.25"h, surface scratches, mint   250-350 June 7, 1998   Sold for $250

3242. Weller LaSa vase, decoration of landscape and shoreline with sunset in ground, metallic glaze, 12.5"h, minor wear, minor chip to foot   700-800   June 7, 1998 Sold for $400

3243. Weller Louwelsa mug, brown glaze with cherry and leaf, artist initialed, 5.5"h, flakes to top   100-150
July 13, 1999   Sold for $40

3244. Weller Louwelsa jug, brown glaze with leaf and berries, artist signed, 5.5"h, mint   150-250
July 13, 1999   Sold for $260

3245. Weller Louwelsa jardinere, attribution, brown glaze with two pansies, 9"dia. x 6.5"h, scratches to top   200-300   July 13, 1999   Sold for $80

3246. Weller Louwelsa ewer, brown glaze, artist initialed, 6.5"h, mint   200-300   July 13, 1999   Sold for $170

3247. Weller Louwelsa lamp base, attribution, brown glaze, 10.5"h, minor glaze flaws   150-250   July 13, 1999
Sold for $90

3248. Weller Louwelsa vase, brown glaze with pansies, two-handled, artist signed Hester Pillsbury, 13"h, flake to top   200-300   July 13, 1999   Sold for $400

3249. Weller Louwelsa vase, four handles, wild rose decoration, artist signed, 6.5"h, minor line to top   150-250
July 13, 1999   Sold for $80

3250. Weller Dickensware jug, artist signed Elliott Roberts, original label, 8"h, mint   300-500   July 13, 1999
Sold for $550

3251. Weller Aurelian tankard, raspberries against brown, yellow, and orange ground, artist signed LJ Burgess, 17"h, minute flake to top   550-750   July 13, 1999
Sold for $325

3252. Weller Louwelsa tankard, attribution, brown glaze with poppy decoration, 11.5"h, mint   200-300
July 13, 1999   Sold for $160

3253. Owens jardinere, attribution, brown glaze with tulips, fluted rim, 8.25"h, mint   250-350   July 13, 1999
Sold for $160

3254. Weller Louwelsa vase, brown glaze, three footed form, artist initials, 4.5"h, mint   150-250   July 13, 1999
Sold for $140

3255. RV Rozane vase, two handles, artist initialed, 5.75"h, mint   200-250   July 13, 1999   Sold for $325

3256. Weller Louwelsa candleholder, brown glaze, artist initialed, 5"h, mint   150-250   July 13, 1999
Sold for $300

Not Pictured:

3257. Weller Louwelsa lamp, green and yellow grapes with green leaves on a green to brown and orange ground, impressed mark, signed Hester Pillsbury, kerosene fittings, 25"h, mint   800-1100   July 13, 1998
Sold for $1100

3258. Weller Louwelsa tankard, brown hi-glaze with corn design, signed, 17"h, glaze bubbles; with a **Weller Louwelsa** vase, three handles, three feet, hairline to rim   300-400   July 14, 1998   Sold for $425

3259. Weller Louwelsa vase, brown hi-glaze, green and brown grapes, artist signed H. Roth, impressed marks, 12"h, restored   250-350   July 14, 1998
Sold for $200

3260. Weller Louwelsa vase, brown glaze, artist initialed, 9"l x 5"h, mint   250-350   July 13, 1999   Sold for $230

3261. Weller Floretta jug, 6"h, mint   100-200   July 13, 1999   Sold for $110

3262. Weller Louwelsa jug, brown glaze with cherries and leaves, 5.5"h, mint   150-250   July 13, 1999   Sold for $170

3263. Weller Floretta vase, 7.5"h, minor flake to top   100-200   July 13, 1999   Sold for $70

3264. Weller Louwelsa vase, brown glaze with daffodils, artist signed, 5"h, mint   150-200   July 13, 1999   Sold for $210

3265. Weller Dickensware vase, leaf and berry design, artist signed, paper label, artist signed, 11"h, mint   800-1100   July 13, 1999   Sold for $550

3266. Weller Louwelsa vase, brown glaze with daffodil, 6.75"h, restored   100-150   July 13, 1999   Sold for $50

3267. Weller Louwelsa vase, brown glaze, artist initialed, 8.25"h, mint   200-300   July 13, 1999   Sold for $220

3268. Weller Aurelian vase, raspberries against brown, yellow, and orange ground, artist signed, 15"h, mint   1000-1500   July 13, 1999   Sold for $800

3269. Weller Louwelsa candleholder, brown glaze, signed, 4.5"h, mint   150-250   July 13, 1999   Sold for $220

3270. Weller Louwelsa candle vase, brown glaze, artist initialed, 8"h, restored   100-150   July 13, 1999   Sold for $90

3271. Weller Aurelian mug, plums against brown, yellow, and orange ground, 6.25"h, restored chips, bruise to lip   50-100   July 13, 1999   Sold for $20

3272. Weller Louwelsa vase, brown glaze with iris, artist signed, 7"h, mint   200-300   July 13, 1999   Sold for $240

3273. Weller Louwelsa pillow vase, brown glaze with flower and thorns, artist initialed, 7"h, mint   200-300   July 13, 1999   Sold for $230

3274. Weller Aurelian jug, raspberries against brown, yellow, and orange ground, good artwork, signed Ed Able, 6.5"h, mint   300-400   July 13, 1999   Sold for $270

Not Pictured:

3275. Weller Louwelsa vase, blue berry and green leaf design, signed, 15"h, restored top   250-350   July 14, 1998   Sold for $200

3276. Weller Louwelsa vase, brown glaze ground, decorated with grape cluster and large green leaves, impressed mark, 7" x 6", mint   200-300   June 7, 1998   Sold for $375

3277. Weller Turada jardiniere, attribution, brown and yellow with blue and yellow cut-out decoration at middle, minor flakes   400-600   June 7, 1998   Sold for $240

3278. **Weller Muskota** frog and fly, 5"w, minor flaws
100-200   July 13, 1999   Sold for $180

3279. **Weller Knifewood** vase, molded design of chickens in
grapevines with foxes below, 10"h, mint   300-400
July 13, 1999   Sold for $1700

3280. **Weller Woodcraft** jardinere, molded decoration of
woodpecker, 5"h, small chip to woodpecker   400-500
July 13, 1999   Sold for $600

3281. **Weller Woodcraft** jardinere, molded decoration of three
foxes, 6"h, minor roughness to interior lip   250-350
July 13, 1999   Sold for $325

3282. **Weller Woodcraft** wallpocket, molded decoration of
owl, 11"l, mint   250-350   July 13, 1999   Sold for $450

3283. **Weller Woodcraft** vase, molded squirrel and owl, mint
900-1200   July 13, 1999   Sold for $1300

3284. **Weller Flemish** vase, molded floral decoration, 6"w,
minor chip to interior foot   100-150   July 13, 1999
Sold for $70

3285. **Weller Rosemont** vase, molded leaves and blue jay,
9.5"h, mint   500-700   July 13, 1999   Sold for $500

3286. **Weller Woodcraft** jardinere, molded decoration of
mushroom and flowers, 5"h, mint   400-600
July 13, 1999   Sold for $700

3287. **Weller Woodcraft** vase, molded decoration, 8"h, mint
200-300   July 13, 1999   Sold for $170

3288. **Weller Knifewood** vase, molded design of four
squirrels, 11"h, mint   400-600   July 13, 1999
Sold for $400

3289. **Weller Muskota** crab, 6"dia, minor flakes to foot
100-200   July 13, 1999   Sold for $130

3290. **Weller Pop-eyed** dog, incised mark, 10"h, minor flake
to foot   3500-5500   July 13, 1999   Sold for $4250

3291. **Weller Pop-eyed** dog, black, 4"h, minor chips to feet
500-700   July 13, 1999   Sold for $650

3292. Weller Dickensware tobacco jar, Irishman, 6"h, mint 500-700 July 13, 1999 Sold for $650

3293. Weller Dickensware vase, incised Dombey & Sons scene, marked, 13"h, factory chip to side, glaze flake to lip 500-700 July 13, 1999 Sold for $800

3294. Weller Flask Suffer-E-Get, 6"h, chip to top 200-300 July 13, 1999 Sold for $220

3295. Weller Dickensware tobacco jar, Chinaman, 6"h, mint 600-800 July 13, 1999 Sold for $500

3296. Weller Dickensware tobacco jar, Turk, 7"h, factory chips to base and chip to interior 500-700 July 13, 1999 Sold for $450

3297. Weller Woodcraft wallpocket, two robins in nest, 13.5"h, repaired 1000-1500 July 13, 1999 Sold for $950

3298. Weller Champrel men's talc bottle, green with brown cap, 4.75"h, mint 100-200 July 13, 1999 Sold for $100

3299. Weller Louwelsa vase, portrait of Jean Francois Millet, decorated and signed by L.J. Burgess, brown glaze, label, 13.5"h, mint 2500-3500 July 13, 1999 Sold for $1600

3300. Weller Louwelsa tankard, brown glaze decoration with bird on fence, painted by and signed Abel, 16.5"h, minor repair 1000-1500 July 13, 1999 Sold for $750

Not Pictured:

3301. Weller Louwelsa vase, attribution, pansies, 9.5"h, mint 200-300 July 13, 1998 Sold for $300

3302. Weller Louwelsa clock, nasturtiums, signed M. Mitchell, 11.5"w x 11"h, missing hands 500-700 July 13, 1998 Sold for $425

3303. Weller Sicard vase, iridescent floral decoration, signed, 5.5"h, mint 400-600   June 12, 1995   Sold for $450

3304. Weller LaSa vase, landscape design in iridescent red and gold, 5.5"h, mint   250-350   June 12, 1995   Sold for $200

3305. Weller Sicard vase, tapered form in decoration of twisting cyclamen, signed on side, blue, silver and red iridescent glaze, 7"h, mint   700-900   June 12, 1995   Sold for $600

3306. Weller Sicard vase, iridescent floral decoration in green and violet, signed, 4.5"h, base chip   250-350   June 12, 1995   Sold for $475

3307. Weller LaSa vase, iridescent tropical landscape in red and gold, 8.5"h, mint   500-700   June 12, 1995   Sold for $375

3308. Weller Sicard vase, iridescent floral decoration on four-footed form, signed, 4.5"h, hairline   300-400   June 12, 1995   Sold for $240

3309. Weller LaSa vase, landscape decoration in orange, violet and gold iridescence, 7.5"h, mint   200-300   June 12, 1995   Sold for $250

3310. Weller Sicard vase, iridescent stylized leaf design in vivid green and purple, signed, 9"h, mint   500-700   June 12, 1995   Sold for $650

3311. Weller Sicard vase, iridescent floral decoration, signed, 5.5"h, drilled   250-350   June 12, 1995   Sold for $350

Not Pictured:

3312. Weller Sicard vase, mums on whiplash stems in a gold, green and rose iridescence against a spotted iridescent ground, signed Sicardo Weller, 13.5"h, mint   1000-1500   July 13, 1993   Sold for $2200

3313. Weller Sicard vase, deep purple and green glaze with pink and gold highlights, decoration of mums, 12", impressed Weller, repaired flake at top   400-600   July 17, 1991   Sold for $700

3314. Weller Eocean vase, seagulls soaring over waves, birds of white and gray against a ground of medium green shading to lighter green, incised mark, 10"h, mint   1000-1500   June 10, 1995   Sold for $1000

3315. **Weller Louwelsa** ewer, brown glaze, artist initialed, 6.5"h, mint 150-250 July 13, 1999 Sold for $110

3316. **Owens Utopian** vase, brown glaze with wild rose decoration, impressed mark, 11"h, surface scratches, mint 250-350 July 13, 1999 Sold for $160

3317. **Owens Lotus** pitcher, decoration of water bird and water lily, 9"h, restored 200-300 July 13, 1999 Sold for $150

3318. **Weller Louwelsa** vase, brown glaze with plum, 7"h, mint 200-300 July 13, 1999 Sold for $180

3319. **Weller Turada** bowl with lid, impressed mark, 5.5"w x 4"h, hairline to lid 250-350 July 13, 1999 Sold for $190

3320. **Owens Utopian** vase, clover decoration, 8"h, mint 200-300 July 13, 1999 Sold for $160

3321. **Weller Aurelian** umbrella stand, daffodil decoration, 24"h, minor glaze flakes 900-1200 July 13, 1999 Sold for $1100

3322. **Weller Louwelsa** vase, brown glaze with orange flowers, artist initialed, 4"h, mint 100-200 July 13, 1999 Sold for $130

3323. **Weller Louwelsa** vase, brown glaze, three footed, 4.5"h, mint 100-200 July 13, 1999 Sold for $130

3324. **Owens Matt Utopian** vase, matt glaze with cherry decoration, impressed mark, artist initialed, 13"h, mint 400-600 July 13, 1999 Sold for $425

3325. **Weller Louwelsa** vase, brown glaze with orange toadstools, 7"h, bruise to top 150-200 July 13, 1999 Sold for $100

3326. **Owens Utopian** lamp base, attribution, brown glaze with pansy decoration, 10.5"h, flake to base 150-250 July 13, 1999 Sold for $100

3327. **Weller Louwelsa** pillow vase, brown glaze with orange flowers, artist initialed, 4"h, mint 150-250 July 13, 1999 Sold for $160

3328. **Weller Louwelsa** vase, three fish, seaweed in ground, impressed mark, artist signed Ed Abel, 10.5"h, mint 2000-3000 July 13, 1999 Sold for $2900

3329. **Weller Voile** wallpocket, 6.75"l, mint 150-250
July 14, 1999 Sold for $280

3330. **Weller Noval** compote, brown, 7"h, without lid, mint
100-150 July 14, 1999 Sold for $75

3331. **Weller Woodrose** wallpockets, pair, molded decoration,
6"h, one with minor chip 200-300 July 14, 1999
Sold for $90

3332. **Weller Woodrose** vase, molded decoration, 7"h, tight
hairline 50-100 July 14, 1999 Sold for $30

3333. **Weller Woodcraft** bud vase, molded decoration, 9.5"h,
mint 100-150 July 14, 1999 Sold for $90

3334. **Weller Woodrose** vase, molded decoration, 10"h,
minute flake 150-250 July 14, 1999 Sold for $70

3335. **Weller Baldin** vase, molded decoration, 6"h, mint
50-100 July 14, 1999 Sold for $40

3336. **Weller Klyro** planter, 3.5"h x 8"dia., minor line
100-150 July 14, 1999 Sold for $50

3337. **Weller Voile** fan vase, original label, 7.25"h, mint
150-250 July 14, 1999 Sold for $120

3338. **Weller Baldin** vase, molded decoration, 9.5"h, mint
200-300 July 14, 1999 Sold for $210

3339. **Weller Flemish** vase, molded floral decoration, 9"h,
mint 100-200 July 14, 1999 Sold for $130

3340. **Weller Woodcraft** bud vase, molded decoration, 10"h,
mint 100-200 July 14, 1999 Sold for $80

3341. **Weller Baldin** vase, molded decoration, 8.5"h, mint
150-250 July 14, 1999 Sold for $160

3342. **Weller Woodrose** wallpocket, molded decoration, 6"h,
repair 50-100 July 14, 1999 Sold for $80

3343. **Weller Voile** vase, 7.25"h, mint 100-150
July 14, 1999 Sold for $100

3344. **Weller Rabbit** lawn or garden ornament, 15"h, mint
3000-4000 July 14, 1999 Sold for $7000

3345. **Weller Rabbit** lawn or garden ornament, 12"l, repair
to ears 1500-2500 July 14, 1999 Sold for $900

Not Pictured:

3346. **Weller Rabbit** lawn or garden ornament, gray,
yellow and brown matt glaze, incised mark, 15"h,
repair to ear 1200-1700 July 15, 1996
Sold for $3500

3347. **Weller Rabbit** lawn or garden ornament, brown, gray
and yellow matt glaze, ink mark, 7.5"h, mint
1200-1700 July 15, 1996 Sold for $1700

3348. Weller Lustre vase, stamped mark, 7"h, mint   150-250
July 14, 1999 Sold for $150

3349. Weller Brighton bird figural, 6"h, mint   200-250
July 14, 1999 Sold for $210

3350. Weller Copra jardinere, daffodils, 8"h, tiny flake to foot
300-400   July 14, 1999 Sold for $250

3351. Weller Woodcraft wallpocket, 9"l, minor flake to back
150-250 July 14, 1999 Sold for $220

3352. Weller Baldin vase, blue, molded decoration of apples
and foliage, 9"h, mint   500-700 July 14, 1999
Sold for $550

3353. Weller Melrose basket, 10"h, mint   300-400
July 14, 1999 Sold for $200

3354. Weller Hudson vase, raspberries, label, 4.5"h, mint
150-250   July 14, 1999 Sold for $270

3355. Weller Greora strawberry jar, 8.5"h, mint   300-500
July 14, 1999 Sold for $750

3356. Weller Kenova vase, molded rose branch, 8"h, tight
hairline to top   200-300   July 14, 1999 Sold for $150

3357. Weller Brighton kingfisher figural, 9"h, mint   250-350
July 14, 1999 Sold for $375

3358. Weller Flemish wall vase, 9.5"l, mint   150-250
July 14, 1999 Sold for $130

3359. Weller Etna jardinere, pale blue with pink flowers,
undulating rim, 9.5"w, mint   300-400   July 14, 1999
Sold for $300

3360. Weller Hudson white and decorated, 7.5"h, mint
200-250   July 14, 1999 Sold for $325

3361. Weller Brighton bird figural, 6"h, mint   200-250
July 14, 1999 Sold for $230

3362. Weller Aurelian vase, painted palm leaves, signed in
full by Albert Halbrich, impressed mark, 14"h, mint
2500-3500 July 14, 1999 Sold for $2700

209

3363. Weller Woodcraft bowl, molded decoration of squirrel, 7"l, mint 250-350   July 14, 1999 Sold for $260

3364. Weller Woodcraft jardinere, molded decoration of three foxes, 4"h, mint 300-400   July 14, 1999 Sold for $210

3365. Weller Woodcraft hanging basket, molded decoration of three foxes, 4.5"h, minor repairs 200-250 July 14, 1999 Sold for $210

3366. Weller Glendale wallpocket, pointing left, molded design, 13"l, reglued tip 300-400   July 14, 1999 Sold for $250

3367. Weller Knifewood vase, molded design of daisies, 7.5"h, mint 250-350   July 14, 1999 Sold for $300

3368. Weller Woodcraft wallpocket with squirrel, 9"l, mint 300-400   July 14, 1999 Sold for $325

3369. Weller Glendale vase, molded design of birds, paper label, 12"h, minor repair to top 500-700   July 14, 1999 Sold for $450

3370. Weller Knifewood vase, molded design of, 5"h, mint 100-150   July 14, 1999 Sold for $450

3371. Weller Woodcraft wallpocket, molded decoration of owl, 11"h, mint 300-400   July 14, 1999 Sold for $425

3372. Weller Woodcraft owl lamp, molded decoration, 13.5"h, mint 650-850   July 14, 1999 Sold for $650

3373. Weller Glendale vase, two yellow birds around nest, stamp mark, 8.5"h, mint 500-700   July 14, 1999 Sold for $700

3374. Weller Glendale wallpocket, pointing right, molded design, 13"l, mint 600-800   July 14, 1999 Sold for $600

3375. Weller Forest hanging basket, molded landscape design, 5"h, small chip and flaking 250-350 July 14, 1999 Sold for $130

3376. Weller Forest jardinere, molded landscape design, 6.75"h, mint 300-400   July 14, 1999 Sold for $450

3377. Weller Hudson Pictorial vase, landscape with snow laden road bordered by brown fence running alongside tree line, signed by McLaughlin, incised mark, 11.5"h, harmless flake to bottom 4000-6000   July 14, 1999 Sold for $3250

3378. Weller Brighton kingfisher figural, hi-glaze, 6.5"h, minor restoration   150-250   July 14, 1999 Sold for $350

3379. Weller Brighton figural with chicks, 5.5"h, minor restoration to beak   150-250   July 14, 1999 Sold for $280

3380. Weller Muskota turtle, 4.25"h, minor chips   350-450 July 14, 1999 Sold for $425

3381. Weller Coppertone vase, two frogs on side, 8"h, mint 750-1000   July 14, 1999 Sold for $1100

3382. Weller Brighton wallpocket, double bud vase, 12.5"l, minute chips and restoration   400-500   July 14, 1999 Sold for $325

3383. Weller Muskota swan, 5"h, mint   400-600 July 14, 1999 Sold for $650

3384. Weller Muskota branch, 4.5"l, minor chips   100-150 July 14, 1999 Sold for $90

3385. Weller Coppertone frog figurine, 2"h, repaired 100-150   July 14, 1999 Sold for $200

3386. Weller Coppertone turtle, 2"h x 5.5"l, minor chip to foot   150-250   July 14, 1999 Sold for $160

3387. Weller Brighton parrot figural, hi-glaze, 13"h, minor restoration   700-900   July 14, 1999 Sold for $1000

3393. Weller Drunken Ducks lawn or garden ornament, stamped mark, 15"h, mint   4000-6000   July 14, 1999 Sold for $2900

3394. Weller Pop-eyed dog, incised mark, 4"h, minor flakes 400-600   July 14, 1999 Sold for $425

3388. Weller Brighton parrot figural, 12.5"h, restoration 650-850   July 14, 1999 Sold for $600

3389. Weller Muskota hunting dog figural, 12"l x 7.5"h, restoration   500-700   July 14, 1999 Sold for $600

3390. Weller Coppertone vase, single frog on side, 9"h, mint 450-650   July 14, 1999 Sold for $850

3391. Weller Muskota swan, 4.5"h, mint   400-600 July 14, 1999 Sold for $450

3392. Weller Coppertone frog figurine, 4"h, mint   200-300 July 14, 1999 Sold for $475

3395. Weller Eocean mug, artist signed LJB, 5.25"h, repair and chip 50-100 July 14, 1999 Sold for $40

3396. Weller Etna vase, molded decoration, 6"h, minute flake to top 50-100 July 14, 1999 Sold for $60

3397. Weller Eocean vase, painted holly design with handles, signed and artist initialed, 6.5"w, mint 300-400 July 14, 1999 Sold for $325

3398. Weller Etna vase, molded floral decoration, impressed mark, 7"h, mint 150-250 July 14, 1999 Sold for $350

3399. Weller Eocean vase, daffodils, 9.5"h, mint 400-600 July 14, 1999 Sold for $650

3400. Weller Eocean vase, incised mark, 6.5"h, mint 250-350 July 14, 1999 Sold for $375

3401. Weller Eocean vase, carnation decoration, four handles at top, incised mark, signed Chilcotte, 7.75"h, mint 700-900 July 14, 1999 Sold for $600

3402. Weller Etna vase, marked, 8.5"h, line to top 150-250 July 14, 1999 Sold for $110

3403. Weller Etna vase, molded floral decoration, 5"h, mint 150-250 July 14, 1999 Sold for $220

3404. Weller Eocean vase, incised mark, 7.25"h, mint 400-600 July 14, 1999 Sold for $550

3405. Weller Eocean vase, painted design with cherries, impressed mark, 10.5"h, mint 450-650 July 14, 1999 Sold for $500

3406. Weller Etna vase, molded decoration, impressed signature, 8.25"h, mint 200-250 July 14, 1999 Sold for $230

3407. Weller Etna vase, molded poppy decoration, signed, 10"h, mint 300-500 July 14, 1999 Sold for $375

3408. Weller Etna vase, painted wild rose decoration, 6"h, mint 250-350 July 14, 1999 Sold for $190

3409. Weller Rochelle vase, impressed mark, 6.25"h, tight line to top 100-200 July 14, 1999 Sold for $60

3410. Weller Etna mug, molded grapes, impressed mark, 6"h, mint 150-250 July 14, 1999 Sold for $130

3411. Weller rooster, incised mark, artist signed H. Pillsbury, 9.5"h, minor flakes 2500-3500 July 14, 1999 Sold for $1600

3412. Weller hen with chicks, six chicks beneath hen, incised mark, 8"h, minor flakes 2000-3000 July 14, 1999 Sold for $1600

3413. Weller Roma compote, molded floral design with birds, 11"l, mint 200-300 July 14, 1999 Sold for $160

3414. Weller Roma planter, molded lions at four corners, 6"w x 6"l x 3.5"h, mint 100-150 July 14, 1999 Sold for $150

3415. Weller Ivory jardinere, molded floral, ink mark, 8"h, flaw to lip 100-150 July 14, 1999 Sold for $60

3416. Weller Roma wall vase, original label, 9"l, minor flake and harmless line to top 100-200 July 14, 1999 Sold for $90

3417. Weller Roma wall vase, 7"l, mint 150-250 July 14, 1999 Sold for $220

3418. Weller jardinere, birds-on-a-line, nice design, 7.5"h, mint 250-350 July 14, 1999 Sold for $240

3419. Weller Roma planters, pair one shown, molded floral design, octagonal, 4.75"h, one mint, other with bruise to lip 150-250 July 14, 1999 Sold for $110

3420. Weller Ivory wall vase, 8"l, mint 150-250 July 14, 1999 Sold for $70

3421. Weller Roma planter, molded floral design, 4" square, mint 100-150 July 14, 1999 Sold for $60

3422. Weller Ivory wall shelf, protruding flowers, artist signed, 12"l, mint 300-400 July 14, 1999 Sold for $240

3423. Weller Experimental white vase, round with handles, sea horse, mermaid riding a sea lion, stamped on bottom, 9"h, mint 600-800 July 14, 1999 Sold for $350

3424. Weller Dupont hanging basket, molded floral design, 10"dia. x 5"h, mint 300-400 July 14, 1999 Sold for $350

3425. Weller Roma doorstop, molded floral design, 9.5"h, minor repair 200-300 July 14, 1999 Sold for $220

3426. Weller Roma compote, molded floral design, 6.5"h, mint 200-250 July 14, 1999 Sold for $90

3427. Weller Roma hanging basket, molded floral design, 4.5"h, mint 200-250 July 14, 1999 Sold for $130

3428. Weller Sicard vase, large bulbous form with metallic glaze, raised leaf design on body, large script signature and numbered on base, 15"h, mint 3500-5500 July 14, 1999 Sold for $6500

3429. Good **Weller Roma** jardinere and pedestal, molded design, 35"h, both mint   1000-1500   July 14, 1999 Sold for $800

3430. **Weller Ivory** umbrella stand, white panels with corn and apples, 21.5"h, mint   500-700   July 14, 1999 Sold for $750

3431. **Weller Roma** jardinere and pedestal, molded design, 35"h, minor glaze flaws and lines in making, mint 1000-1500   July 14, 1999   Sold for $950

Not Pictured:

3432. **Weller Forest** jardiniere and pedestal, designed by R. Lorber, landscape in earth tones, blue sky in ground, 11"dia. jardiniere, total 28"h, mint   1500-2000 June 7, 1998   Sold for $1300

3433. **Weller Ivory** jardiniere and pedestal, matt glaze with fish, shells, flowers and leaves in cream and brown, impressed marks, jardiniere 12"dia. x 11.5"h, pedestal 24"h, chip to bases of both, lines to top of pedestal 700-900   July 15, 1997   Sold for $650

3434. **Weller Forest** jardiniere and pedestal, brown, green and blue, impressed marks, jardiniere 12"dia. x 11"h, pedestal 17"h, chips to base of jardiniere, pedestal mint 900-1200   July 15, 1997   Sold for $900

3435. **Weller Ivory** jardiniere and pedestal, matt glaze with design of columns and roses in cream and brown, impressed marks, jardiniere 16"dia. x 13.5"h, all 37.5"h, both have chips to roses, jardiniere has line to rim 500-700   July 15, 1997   Sold for $475

3436. **Weller Glossy Hudson** vase, painted floral decoration, signed, 17.5"h, mint   3500-4500   July 14, 1999 Sold for $5500

3437. Weller Forest jardinere and pedestal, molded landscape design, 29"h, mint   1500-2000   July 14, 1999 Sold for $1900

3438. Weller Patricia vase, original paper label, 18"h, mint 500-700   July 14, 1999   Sold for $450

Not Pictured:

3440. Weller Claywood vase, Egyptian design, minor flakes, 10"h, mint   250-350   July 15, 1998   Sold for $375

3441. Weller Ardsley bowl, 12"dia., mint   200-300 June 6, 1999   Sold for $260

3442. Weller Aurelian jardinere and pedestal, Iris decoration, signed by Ferrell, 29"h, both with damage   500-700 July 13, 1999   Sold for $270

3443. Weller Claywood jardinere, Bells of San Juan, 6.75"h, minute chips to side   250-350   June 6, 1999 Sold for $250

3444. Weller Forest umbrella stand, landscape decoration, 20"h, cracks   400-600   June 6, 1999   Sold for $400

3445. Weller Flemish jardinere, tree and bird decoration, 11"w, mint   250-350   June 6, 1999   Sold for $300

3446. Weller Eocean vase, decorated and signed by Claude Leffler, incised mark, 17"h, mint   5500-7500 July 14, 1999   Sold for $9500

3439. Weller Ardsley jardinere and pedestal, 30"h, tight line in base of jar does not go through   1200-1700 July 14, 1999   Sold for $1500

3447. Weller Muskota salamander on lily pad, 4.5"h, mint 150-250 July 14, 1999 Sold for $325

3448. Weller Muskota geese, pair, white hi-glaze, 5.5"h, mint 300-400 July 14, 1999 Sold for $290

3449. Weller Muskota bowl with three swans, 10.5"dia. x 7"h, a few minute flakes 800-1100 July 14, 1999 Sold for $525

3450. Weller Muskota frog, 5.5"dia., mint 250-350 July 14, 1999 Sold for $475

3451. Weller Muskota swan, 5.5"dia., mint 200-300 July 14, 1999 Sold for $325

3452. Weller Brighton kingfisher figural, hi-glaze, 8.5"h, minor repair 200-300 July 14, 1999 Sold for $325

3453. Weller Muskota retriever with duck figural, 6"h, mint 450-650 July 14, 1999 Sold for $650

3454. Weller Woodcraft fisher boy on fish bowl base, molded decoration, 11.5"dia. x 12"h, mint 700-900 July 14, 1999 Sold for $950

3490. Weller Squirrel garden ornament, standing squirrel eating nut, 12"h, mint 2000-3000 July 14, 1999 Sold for $2500

3491. Weller Squirrel garden ornament, for hanging on tree side, 13"l, mint 1500-2000 July 14, 1999 Sold for $1400

3455. Weller Brighton parrot figural, hi-glaze, 11"h, mint 1000-1500 July 14, 1999 Sold for $1300

3456. Weller Muskota cats on gate, with pots, 7"w x 7"h, mint 800-1100 July 14, 1999 Sold for $1300

3457. Weller Muskota geese figural, 9.5"w x 6.5"h, mint 800-1100 July 14, 1999 Sold for $650

3458. Weller Muskota kneeling woman figural, 6"h, mint 300-400 July 14, 1999 Sold for $350

3489. Weller Muskota swan, 6"l, mint 250-350 July 14, 1999 Sold for $350

3492. Weller Glendale vase, molded design of birds, 4"h, mint 250-350 July 14, 1999 Sold for $300

3493. Weller Glendale vase, walking bird at nest with white eggs, 6.25"h, mint 300-400 July 14, 1999 Sold for $500

3494. Weller Glendale double bud vase, molded design of birds, paper label, 7.5"h, mint 300-400 July 14, 1999 Sold for $425

3495. Weller Glendale vase, yellow birds at nest, 8.25"h, mint 500-700 July 14, 1999 Sold for $800

3496. Weller Glendale wallpocket, pointing right, molded design with birds, 13"l, mint 450-650 July 14, 1999 Sold for $475

3497. Weller Glendale candleholders, pair, molded design of birds, 5.5"dia., mint 300-400 July 14, 1999 Sold for $280

3498. Weller Glendale vase, molded design of birds, 8.5"h, mint 550-750 July 14, 1999 Sold for $850

3499. Weller Glendale vase, yellow finch on branch, red flowers, blue eggs, 7.5"h, mint 300-500 July 14, 1999 Sold for $550

3500. Weller Glendale vase, molded design of birds, 6"h, mint 250-350 July 14, 1999 Sold for $400

3501. Weller Glendale wallpocket, pointing left, molded design, 13"l, reglued bottom and chip to back 300-400 July 14, 1999 Sold for $180

3502. Weller Glendale vase, molded design of birds, 12"h, mint 650-850 July 14, 1999 Sold for $1100

3503. Weller Glendale wallpocket, molded bird design, 9"l, factory chip to foot, otherwise mint 400-600 July 14, 1999 Sold for $375

3504. Weller Glendale double bud vase, molded design of birds, 8.5"w, mint 350-450 July 14, 1999 Sold for $350

3505. Weller Glendale vase, molded design of birds, remnant of paper label, 7"h, mint 350-550 July 14, 1999 Sold for $600

3506. Weller Glendale vase, molded design of birds, 5"h, mint 250-350 July 14, 1999 Sold for $250

3507. Weller Glendale vase, duck in reeds at nest with speckled eggs, 7"h, mint 450-650 July 14, 1999 Sold for $300

3508. Weller Glendale vase, molded design of birds, 9"h, mint 900-1200 July 14, 1999 Sold for $1300

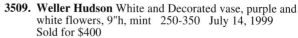

3509. Weller Hudson White and Decorated vase, purple and white flowers, 9"h, mint   250-350   July 14, 1999 Sold for $400

3510. Weller Hudson vase, blue floral design, signed McLaughlin, label, 12"h, mint   1500-2500 July 14, 1999   Sold for $2400

Not Pictured:

3511. Weller Hudson vase, detailed floral decoration in blue and pink with green leaves, ground shades from green to blue, executed by S. McLaughlin, 12"h, glaze burst to top edge   1500-2500   June 6, 1999   Sold for $1100

3512. Weller Eocean vase, painted design, on a twisted form, artist signed Hester Pillsbury, 12.5"h, mint 1500-2500   July 14, 1999   Sold for $1200

3513. Weller Hudson White and Decorated vase, hi-glaze with decoration of Pekinese dog, signed Hester Pillsbury, label, 7"h, mint   2000-2500 July 14, 1999 Sold for $1800

3514. Weller Eocean floor vase, painted design with Calla Lily, artist signed Marie Rauchfuss, 21"h, mint 5000-10,000   July 14, 1999   Sold for $5500

Not Pictured:

3515. Weller Eocean vase, red and green leaves on a olive, green to pink ground, 14"h, mint   800-1100 July 14, 1998   Sold for $800

3516. Weller Eocean vase, red carnations on green stems, no mark, 6.5"h, mint   200-300   July 15, 1997 Sold for $240

3517. Weller Muskota swan, ivory with green, marked, 2.5"h, minor chip; with a **Weller Muskota** frog, green base with frog decoration, 4.5"h, mint   200-300 July 14, 1998   Sold for $280

3518. Weller Burntwood vase, flowers in tan on dark brown ground, impressed mark, 9.25"h, minor flakes   200-300 June 7, 1998   Sold for $260

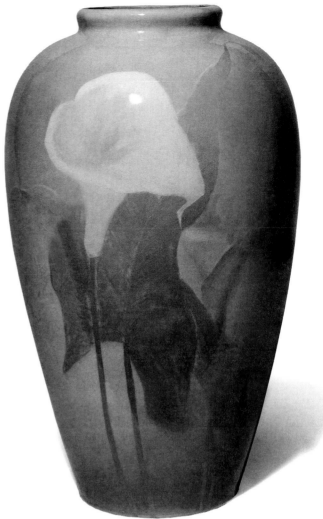

3519. Weller Hudson vase, painted decoration of iris, signed Timberlake, 15"h, kiln chips to foot, mint 2750-3750   July 14, 1999   Sold for $4000

3520. Weller Hudson vase, painted decoration of dogwood, signed Timberlake, 7"h, mint   300-400 July 14, 1999   Sold for $800

Not Pictured:

3521. Weller Hudson vase, broad-shouldered form painted with beautiful blue and pink flowers on two-tone green leaves and stems, artist signed Pillsbury, stamped mark, 12.5"h, mint   700-900 June 7, 1998   Sold for $950

3522. Weller Turada lamp, oil version, with glass shade, impressed mark, base 10"h, minor flaws to base, some damage to shade   500-700   July 13, 1999 Sold for $250

For more details please call:
(513) 321-6742

3523. **Weller Sicard** vase, metallic glaze with floral design, signed, 6.5"h, mint   500-700   July 14, 1999 Sold for $550

3524. **Weller Sicard** vase, metallic glaze with mistletoe design, signed, 5.5"h, minor scratches   450-650 July 14, 1999   Sold for $330

3525. **Weller LaSa** vase, metallic glaze with landscape design, signed, 10.5"h, minor chip to top   300-500 July 14, 1999   Sold for $375

3526. **Weller Sicard** vase, floral design in metallic glaze, signed, 5"h, mint   800-1100   July 14, 1999 Sold for $950

3527. **Weller LaSa** vase, metallic glaze with landscape design, signed, 5"h, mint   300-500   July 14, 1999 Sold for $450

3528. **Weller Sicard** vase, floral design in metallic glaze, signed, 7"h, mint   800-1100   July 14, 1999 Sold for $1500

3529. **Weller Sicard** vase, floral design, metallic glaze, signed, 5"h, mint   650-850   July 14, 1999 Sold for $1300

Not Pictured:

3530. **Weller Sicard** vase, metallic glaze with floral design, painted signature, 4.5"h, mint   450-650   July 14, 1999 Sold for $425

3531. **Weller Sicard** vase, metallic glaze with floral design on ribbed and twisted form, signed, 8.5"h, mint   650-850 July 14, 1999   Sold for $650

3532. **Owens Utopian** vase, portrait of Native American Indian in brown glaze, artist signed, titled High Bear Sioux, impressed mark, 12"h, mint   4000-6000 July 13, 1999   Sold for $7500

3533. Weller Woodcraft planter, molded decoration of three foxes, 6"h, mint   400-600   July 14, 1999   Sold for $290

3534. Weller Woodcraft mug, molded decoration of three foxes, 6"h, minute chip to base   250-350   July 14, 1999   Sold for $270

3535. Weller Glendale bowl and flower frog with molded design of seagulls, bowl 15"dia., frog is 3"h, minor chip to bowl, frog has chip to foot   700-900   July 14, 1999   Sold for $300

3536. Weller Glendale vase, molded design of birds, 4"h, mint   250-350   July 14, 1999   Sold for $230

3537. Weller Glendale vase, wading bird with three speckled eggs in nest, 11"h, short tight line to top that does not go through   700-900   July 14, 1999   Sold for $375

3538. Weller Woodcraft hanging basket, molded decoration of owls, 5"h x 10"dia., minor chip   350-550   July 14, 1999   Sold for $240

3539. Weller Knifewood vase, molded design of yellow breasted birds in apple tree, 6"h, mint   350-550   July 14, 1999   Sold for $1000

3540. Weller Woodcraft vase, molded decoration of an owl on tree trunk, 16"h, two hairlines   700-900   July 14, 1999   Sold for $1500

3541. Weller Glendale vase, molded design of birds, 5"h, mint   250-350   July 14, 1999   Sold for $210

3542. Weller Glendale bowl and frog, molded design of birds, bowl 16"dia., frog 5"dia., both mint   800-1100   July 14, 1999   Sold for $550

3543. Weller Glendale wallpocket, molded design of birds, 7"w, mint   400-600   July 14, 1999   Sold for $450

3544. Weller Glendale vase, molded design of birds, 6.5"h, mint   300-400   July 14, 1999   Sold for $475

3545. Weller Swan garden ornament, male, 19"h, chip to tail and a reglue   4000-6000   July 14, 1999   Sold for $7000

3546. Weller Swan garden ornament, female, 14.5"h, chips to base   4000-6000   July 14, 1999   Sold for $11,000

221

3547. Weller Sicard covered vessel, crimped and twisted form with iridescent glaze of red, blue and green with gold floral decoration, marked, 6"h, repaired   500-700
June 7, 1998 Sold for $375

3548. Weller Hudson vase, blue with floral decoration, signed McLaughlin, original label, stamp mark, 7"h, mint
250-350 June 7, 1998 Sold for $375

3549. Weller Muskota covered powder jar, yellow, 7"h, mint
150-200 June 7, 1998 Sold for $100

3550. Weller Hudson vase, light blue dogwood on green to pink ground, artist signed, 7"h, mint   300-400
June 7, 1998 Sold for $375

3551. Weller Blue Ware vase, female figure, 10"h, minor flake   100-200 June 7, 1998 Sold for $200

3552. Weller Silvertone vase, floral design, 12"h, mint
250-350 June 7, 1998 Sold for $260

3553. Weller Woodcraft candlestick with owl, 14"h, mint
300-400 June 7, 1998 Sold for $400

3554. Weller Matt vase, three mushrooms on a mottled blue ground, impressed mark, 6.5"h, mint   350-450
June 7, 1998 Sold for $475

3555. Weller Sicard vase, poppy with circles in ground, red, green and gold lustre, impressed numbers, 12.25"h, rough spot on side in making, mint   1200-1700
June 7, 1998 Sold for $900

3556. Weller Sicard jardiniere, footed form with gold iridescent glaze with red, green and blue highlights, red, interior, marked on side, 8"dia. x 7"h, minor scratches, mint   600-800 June 7, 1998 Sold for $650

3557. Weller Muskota fishing boy, 7"h, repaired chip
150-200   June 7, 1998 Sold for $140

3558. Weller Silvertone vase, floral design, 8"h, mint
200-300   June 7, 1998 Sold for $325

3559. Weller Muskota flower frog, woman on rock, 7"h, minor flakes   200-300 June 7, 1998 Sold for $180

3560. Weller Coppertone turtle, green and brown glaze, 5"l, mint   200-300 June 7, 1998 Sold for $240

3561. Weller Blue & Decorated Hudson vase, floral design in band, 9.5"h, mint   200-300 June 7, 1998
Sold for $230

3562. Weller Coppertone bowl with flower frog, frog on end covered in a green and brown glaze, ink mark, 10"l x 5"h, minor bruise   400-600 June 7, 1998
Sold for $375

3563. RV planter with liner, Rhead design, water lilies in yellow and black on a green ground, 5"h, minor flakes
250-350 June 7, 1998 Sold for $250

Not Pictured:

3564. Weller Sicard covered vessel, twisted and ribbed form with a metallic floral decoration, two painted signatures, 8.5"w, restored chip to top   800-1100 July 14, 1999
Sold for $650

3565. Weller Coppertone vase, two frogs at each end under a brown, green and black matt glaze, 8.5"h, mint
800-1100 June 7, 1998 Sold for $950

3566. Weller LaSa vase, metallic glaze with landscape decoration, 5"h, mint   350-450 July 14, 1999
Sold for $425

3567. Weller Camelot vase, olive and ivory glaze with geometric designs, 6.5"h, repaired top 150-250 June 7, 1998 Sold for $110

3568. Weller Klyro vase, four legs, 6.5"h, minor lines 100-200 June 7, 1998 Sold for $60

3569. Weller Claywood vase, cylindrical shape with four panels of spider webs, 5.75" x 2.75", mint 150-250 June 7, 1998 Sold for $150

3570. Weller Art Nouveau vase, four-sided form with molded decoration of woman, grapes and flowers, impressed mark, 9"h, mint 250-350 June 7, 1998 Sold for $300

3571. Weller Greenbriar vase, lime green glaze with maroon streaks, 7", mint 200-300 June 7, 1998 Sold for $200

3572. Weller Claywood vase, four panels with Arts & Crafts floral design, 8.5"h, hairlines 100-200 June 7, 1998 Sold for $130

3573. Weller Jewel vase, design of stylized tree with red-centered flowers, incised decoration filled in with green on a yellow, gray and rose matt ground, impressed mark, 9"h, harmless line to lip 350-450 June 7, 1998 Sold for $550

3574. Weller Glendale vase, decoration of bird in brown with wetlands in ground, 6.5"h, mint 250-350 June 7, 1998 Sold for $450

3575. Weller Coppertone bowl, ivory, green and brown matt glaze, molded fish on side below perched frog, incised mark, 10"l, mint 550-750 June 7, 1998 Sold for $950

3576. Weller White and Decorated Hudson vase, octagon shape in an ivory matt glaze with floral decoration, impressed mark, 10"h, repaired chip to body 150-200 June 7, 1998 Sold for $140

3577. Weller Etched Matt vase, decoration of branches, berries and leaf covered in a orange, tan and green matt glaze, impressed mark, 12.5"h, mint 450-650 June 7, 1998 Sold for $850

3578. Weller Dickensware II vase, woodpeckers on tree branch, incised and painted trees in ground, impressed mark, 9.5"h, mint 750-950 June 7, 1998 Sold for $850

3579. Weller Roma vase, bulbous cylindrical shape with pinecones and needles, impressed mark, 7"h, minute flake to top 100-200 June 7, 1998 Sold for $90

3580. Weller Marvo bowl, molded fern and flower design encircles bowl, orange and green matt glaze, stamped mark, 8.5" x 9.75", harmless line to top 200-300 June 7, 1998 Sold for $160

3581. Weller Pearl vase, multicolored decoration on cream color with a black rim, impressed mark, 7" x 4.75", insignificant tight lines to rim 100-200 June 7, 1998 Sold for $200

3582. Weller Woodcraft vase, goblet-shaped with three trees as supports, 9.25"h, repaired chip 100-200 June 7, 1998 Sold for $140

3583. Weller Woodcraft bowl, four legs, squirrel design, stamped mark, 3.25"h, mint 100-200 June 7, 1998 Sold for $100

223

3584. Weller Roma vase, three panels, cream with pink grapes, green leaves, 4.5"w x 10"h, mint 100-200 July 13, 1998 Sold for $150

3585. Weller Dickensware mug, brown with Indian Chief, Ghost Bull, marked and signed C.B. Upjohn, 5"w x 5.5"h, mint 450-650 July 13, 1998 Sold for $550

3586. Weller Silvertone vase, pastel colors, lily decoration, marked and paper label, 5"w x 11.75"h, mint 200-300 July 13, 1998 Sold for $550

3587. Weller Dickensware tankard, brown, four men at table, Dombey & Sons, marked, 12.25"h, crazing, flakes to top 350-550 July 13, 1998 Sold for $600

3588. Weller Bonito vase, cream with stylized flowers, marked and initialed N. Walsch, 8"w x 11"h, mint 200-300 July 13, 1998 Sold for $325

3589. Weller Chase vase, blue with white Hunter on horse with dog, excellent color, marked, 5"w x 9.25"h, mint 250-350 July 13, 1998 Sold for $210

3590. Weller Hunter pillow vase, tan with rabbit decoration, marked, 6.25"w x 5"h, fracture to top 200-300 July 13, 1998 Sold for $400

3591. Weller Blueware vase, blue with classical figures, 5"w x 10.5"h, repaired base chips 150-250 July 13, 1998 Sold for $140

3592. Weller Art Nouveau ewer, pink and green with poppies, marked, 3.75"w x 11.75"h, flaw to top and handle 300-400 July 13, 1998 Sold for $450

3593. Weller Blue Ware vase, figures against blue ground, marked, 6"w x 12"h, mint 300-400 July 13, 1998 Sold for $475

3594. Weller Dickensware vase, beige, deer head and trees on sides, marked, 6.5"h, flake on base 250-350 July 13, 1998 Sold for $325

3595. Owens Matt vase, pale orange with gray flowers, marked and signed Tot Steele, 5"w x 10.5"h, bruise to top 100-200 July 13, 1998 Sold for $100

3596. Weller Dickensware vase, brown hi-glaze, Withers Dombey & Sons, marked, A.D., 3.75"w x 10"h, heavy crazing, mint 350-450 July 13, 1998 Sold for $270

3597. Weller Dickensware mug, tan with people in front, marked, 4"w x 5.5"h, mint 300-500 July 13, 1998 Sold for $400

3598. Weller Dickensware vase, tall standard glaze with man, marked, 17"h, minute flaking to rim 300-500 July 13, 1998 Sold for $650

3599. Weller Dickensware vase, brown to blue with male golfer, marked, 4"w x 9"h, two glaze misses 800-1100 July 13, 1998 Sold for $1200

3600. Weller Roma vase, cream in three panels, stylized flowers, marked, 3.75"w x 9"h, mint 100-200 July 13, 1998 Sold for $260

Not Pictured:

3601. Weller Dickensware vase, incised and painted Monk portrait, 16.5"h, chip 300-400 June 7, 1998 Sold for $240

3602. Weller Dickensware tankard, monk design, impressed mark, 12"h, repaired 250-350 July 14, 1998 Sold for $250

3603. Weller Silvertone vase, poppies with green leaves against a purple ground, ink mark, 6.5"h, mint 200-300 July 14, 1998 Sold for $375

3604. **Weller Dickensware** ewer, blue, yellow to brown with incised and painted decoration of yellow pears on brown branches with green leaves, incised mark, incised B.L., 13.5"h, mint   500-700   July 13, 1998   Sold for $425

3605. **Weller Bonita** vase, cream with pink, blue and brown flowers with green and brown leaves, 7.5"h, mint; with a **Weller Wild Rose** vase not shown, pink to green with large white and pink flower, both with script signature, 7"h, chip inside top   150-250   July 13, 1998   Sold for $80

3606. **Weller Dickensware** jug, tan to green, incised and painted fish swimming through waves, impressed mark, artist initial, 5.5"h, mint   250-350   July 13, 1998   Sold for $325

3607. **Weller Blue Ware** lamp, dark blue with girl and yellow garlands, 5"w x 11"h, hairline   150-250   July 13, 1998   Sold for $200

3608. **Weller Claremont** vase, brown and green with molded floral design, impressed Weller, 6"h, with a **Weller Warwick** bud vase not shown, tree branch design in brown and green with pink berries, stamp mark, 7"h, both mint   200-300   July 13, 1998   Sold for $110

3609. **Weller Baldin** bowl, yellow and red molded apples, 7"dia. x 4.25"h; with a **Weller Baldin** vase, not shown, impressed Weller, 6"h, both mint   200-300   July 13, 1998   Sold for $325

3610. **Weller Bronzeware** lamp, green and gold metallic glaze, 9"h, mint   250-350   July 13, 1998   Sold for $400

3611. **Weller Blue Drapery** bowl, blue with pink flowers, 3.5"h, rough spots in making; with a **Weller Blue Drapery** planter, not shown, blue with pink flowers, marked, 3.5"h, mint   150-250   July 13, 1998   Sold for $160

3612. **Weller Dickensware** jug, yellow, green, orange and brown berry and leaf decoration, marked, initialed R.G., 10.5"h, minor scratches   200-300   July 13, 1998   Sold for $270

3613. **Weller Flemish** jardiniere, brown and green with molded leaf design and band of dark pink flowers, 9"h, tiny chip to bottom; with a **Weller Woodrose** bowl (not shown), greens and browns with molded roses, 8"dia. x 2.5"h, mint   250-350   July 13, 1998   Sold for $240

3614. **Weller Manhattan** vase, orange matt with two handles are molded leaf decoration, script Weller Pottery, 8"h; with a **Weller Golden Glow** footed vase, mottled orange and yellow glaze with molded green leaf design, both mint   250-350   July 13, 1998   Sold for $160

3615. **Weller Burntwood** vase, cream and dark brown with birds and flowers banded in dark brown, 8.25"h, mint; with a **Weller Cornish** vase, blue matt with blue and pink berries both marked, 8.5"h, mint   250-350   July 13, 1998   Sold for $225

3616. **Weller Velva** vase, flared shape, orange to green with panel of flowers and leaves, script Weller Pottery, 6"dia. x 5"h; with a **Weller Flemish** basket (not shown), molded dark pink rose decoration, 8"dia. x 4"h, both mint   150-250   July 13, 1998   Sold for $140

3617. **Weller Flemish** basket, pink rose decoration, 8"dia. x 5.5"h; with a **Weller Flemish** basket not shown, molded rose decoration, 8"dia. x 4.5"h, both mint   200-250   July 13, 1998   Sold for $250

Not Pictured:

3618. **Weller Bronzeware** vase, metallic red glaze, 11"h, mint   400-600   June 7, 1998   Sold for $800

3619. Weller Blue & Decorated Hudson vase, flowers in red and lavender with yellow centers, green leaves on a blue ground, impressed mark, 9"h, mint 200-300 July 13, 1998 Sold for $260

3620. Weller Eocean vase, yellow daffodils on green stems with green and lavender leaves on a dark olive to green to lavender ground, impressed mark, 12"h, mint 450-650 July 13, 1998 Sold for $750

3621. Weller Eocean vase, red flowers and green leaves on a green to lavender to gray ground, impressed, 6.5"h, mint 250-350 July 13, 1998 Sold for $130

3622. Weller Eocean mug, red flower with green leaves, green ground, 5"h, mint 150-250 July 13, 1998 Sold for $110

3623. Weller Louwelsa vase, attribution, flattened form with two open handles and crimped top, yellow and orange pansies on a green to brown ground, artist signed, impressed numbers, 10"w, mint; with a **Weller Louwelsa** mug, orange berry, artist signed and impressed mark, 6"h, scratches to glaze and flakes to lip 350-450 July 13, 1998 Sold for $375

3624. Weller Etna pitcher, raised pink and white mums on green stems against a gray to pink ground, incised Weller on front, impressed Etna on bottom, 10.5"h, minor roughness around base 150-250 July 13, 1998 Sold for $220

3625. Weller vase, Arts & Crafts style English roses in pink with yellow centers and green leaves with floral continuing around vase, impressed mark, 8.5"h, mint 400-600 July 13, 1998 Sold for $250

3626. Weller Louwelsa floor vase, attribution, four-sided with blown out top and scalloped rim, orange and brown poppies with green leaves, unmarked, 23"h, minor flakes to top 500-750 July 13, 1998 Sold for $1100

3627. Weller Hudson vase, peach and blue irises with green leaves, all outlined in black, painted and signed by Walch, 8.5"h, mint 450-650 July 13, 1998 Sold for $800

3628. Weller White & Decorated Hudson vase, white roses with yellow centers and pink buds on an ivory to gray ground, impressed mark, 7.5"h, minor flake to interior lip 150-250 July 13, 1998 Sold for $180

3629. Weller Eocean vase, carp in green, pink and cream on a green to pink ground, incised signature, 6.5"h, mint 650-850 July 13, 1998 Sold for $1500

3630. Weller Etna vase, red and lavender flowers with yellow centers on a gray to ivory ground, 5.5"h, mint 200-300 July 13, 1998 Sold for $160

3631. Weller Dickensware vase, floral in green, brown and cream against a green and brown ground, artist initials, impressed mark, 11"h, mint 250-350 July 13, 1998 Sold for $425

3632. Weller Jap Birdimal jardiniere, landscape in squeeze bag technique, blue trees, yellow moon, impressed mark, 8.5"h, hairline crack 200-300 July 13, 1998 Sold for $210

3633. Weller Eocean vase, red flowers and green leaves on a gray to lavender to ivory ground, impressed, 9"h, mint 250-350 July 13, 1998 Sold for $260

3634. Weller White and Decorated Hudson vase, green leaves with pink grapes, marked, 6.5"h, mint 200-300 July 13, 1998 Sold for $240

3635. Weller Hudson vase, blue to pink, marked, artist signed by Walsh, 15.25"h, minor flake to base 150-250 July 13, 1998 Sold for $240

3636. Weller Blue and Decorated Hudson vase, blue with elaborate flowers, marked, 7.5"h, mint 150-250 July 13, 1998 Sold for $220

3637. Weller Blue and Decorated Hudson vase, two finely painted birds on limbs/flowers, marked, 13"h, mint 900-1200 July 13, 1998 Sold for $1600

3638. Weller Hudson Perfecto vase, attribution, blue and lavender with design floral border at rim, marked, 8"h, mint 200-300 July 13, 1998 Sold for $190

3639. Weller Hudson Perfecto vase, pale purple with leaves and berries, marked and signed Leffler, 5.75"h, mint 150-250 July 13, 1998 Sold for $250

3640. Weller White and Decorated Hudson bowl, white with multicolored flowers and cameo heads, marked, 6"w x 3.75"h, mint 300-400 July 13, 1998 Sold for $500

3641. Weller Hudson vase, blue to pink with iris decoration, painted and signed by Timberlake, marked, 15.25"h, mint 1500-2500 July 13, 1998 Sold for $3500

3642. Weller Blue and Decorated vase, blue with small flowers around top, marked, 7.25"h, mint 100-200 July 13, 1998 Not Sold

3643. Weller Hudson vase, pale pink and light green with stylized flowers, marked, 6.5"h, glaze chip in making, mint 350-550 July 13, 1998 Sold for $260

3644. Weller White and Decorated Hudson vase, white with detailed pink wisteria decoration, green leaves, 8"h, mint 250-350 July 13, 1998 Sold for $280

3645. Weller Hudson vase, blue with iris decoration, marked and signed D. England, 8.5"h, mint 300-500 July 13, 1998 Sold for $600

3646. Weller Blue and Decorated Hudson vase, blue with floral decoration, marked, 7.5"h, mint 100-200 July 13, 1998 Sold for $230

3647. Weller White and Decorated Hudson vase, iris decoration, marked, signed Timberlake, 12"h, mint 250-350 July 13, 1998 Sold for $375

3648. Weller Hudson vase, blue top with gray and pink bottom, pink and blue flowers at top, marked, signed Walsh, 7"h, mint 250-350 July 13, 1998 Sold for $450

3649. Weller Hudson vase, pink to green ground with pink ad white dogwood decoration with green leaves ad branches, 9"h, mint   350-450   July 14, 1998   Sold for $450

3650. Owens vase, orange, grapes, vines and leaves, pink to green ground, impressed Owens 7.5"h, mint   250-350   July 14, 1998   Sold for $300

3651. Weller vase, yellow daffodil decoration with green leaves and stems, original lamp hole in base, 10"h, mint   200-300   July 14, 1998   Sold for $190

3652. Weller Hudson vase, green matt with floral decoration, script mark, signed Timberlake, 7"h, mint   250-350   July 14, 1998   Sold for $550

3653. Weller Jewel vase, rose with green on molded vine and leaf design with raised red flowers and jewels, impressed mark, 11"h, mint   500-700   July 14, 1998   Sold for $800

3654. Weller Eocean vase, cat portrait in burgundy, lavender and white with black and yellow eyes on a gray ground, artist signed E. Blake, incised mark, 5"h, mint   1500-2000   July 14, 1998   Sold for $2500

3655. Weller Dickensware vase, hunter behind haystack with decoys on fence, all incised and in green, brown and yellow against a brown, green and tan ground, incised mark, 11"h, mint   700-900   July 14, 1998   Sold for $700

3656. Weller Matt Louwelsa with Dresden decoration vase, green/blue to light blue with Dutch scene and sailboats, 11"h, mint   450-650   July 14, 1998   Sold for $700

3657. Weller Blue Louwelsa vase, white crocuses against a multi-tone blue ground, impressed mark, 10.5"h, mint   1200-1700   July 14, 1998   Sold for $1800

3658. Weller experimental vase, cream matt ground with black banding top an bottom, two panels with incised and painted Dutch scenes, 9"h, mint   500-700   July 14, 1998   Sold for $2100

3659. Weller Art Nouveau vase, bisque finish in green with cream and peach, shell design on one side, other side has female with blonde hair and floral decoration, impressed mark, 9"w x 11"h, mint   350-450   July 14, 1998   Sold for $450

3660. Weller Eocean vase, painted mushroom decoration in burgundy, lavender and white on a gray ground, incised and painted mark, 5"h, mint   800-1100   July 14, 1998   Sold for $1100

3661. Weller Hudson vase, berry decoration and green leaves, impressed mark, 11"h, mint   250-350   July 14, 1998   Sold for $300

3662. Weller Blue and Decorated vase, bulbous bottom with stove pipe neck, blue with light and dark pink band with multicolored flowers, impressed mark, 10"h, mint   200-300   July 14, 1998   Sold for $260

Not Pictured:

3663. Weller Aurelian umbrella stand, brown with red, orange and yellow painted ground, large yellow daffodils with green leaves, ruffled top, artist signed, 24"h, chips, minor lines and slight loss of glaze   700-900   June 7, 1998   Sold for $550

3664. Weller Bronzeware lamp, deep red and purple with iridescent finish, marked 6"w x 12"h, mint   300-400   July 13, 1998   Sold for $550

3665. Weller Louwelsa vase, brown glaze with nasturtiums, 10"h, cracked; with a **Weller Louwelsa** vase, orange roses, signed Eugene Roberts, 4.5"w x 11"h, mint   200-300   July 13, 1998   Sold for $400

3666. Weller Wild Rose letter holder, brown and green with pink flowers, green branches, 7.25"w x 4.5"h, mint 100-200 July 14, 1998 Sold for $1500

3667. Weller White and Decorated Hudson vase, iris in rose and pink with yellow centers, ground yellow to gray, 9.5"h, mint 200-300 July 14, 1998 Sold for $240

3668. Weller Woodcraft vase, three handles at bottom, impressed mark, 9.5"h, mint 100-200 July 14, 1998 Sold for $170

3669. Weller Ivoris vase, two ring handles with leaf design, ivory glaze, 13"h, hairline; with a **Weller Ivory** vase, 10"h, hairline 200-300 July 14, 1998 Sold for $140

3670. Weller Roma planter, baskets of roses, 8"l x 4", mint; with a **Weller Roma** wallpocket, not shown, 7"h, line to top; and a **Weller Roma** wallpocket, not shown, 7"h, tiny flake to top 200-300 July 14, 1998 Sold for $170

3671. Weller Wild Rose vase, two handles, green, impressed mark, 12.5"h; with a **Zanesville** Stoneware vase, attribution, molded woman pouring water at brick wall, green and blue hi-glaze, 10.5"h, both mint 200-300 July 14, 1998 Sold for $375

3672. Weller Coppertone bowl, frog to edge covered in a green to brown matt glaze, 15.5"l, mint 600-800 July 14, 1998 Sold for $600

3673. Weller Cornish vases, two closed handles, brown ground, incised marks, one 9.5"h, other 8.5"h, both mint 400-500 July 14, 1998 Sold for $180

3674. Weller Silvertone wallpocket, multicolored ground and floral design, stamp mark, 10"h, minute bruise to top 150-250 July 14, 1998 Sold for $350

3675. Weller vase, floral on white and green ground, 8"h, mint; with a **RV Peony** pitcher, not shown, yellow and green, 8"h, chips and repairs 100-200 July 14, 1998 Sold for $180

3676. Weller Barcelona basket, floral decoration, stamped mark, 8"dia; with a **Weller Bonito** vase, cream with purple and pink floral design, incised mark, 9"h, both mint 150-250 July 14, 1998 Sold for $130

3677. Weller Louella vase, floral decoration in purple with green leaves, impressed mark, 6"h; with a **Weller Pearl** wallpocket, not shown, hi-glaze white with ornate floral design and lavender beading draping from top, 7"l, both with chip 100-200 July 14, 1998 Sold for $180

3678. Weller Woodcraft wallpocket, purple plums on branch with green leaves, 9"l, mint 200-300 July 14, 1998 Sold for $450

Not Pictured:

3679. Weller Roma vase, floral design, 9"h, mint; with a **Weller Burntwood** vase, fish design, 5.5"h, mint 400-500 July 15, 1998 Sold for $425

3680. Weller Malverne jardinere, 13"dia. x 11"h, mint 550-750 July 14, 1999 Sold for $750

3681. Weller Baldin vase, brown and green with apples, 6"h; with a **Weller Malverne** vase, embossed floral, incised mark, 5.5"h, both mint 200-300 July 15, 1998 Sold for $210

3682. Weller Floretta vase, molded grapes, marked, 7.5"w, mint 150-250 July 14, 1999 Sold for $70

3683. Weller Turada jardinere, attribution, 7.5"h, mint 400-600 July 14, 1999 Sold for $190

3684. Owens Utopian vase, artist initials, impressed mark, 10.5"h, mint 350-550 July 14, 1999 Sold for $375

3685. Weller Louwelsa vase, attribution, artist signed, impressed numbers, 9"h, mint 300-400 July 14, 1999 Sold for $270

3686. Owens vase, pansies, artist signed, impressed mark, 6"h, mint 150-250 July 14, 1999 Sold for $170

3687. Weller Louwelsa pitcher, floral decoration, impressed mark, 4"w, minor flakes to spout 100-150 July 14, 1999 Sold for $100

3688. RV Rozane vase, wild roses, signed B. Myers, Rozane wafer mark, 7"h, mint 300-400 July 14, 1999 Sold for $300

3689. RV Rozane vase, wild rose decoration, artist signed by Pillsbury, wafer mark, 8.5"h, mint 350-550 July 14, 1999 Sold for $475

3690. Karl Kappes oil painting, oil on board, scene of people at rivers edge, Arts & Crafts oak frame, 6 x 9", excellent condition 800-1100 July 14, 1999 Sold for $800

3691. Weller Louwelsa vase, daffodils, artist signed Sulcer, impressed mark, 14"h, deteriorating repair to top and bottom 200-300 July 14, 1999 Sold for $350

3692. Owens jug, tulip decoration, artist signed Tot Steele, impressed mark, 6.5"w, mint 200-250 July 14, 1999 Sold for $210

3693. Weller Louwelsa vase, floral design, impressed mark, 14.5"h, minor glaze abrasions 400-500 July 14, 1999 Sold for $650

3694. RV Rozane vase, wild rose decoration, artist initial, impressed mark, 4.5"w, mint 150-250 July 14, 1999 Sold for $160

3695. Weller Floretta vase, molded grapes, impressed mark, 7.5"h, mint 100-200 July 14, 1999 Sold for $70

3696. Owens vase, wild rose decoration, artist signed, impressed mark, 10.5"h, mint 350-550 July 14, 1999 Sold for $325

3697. Weller Turada jardinere, attribution, 8.5"h, minor chip 400-500 July 14, 1999 Sold for $170

Not Pictured:

3698. Weller LaSa vase, gold with pine trees and water scene, 5"w x 10"h, mint 500-700 July 13, 1998 Sold for $425

3699. Weller Louwelsa jug, brown glaze with leaves and raspberries, marked, signed Levi J. Burgess, 5.5"w x 6.5"h, mint 100-200 July 13, 1998 Sold for $220

3700. Weller Louwelsa vase, two handles, green leaf and berry design, 12"h, minor scratches to rim 150-250 July 14, 1998 Sold for $350

3701. Peters and Reed vase, handled form with multi-color floral design, 6"h, with a **Peters and Reed** Pretzel vase, molded floral design, 10.5"h, both mint   250-350 July 14, 1999 Sold for $270

3702. RV Rozane vase, floral design, impressed mark, artist signed, 4"h, mint   150-200 July 14, 1999 Sold for $190

3703. Weller Louwelsa vase, Native American father and child, impressed mark, artist signed Anthony Dunlevy, 15"h, mint   3500-4500 July 14, 1999 Sold for $1700

3704. Owens vase, four-sided form with floral design, impressed mark, signed, 6"h, repaired chip   100-150 July 14, 1999 Sold for $40

3705. Weller Louwelsa vase, wild rose design, impressed mark, signed, 6.5"h, flake to foot and top   100-200 July 14, 1999 Sold for $70

3706. Weller Louwelsa vase, dog decoration, impressed mark, signed Blake, 10.5"h, restored   800-1100 July 14, 1999 Sold for $350

3707. Weller Aurelian vase, daffodils on long stems, incised mark, artist signed Ferrell, 16"h, minute harmless flake at base   1500-2000 July 14, 1999 Sold for $1100

3708. Weller Red Louwelsa vase, nasturtium decoration, unmarked, signed Stemm, 10.5"h, minor flaws 1200-1700 July 14, 1999 Sold for $1800

3709. Weller Blue Louwelsa ewer, white flowers on a multi-toned blue ground, impressed mark, 4.5"w, mint 900-1200 July 14, 1999 Sold for $1500

3710. Weller Louwelsa vase, floral design, impressed mark, initialed, 12"h, mint   250-350 July 14, 1999 Sold for $300

3711. Weller Dickensware vase, four handles at top, embossed and painted, embossed mark, artist initialed, 9"h, mint   900-1200 July 14, 1999 Sold for $900

3712. RV Rozane vase, Native American portrait, impressed mark, artist initialed, 14.5"h, beautifully restored chip at top   3000-4000 July 14, 1999 Sold for $2800

3713. Weller Blue Louwelsa vase, floral design, impressed mark, 9"h, cracked   250-350 July 14, 1999 Sold for $350

3714. Lonhuda covered vessel, floral design, impressed mark, artist initials, 4.5"w, mint   300-400 July 14, 1999 Sold for $350

3715. Weller Louwelsa vase, floral design, impressed mark, 5.5"h, mint   150-250 July 14, 1999 Sold for $170

Not Pictured:

3716. Weller Louwelsa vase, clover decoration, marked, 6.5"h, repaired top; with a **Weller Louwelsa** jug, standard glaze with leaves and blackberries, marked, signed Elizabeth A. Edward, 7"h, mint   150-250 July 13, 1998 Sold for $210

3717. Weller Louwelsa humidor, matches, cigars and pipe, artist initials, 5"h, top not original, mint; with a **Weller Louwelsa** jug, blackberries and leaves, artist signed, flaking to top   200-300 July 13, 1998 Sold for $230

3718. Weller Stellar vase, black stars on cream, signed by H. Pillsbury, incised mark, 5"h, flaking to interior rim restored   300-400   July 13, 1998   Sold for $325

3719. Weller Kevona vase, modeled and applied lizard on floral in brown and green, 6"h, mint   600-800   July 13, 1998   Sold for $850

3720. Owens Lotus vase, Iris in rose, pink, purple and yellow with green leaves against an ivory, gray and peach ground, artist signed, impressed mark, 16.5"h, harmless glaze flaws to top   900-1200   July 13, 1998 Sold for $1400

3721. Weller vase, probably experimental, multicolored flowers and leaves on a yellow ground, stamp mark, 6.5"h, minor line to top   250-350   July 13, 1998 Sold for $170

3722. Weller Glendale vase, brown and green with bird nest decoration, marked, 8"w x 9"h, mint   300-400 July 13, 1998   Sold for $1000

3723. Weller Hudson vase, pink ground with red wild roses with green and yellow centers and green leaves, painted and signed by S. Timberlake, incised mark, 7"h, mint 300-400   July 13, 1998   Sold for $375

3724. Weller Perfecto vase, peonies in pinks and purples with brown centers and green leaves, Dorothy England, 9"w x 9"h, mint   800-1100   July 13, 1998   Sold for $650

3725. Owens Lotus vase, bee flying above green blades of grass on an ivory to blue ground, impressed mark, artist initialed, 4"h, mint   400-600   July 13, 1998 Sold for $400

3726. Weller figural, drunken ducks in yellow on a coppertone base, stamped mark, 15"h, small flake to bottom edge 5500-7500   July 13, 1998   Sold for $3250

3727. Weller Etna vase, raised floral design in red and green against a green to light tan ground, impressed mark, 5.5"h, mint   150-250   July 13, 1998   Sold for $110

3728. Weller Hudson vase, lily of valley in cream on a blue to green ground, signed Hood, stamp mark, 9"h, mint 550-750   July 13, 1998   Sold for $950

3729. Weller Eocean vase, white and pink pansies on a lavender to gray ground, impressed numbers, 6.5"h, mint 250-350   July 13, 1998   Sold for $260

3730. Weller Hudson vase, blue ground with white and pink peonies, painted and signed by Pillsbury, marked, 15"h, mint   1500-2500   July 13, 1998   Sold for $4500

3731. Weller Blue Louwelsa vase, holly berries and leaves in various shades of blue, impressed mark, 7.5"h, mint 850-1150   July 13, 1998   Sold for $900

3732. Weller Matt vase, painted and incised flowers in deep red with orange centers and green stems, impressed mark, 6.5"h, mint   500-700   July 13, 1998 Sold for $600

3733. RV Rozane Della Robbia mug, Dutch girls in blue, white and brown against a cut-back ground of dark green bordered by olive green, artist F.B., 4.5"h, mint 900-1200   July 13, 1998   Sold for $750

3734. Weller Matt vase, raised decoration of oak leaves, red, tan and matt glaze, impressed mark, 6.5"h, mint 650-850 July 14, 1999 Sold for $600

3735. Weller Hudson vase, floral decoration, painted and signed by Sarah Timberlake, impressed mark, 7"h, mint 250-350 July 14, 1999 Sold for $300

3736. Weller Hudson vase, stamped and impressed mark, signed Hood, 15"h, mint 3500-4500 July 14, 1999 Sold for $2700

3737. RV Rozane Woodland vase, incised and painted floral design on a bisque ground, all four sides decorated, signed with Rozane seal, 11"h, repaired flakes 750-950 July 14, 1999 Sold for $425

3738. Weller Eocean vase, wild rose decoration, 10"h, mint 450-650 July 14, 1999 Sold for $375

3739. Weller Perfecto vase, peony decoration, impressed mark, artist signed Dorothy England, 9.5"h, mint 800-1100 July 14, 1999 Sold for $475

3740. Weller vase, probably experimental, poppy's and other flowers surround vase, incised mark, 5.5"h, mint 1000-1500 July 14, 1999 Sold for $650

3741. RV Rozane Woodland vase, incised and painted floral design on a bisque ground, signed with Rozane wafer, 7"h, mint 650-850 July 14, 1999 Sold for $425

3742. Weller Dickensware mug, two ducks in body of water with fish handle, impressed mark, 5.5"h, minor flaws 250-350 July 14, 1999 Sold for $120

3743. RV Rozane Woodland vase, incised and painted floral design on a bisque ground, signed with Rozane wafer mark, 10"h, restored chips 650-850 July 14, 1999 Sold for $475

3744. Weller Dickensware vase, scene of revolutionary war soldiers, incised mark, 16"h, firing lines and glaze bubbles 1000-1500 July 14, 1999 Sold for $650

3745. Weller Eocean candlesticks, floral decoration, 8"h, some minor chips 200-300 July 14, 1999 Sold for $150

3746. Weller Etna vase, embossed roses, colorful, 12.5"h, mint 800-1100 July 14, 1999 Sold for $550

3747. Weller Dickensware mug, English characters and quotation from Copperfield, impressed mark, artist signed, 5.5"h, mint 300-400 July 14, 1999 Sold for $325

3748. Weller Dickensware vase, incised portrait of Native American, signed Black Bird, impressed mark, 6.5"h, mint 800-1100 July 14, 1999 Sold for $600

Not Pictured:

3749. Weller Dickensware vase, incised portrait of Indian brave in full headdress, portrait of Chief Black Bear, painted by Upjohn, impressed mark, 14"h, repaired top 400-600 June 6, 1999 Sold for $650

3750. Weller Dickensware vase, two children playing football, impressed mark, 9"h, mint 900-1200 July 14, 1999 Sold for $800

233

3751. Weller Dickens vase, two handles, gray with man in hat, marked, 6"w x 3.75"h, mint   300-400
July 13, 1998 Sold for $260

3752. RV Rozane Home Art vase, green, paper label, 3.5"w x 4.5"h, repair to feet   70-120   July 13, 1998
Sold for $60

3753. Weller Eocean mug, gray with pink and purple cherries, marked, 5.5"w x 6"h, mint   100-150   July 13, 1998
Sold for $140

3754. Weller Jap Birdimal jardiniere, gray with trees and moon, 7.25"w x 6.5"h, mint   200-300   July 13, 1998
Sold for $250

3755. Weller Etna vase, gray with pink carnations, marked, 6.75"w x 8"h, mint   200-300   July 13, 1998
Sold for $290

3756. RV Rozane Royal pillow vase, gray hi-glaze with raspberries, signed Timberlake, Rozane wafer mark, cracked   250-350   July 13, 1998 Sold for $190

3757. Weller Jap Birdimal hair receiver, dark blue with four Norse sailing ships, 4"w x 2"h, mint   150-250
July 13, 1998 Sold for $190

3758. Weller Rochelle vase, gray with multicolored flowers, 2"w x 5"h, mint   100-150   July 13, 1998 Sold for $140

3759. Weller Eocean vase, gray hi-glaze with red cherries and leaves, 4.5"w x 5.5"h, mint   150-250   July 13, 1998
Sold for $170

3760. Weller Eocean vase, gray to pale pink, blue flowers, green leaves, marked, 4.75"w x 4.5"h, mint   150-250
July 13, 1998 Sold for $220

3761. Weller Eocean vase, black top and gray to pink bottom, two white flowers, purple leaves, marked and signed Claude Leffler, 6.5"w x 16"h, mint   900-1200
July 13, 1998 Sold for $1700

3762. RV Rozane Royal pillow vase, green with pink roses and leaves, signed M. Timberlake, 4.5"w x 4.25"h, flake bottom, line to lip   50-100   July 13, 1998
Sold for $100

3763. Owens Lotus pitcher, gray with white stork, 8.25"h, lines in bottom in making   150-250   July 13, 1998
Sold for $260

3764. Weller Rochelle vase, gray glaze with yellow rose, marked, 2"w x 7"h, mint   100-200   July 13, 1998
Sold for $110

3765. Weller Etna jardiniere, gray with pink embossed flowers, marked, 8.5"h, glaze flake; with a **RV Rozane** bowl, (below) cream to gray with blue and pink flowers, signed C. Neff, 4"h, chip   200-300   July 13, 1998
Sold for $190

3766. Weller Eocean vase, dark to light gray, red and gray flowers, 6.25"h, small flake to top; with a **Weller Floretta** mug, dark to light gray, purple grapes, 5"h, flake to top   150-200   July 13, 1998 Sold for $150

Not Pictured:

3767. Weller Eocean vase, pink flowers on green to ivory, 8.5"h, mint   250-350   July 15, 1998 Sold for $375

3768. Weller Aurora vase, hi-glaze, pastel pink, yellow and white iris decoration with green leaves on a multicolored pastel ground, incised mark, 10"h, repaired top 250-350   July 15, 1997 Sold for $250

3769. Zaneware vase, green drip with overall iridescence, 7"h, mint   250-350   July 13, 1998 Sold for $300

3770. Weller Eocean vase, nasturtiums with green leaves on a gray, green and ivory ground, artist initialed, 12"h, mint 550-650   July 13, 1998 Sold for $400

3771. Weller Dickensware vase, young girl and man, signed on reverse Dombey and Son, marked, 8.5"h, mint 450-650   July 13, 1998 Sold for $325

3772. Weller Hudson candlesticks, pair, floral on a two-tone green ground, impressed marks, signed M. Timberlake, 8.5"h, minor flake   300-400   July 13, 1998 Sold for $375

3773. Weller Golden Glow vase, pink and white mottled body with green handles, 7"h; with a **Weller Golden** vase not shown, pedestal form in solid light and dark rusty brown, raised molded leaf and flower design, handles, both script mark, 7.5"h, both mint   200-300 July 13, 1998 Sold for $210

3774. Weller vase, yellow matt with green leaves and white flowers, script mark, 12.5"h, mint   200-300 July 13, 1998 Sold for $180

3775. Weller Eocean vase, purple grapes with green leaves and stems on a lavender to green ground, six handles under top lip, incised mark, artist initialed, 13"h, mint 800-1100   July 13, 1998 Sold for $750

3776. Weller Greora vase, marked, 9"h, mint   200-300 July 13, 1998 Sold for $270

3777. Weller Silvertone vase, two handles, lavender and green with multicolored flowers, stamp mark, 8"h, mint 150-250   July 13, 1998 Sold for $350

3778. Weller Coppertone bowl, lily pads and frogs on sides, 10.5"l x 3.5"h, minute flake to side   250-350 July 13, 1998 Sold for $425

3779. Weller Hudson Perfecto lamp base, lavender to green, watercolor decoration pink with yellow and brown, purple leaves and green leaves, impressed mark, signed Leffler, 10"h, mint   900-1200 July 13, 1998 Sold for $600

3780. Weller Hudson vase, cream to gray with large pink berries, white and yellow flowers, green leaves and vines, impressed mark, 11"h, mint   250-350 July 13, 1998 Sold for $280

3781. Weller Burntwood plate, cream cork-like finish with birds and flowers, brown back, 9"dia., minor flakes to back   100-150   July 13, 1998 Sold for $170

3782. Weller Hudson bowl, gray and pale green with green and pink thistle decoration, pale green leaves, impressed mark, 7.5"h x 3.5"h, mint   200-300 July 13, 1998 Sold for $150

3783. Weller Eocean vase, pansy decoration in pink, purple and ivory on an ivory to green ground, incised signature, artist initialed, 8.5"h, mint   300-400   July 13, 1998 Sold for $280

3784. Weller White and Decorated Hudson vase, cream with blue band at shoulder with multicolored floral decoration, impressed mark, 9.5"h, mint   250-350 July 13, 1998 Sold for $300

Not Pictured:

3785. Weller Oak Leaf vase, brown, 16"h; with a **Weller Oak Leaf** vase, brown, 9"h, both mint   350-450 July 15, 1998 Sold for $300

3786. Weller Glendale vase, molded forest scene with two parakeets on branch, impressed mark, 9"h, roughness in glaze on side in making, mint 350-550 July 14, 1998 Sold for $550

3787. RV Decorated mug, green to white ground, purple grapes and leaves, RPCo. mark, 5"h, mint 150-250 July 14, 1998 Sold for $70

3788. Weller Baldin lamp base, blue with red and yellow apples, green leaves, brown branches, metal base and fittings, 12.5"h, mint 250-350 July 14, 1998 Sold for $800

3789. RV Gold Trace candlestick, cream with gold design around top and base, unmarked, 9"h, mint 100-200 July 14, 1998 Sold for $50

3790. RV Decorated Gold Trace bowl with flower frog top, two pieces, cream with painted green design and gold trace floral and line design, 7"dia. x 3"h, mint 150-250 July 14, 1998 Sold for $80

3791. Weller Ivory vase, cream with brown highlights, ornate design of alternating openings and ram heads around base, floral and fruit design around top, unmarked, 10"h, mint 150-250 July 14, 1998 Sold for $160

3792. Weller Coppertone vase, frog holding flower vase on lily pad, Weller script mark, 4"h, mint 200-300 July 14, 1998 Sold for $250

3793. RV Decorated pitcher, white, yellow and purple flowers with green leaves, ground shades from purple, green to yellow, gold highlights on top and handle, unmarked, 9"h, chip to body; with an **RV early Landscape** pitcher (shown far right), orange to cream with band of green and brown trees and houses, unmarked, 7"h, chip, crack in spout 150-250 July 14, 1998 Sold for $90

3794. Weller Louwelsa vase, brown, green to orange ground with orange and green floral and leaf decoration, artist initials on front, impressed mark, 7"h, mint 100-200 July 14, 1998 Sold for $120

3795. LaMoro pitcher, brown, orange to green with orange and green leaves, impressed mark, 13"h, mint 150-250 July 14, 1998 Sold for $220

3796. RV Creamware mug, cream with blue band, Indian decoration, unmarked, 4.5"h, mint 100-200 July 14, 1998 Sold for $200

3797. Weller Glendale vase, red and blue flowers and berries, blue and yellow bird with nest in tree, molded McLaughlin signature on reverse, impressed mark, 10"h, mint 350-450 July 14, 1998 Sold for $475

3798. Weller Dickensware jardiniere and pedestal, pedestal not shown, caramel hi-glaze with brown and yellow floral decoration with green stems and leaves, impressed mark, 10"dia., pedestal 19"h, hairline in pedestal 550-750 July 14, 1998 Sold for $375

3799. RV Aztec pitcher, blue with squeezebag decoration in blue and white, 4.5"h, mint 300-400 July 14, 1998 Sold for $290

3800. Weller Woodcraft figurine, two hunting dogs in grasses, brown to yellow dogs, base in earth tones and green, impressed block mark, 7"h, minute chip to base 450-650 July 14, 1998 Sold for $650

3801. J.B. Owens vase, footed pillow vase in dark to light brown with yellow ground, Indian portrait with cream and red vest, blue in hair, impressed marks, 8.5"w x 8"h, repaired top 700-900 July 14, 1998 Sold for $1100

3802. Owens vase, yellow chick surrounded by thinly painted grass, four feet, artist signed, 5"w x 4"h, mint   450-650 July 13, 1998 Sold for $300

3803. Weller Hudson vase, butterflies on a blue and green ground with blue and pink flowers on green stems and leaves, signed by M. Timberlake, ink mark, 7"h, harmless tight hairlines   500-700 July 13, 1998 Sold for $1300

3804. Weller Aurora vase, pastel ground of yellow, blue, white and peach with flowers, incised mark, 9"h, mint 600-800 July 13, 1998 Sold for $650

3805. Weller Louwelsa vase, rose in orange with green leaves on a brown and green ground, impressed mark, artist initialed, 8.5"h, small scratch   300-400 July 13, 1998 Sold for $400

3806. Weller Jap Birdimal vase, black cat, green ground, 7.5"h, mint   600-800 July 13, 1998 Sold for $850

3807. Weller Silvertone vase, two handles, red and white embossed flowers on a purple, pink and white ground, original labels, 10"h, mint   350-450 July 13, 1998 Sold for $500

3808. Lessell vase, landscape design with trees in front of water, mountains in ground, red with dark red outlined in white, signed Lessell, 10"h, mint   600-800 July 13, 1998 Sold for $1000

3809. Owens vase, similar to Weller Aurelian with green, yellow and brown leaves on a swirling ground of mahogany, yellow and dark brown, artist initialed, incised bottom, sunburst J.B. Owens, initial A.H., 13.5"h, mint   600-800 July 13, 1998 Sold for $650

3810. Weller Matt Louwelsa vase, oak leaves and acorns in deep rust against a tan ground, signed by Hester Pillsbury, incised and impressed marks, 12"h, mint 900-1200   July 13, 1998 Sold for $1100

3811. Weller Green Louwelsa vase, attribution, roses in yellow against an emerald green ground, signed by H. Pillsbury, incised mark, 10.5"h, mint   800-1100 July 13, 1998 Sold for $2400

3812. Owens Lotus vase, fish in dark green with pink and green sea vegetation, three-handled form decorated and signed by Chilcote, 5"h, mint   600-800 July 13, 1998 Withdrawn

3813. Weller Claywood vase, tan and green decoration on a brown ground, 5"h, mint   150-250 July 13, 1998 Sold for $100

3814. Weller Jewel vase, fern fronds with swirling blue jewels, decorated front and back on a blue, green and pink ground, impressed mark, 7.5"h, mint   500-700 July 13, 1998 Sold for $700

3815. Weller Eocean vase, molded frog clinging to side of vase in green on a gray and beige ground, hi-glaze, impressed mark, 4"h, mint   450-650 July 13, 1998 Sold for $300

3816. Weller Louwelsa vase, yellow daffodil and green and brown leaves, impressed mark, 9"h, mint   300-400 July 13, 1998 Sold for $400

Not Pictured:

3817. Weller Hudson Perfecto vase, lavender ground with nice floral decoration, signed Leffler, 5.5"h, mint 150-250 July 15, 1998 Sold for $350

3818. RV Rochelle candlestick, pink fruit clusters on black ground with greens and yellows, 10.5"h, mint 150-200 July 14, 1998 Sold for $150

3819. RV Rozane Woodland vase, flowers front and back, wafer mark, 10.25"h, minor chip repairs to base 500-700 July 14, 1998 Sold for $425

3820. Weller Hudson vase, multicolored floral decoration, impressed mark, 4.5"h, mint 250-350 July 14, 1998 Sold for $240

3821. Weller Etna ewer, blue, pink and yellow floral decoration, marked, 6"h, mint 150-200 July 14, 1998 Sold for $110

3822. Weller Marbleized vase, cream, green and brown swirls, impressed mark, 9.5"h, mint 250-350 July 14, 1998 Sold for $160

3823. Weller Muskota fence, green and charcoal matt glaze, not marked, 5"h, mint 100-200 July 14, 1998 Sold for $200

3824. Weller White & Decorated vase, cream with pink and burgundy floral, green leaves and black branches, 11.5"h, mint 250-350 July 14, 1998 Sold for $325

3825. Weller Floral vase, tulips with green leaves on a green ground, incised signature, 11.5"h, mint 250-350 July 14, 1998 Sold for $260

3826. Weller Muskota lobster flower frog, impressed mark, 5.5"dia., signed, mint 150-250 July 14, 1998 Sold for $160

3827. Weller Sicard vase, clover in gold on a purple/red ground with iridescent highlights of pink, blue, green, red and gold, signed, 6"h, mint 300-400 July 14, 1998 Sold for $425

3828. Weller Eocean vase, blue to green hi-glaze, pink to burgundy floral with yellow and green leaves, buds and stems, marked, 12.5"h, mint 800-1100 July 14, 1998 Sold for $1500

3829. Weller Muskota gate, unsigned, 7.5"h, minor chip repair 500-700 July 14, 1998 Sold for $475

3830. Weller vase, molded floral decoration covered in a purple hi-glaze, incised mark, 5.5"h, mint 250-350 July 14, 1998 Sold for $250

3831. Weller Sicard vase, purple and red body with golden floral decoration, overall blue, green, pink and gold highlights, signed, 3"h, roughness around bottom 200-300 July 14, 1998 Sold for $280

3832. Weller LaSa vase, landscape in red, yellow, green and blue, signed, 9.5"h, mint 500-700 July 14, 1998 Sold for $375

3833. Weller Cornish vase, experimental, marked, 6"h, mint 200-300 July 14, 1998 Sold for $100

3834. RV Woodland vase, twisted form with cream finish, orange, brown and green glossy decoration, wafer mark, 6"h, minor flaking to top 350-550 July 14, 1998 Sold for $300

3835. Weller LaSa vase, landscape with green, gold and red with purple highlights, 5"h, repaired top 100-200 July 14, 1998 Sold for $140

3836. Weller LaSa vase, evergreen tree on shore of lake, mountains, iridescent green, red and gold, paper label, signed, 3.5"h, mint 350-450 July 14, 1998 Sold for $260

3837. Weller Sicard vase, floral decoration in green and gold iridescent glaze, signed, 5"h, mint 400-600 July 14, 1998 Sold for $375

3838. Weller Louwelsa vase, green palm leaves on a brown, orange and green ground, artist signed, 6"h, mint 150-250 July 14, 1998 Sold for $110

3839. Weller Dickensware vase, incised scene of boys playing football in period gear, impressed marks, 9"h, small chip repair to rim 1200-1700 July 14, 1998 Sold for $1000

3840. Weller Louwelsa jardiniere, daffodils, green leaves on a brown, orange and green ground, impressed mark, artist signed, 10"dia. x 8"h, surface scratches, mint 350-450 July 14, 1998 Sold for $230

3841. Weller Louwelsa vase, two-handled form with brown and yellow cherries on brown stems with brown and green leaves, artist initialed and impressed mark, 12"h, mint 450-650 July 14, 1998 Sold for $700

3842. Weller Dickensware vase, female golfer in period clothing, impressed mark, 8"h, mint 1000-1500 July 14, 1998 Sold for $1300

3843. RV Rozane Royal vase, yellow lily of the valley with green leaves on a green, orange and brown ground, impressed mark, artist signed, 18"h, damage and deteriorating repair to top 250-350 July 14, 1998 Sold for $110

3844. Weller Louwelsa vase, yellow mums with green leaves against a brown and yellow ground, artist signed by C.L. Leffler, impressed mark, 10.5"h, minute flake to top 250-350 July 14, 1998 Sold for $400

3845. Weller Louwelsa candlestick, clover in green and ivory on a brown and yellow ground, marked, artist signed, 11"h, mint 250-350 July 14, 1998 Sold for $260

3846. Weller Louwelsa vase, long-beaked bird sitting amongst palm leaves, bird in green, yellow and brown against a yellow and brown ground, signed by Ed Able, impressed mark, 14.5"h, harmless lines to body 2000-3000 July 14, 1998 Sold for $3000

3847. Weller Jap Birdimal vase, Geisha girl in colorful clothing holding umbrella, trees in ground, incised Weller Rhead Faience, artist initialed L.S., 10.5"h, mint 1200-1700 July 14, 1998 Sold for $1800

3848. Weller Dickensware vase, Native American brave marked Blackbird, impressed mark, 6.5"h, mint 550-750 July 14, 1998 Sold for $500

3849. RV Rozane vase, yellow rose with green leaves, marked, artist initials, 5"w, mint 150-250 July 14, 1998 Sold for $110

3850. Owens Utopian vase, rose with green leaves and brown stems on an orange and brown ground, marked, artist signed, 11"h, minor flakes 200-300 July 14, 1998 Sold for $260

3851. RV Rozane vase, attribution, two-handled form with ruffed top, painting of hunting dog with pheasant in his mouth, unmarked, 9"h, well repaired chips to lip 800-1100 July 14, 1998 Sold for $1300

3852. Weller vase, two-handled form with bearded man with crown, impressed mark, 11.5"h, minor chips 500-700 July 14, 1998 Sold for $270

3853. LaMoro vase, two-handles, orange pansy, impressed mark, 7"h, mint 150-250 July 14, 1998 Sold for $160

3854. Weller Aurelian vase, molded ground of green, yellow, orange and brown with pansy decoration, impressed mark, 8"w, roughness at handle 500-700 July 14, 1998 Sold for $400

239

3855.Brush McCoy vase, brown glaze with corn design, signed Rosewood, 13"h, restored; with a **Peters and Reed** vase (shown far right), decorated with two handles, 15"h, restored 250-350 July 15, 1998 Sold for $180

3856. Weller Dickensware vase, green ground and a monk design, impressed mark, 17"h, restored 500-750 July 15, 1998 Sold for $425

3857. RV Rozane Light pitcher, plum design on ivory to gray ground, impressed number, 5"h, restored; with an **Owens Lotus** pitcher (shown to right), stork design on gray to white, 9"h, restoration to lip 300-400 July 15, 1998 Sold for $280

3858. Weller Louwelsa candleholder, brown glaze with floral decoration, handle, impressed mark, artist initials, 6"h, mint 200-300 July 15, 1998 Sold for $260

3859. Weller Eocean vase, berry design in pink and red on green, impressed mark, 12"h, mint 550-750 July 15, 1998 Sold for $850

3860. Weller Blue Louwelsa tankard, white grapes on blue ground, impressed marks, signed C. Leffler, 12"h, restored 450-650 July 15, 1998 Sold for $700

3861. Weller Eocean vase, floral design, 5"h, mint 200-300 July 15, 1998 Sold for $375

3862. RV Rozane Royal pitcher, fruit decoration in yellow and green on a brown ground, wafer mark, 14"h, mint 250-350 July 15, 1998 Sold for $200

3863. RV Rozane Royal Light vase, oak leaves and acorns in green and brown, wafer mark, artist signed W. Meyers, 14"h, restored 300-400 July 15, 1998 Sold for $500

3864.Weller Glossy Hudson lamp, flowers on a gray ground, 13"h, restored original lamp base 250-350 July 15, 1998 Sold for $290

3865.RV Rozane Royal vase, Indian brave, impressed mark, 16"h, repaired chip to top 1000-1500 July 15, 1998 Withdrawn

3866. Weller LaSa vase, trees along riverbank, mountains and clouds in ground, metallic iridescence, signed, 9"h, minor roughness to top; with a **Weller Louwelsa** vase, floral design of yellow roses, impressed mark, artist initials, 7"h, restoration to top 500-700 July 15, 1998 Sold for $375

3867. Weller Floretta vase, pink floral design on green to ivory ground, impressed mark, 14"h, mint 350-550 July 15, 1998 Sold for $350

Not Pictured:

3868. Weller Louwelsa vase, brown glaze with asters, marked, signed Eugene Roberts, 6"w x 11.5"h, mint 200-300 July 13, 1998 Sold for $450

3869. Weller Louwelsa vase, brown glaze with flowers, marked, signed E. Roberts, 3"w x 12.5"h, mint 300-400 July 13, 1998 Sold for $475

3870. Weller Louwelsa vase, roses, marked, artist signed, 14.5"h, mint 300-500 July 13, 1998 Sold for $650

3871. Weller Matt vase, beetles on a red ground with green leaves, incised signature, 5"h, mint 550-750 June 7, 1998 Sold for $700

3872. Weller Fleron vase, green matt, incised mark, 8"h; with a **Weller Woodrose** wallpocket, 6"l, both mint 200-300 June 7, 1998 Sold for $300

3873. Weller Hudson vase, lily of valley in white with green leaves, signed by Pillsbury, ink mark, 9"h, mint 550-750   July 14, 1998   Sold for $650

3874. Weller Sicard vase, wheat in gold on an iridescent ground of purple, blue, green and red, signed Weller Sicard, 9"h, mint   1200-1700   July 14, 1998 Sold for $2000

3875. Weller Eocean vase, two egrets in white, lavender, orange and red against a green, cream and lavender ground, incised signature, impressed mark, 11"h, mint 2000-3000   July 14, 1998   Sold for $2500

3876. Weller vase, experimental design with cameo style decoration of stylized flowers, multi-tone blue matt glaze, impressed mark, 8.5"h, mint   700-900 July 14, 1998   Sold for $1300

3877. Weller Coppertone bowl, frog on end covered in green and brown matt glaze, 5"h, mint   600-800 July 14, 1998   Sold for $550

3878. Weller Hudson Pictorial vase, landscape with snow laden road bordered by brown fence running alongside tree line, signed McLaughlin, incised mark, 11.5"h, harmless flake to bottom   5500-7500   July 14, 1998 Sold for $4250

3879. Owens Matt vase, poppy in pink with green stems and leaves on a pink, ivory and light blue ground, artist initialed, impressed mark, 12.5"h, mint   350-450 July 14, 1998   Sold for $600

3880. Weller Sicard vase, gold mums with green highlights against a purple, blue and red ground, signed Weller Sicard, 10.5"h, mint   1000-1500   July 14, 1998 Sold for $1700

3881. Weller Figural hen, six chicks around base, incised mark, 8"h, restored minor flakes   2000-3000 July 14, 1998   Sold for $1600

3882. RV Rozane Della Robbia vase, flaring waisted form with incised and cut-back tulips in olive green against a cut-back ground of aqua, Rozane wafer, artist signed, 11"h, a couple of repaired chips   2000-3000 July 14, 1998   Sold for $1300

3883. RV Rozane Royal vase, ivory and green colored irises, signed J. Imlay, wafer seal, 14.5"h, hairlines to top 250-450   July 14, 1998   Sold for $325

3884. Weller Kenova vase, molded floral decoration under applied lizard, covered in a rust, brown and green matt glaze, 6"h, mint   800-1100   July 14, 1998 Sold for $850

3885. Weller Delta vase, Irises with yellow and brown centers and green leaves with a blue ground, signed by Pillsbury, stamp mark and Greek letters, 15.5"h, mint 1500-2500   July 14, 1998   Sold for $3250

3886. Weller Blue Louwelsa vase, crocus design in cream and blue with dark and light blue leaves against a multi-tone blue ground, impressed mark, 6.5"h, mint   700-900 July 14, 1998   Sold for $1100

3887. Weller Matt vase, molded morning glory decoration and leaves covered in a green, blue and red matt glaze, incised mark, 5"h, mint   450-650   July 14, 1998 Sold for $600

3888. RV Decorated Pauleo vase, floral decoration in middle, gray ground, 19.5", restored drill hole   550-750 July 15, 1998 Sold for $500

3889. Brush jewel bud vases, pair, 10"h, both mint   250-350 July 15, 1998 Sold for $850

3890. Peters and Reed vase, cream ground, blue drip glaze, 11", mint 250-350 July 15, 1998 Sold for $550

3891. Weller Muskota flower frog in a lily pad, 4.5"h, repaired; with a **Brush McCoy** frog, (at right) attribution, green and brown, 14.5"l, mint   400-600 July 15, 1998 Sold for $425

3892. Weller Hudson vase, rose decoration, 15"h, repaired 500-700 July 15, 1998 Sold for $200

3893. Weller Hudson vase, floral design on gray to ivory ground, 14", repaired chips   150-250 July 15, 1998 Sold for $160

3894. Weller Chengtu vase, orange matt, stamp mark, 7.5"h, mint 100-150 July 15, 1998 Sold for $200

3895. Weller Hudson vase, gray to blue with floral decoration, artist initialed, 14"h, mint 700-900 July 15, 1998 Sold for $900

3896. Weller Matt Louwelsa vase, nicely decorated with peach grapes on a gray to green ground, signed Farrell, impressed Louwelsa and Perfecto marks , 18"h, drilled for lamp 500-750 July 15, 1998 Sold for $900

3897. Weller Hudson vase, gray and cream ground and roses, 15"h, restored drill hole   300-400 July 15, 1998 Sold for $600

3898. Weller Frosted Matt vase, green to yellow/brown, unmarked, 7.5"h, chip to foot   100-150 July 15, 1998 Sold for $130

3899. Weller Dickensware vase with matt finish, incised decoration of man with staff among two trees, impressed mark, 15"h, restored chips   450-650 July 15, 1998 Sold for $425

3900. Weller Floretta ewer, peach design on green and brown matt, incised marks, 11"h, restored top   250-350 July 15, 1998 Sold for $90

3901. Weller Dickensware pillow vase, incised Indian, 6", restoration to base and top   350-550 July 15, 1998 Sold for $200

3902. Weller Hudson vase, green to pink, pansy decoration, artist signed Pillsbury, 7.5"h, mint   350-450 July 15, 1998 Sold for $600

3903. Weller Dickensware Dombey and Sons vase, 11"h, restored chips   350-550 July 15, 1998 Sold for $650

Not Pictured:

3904. Weller Dickensware oil lamp, standard glaze brown to green with floral decoration, artist signed, 16"h, comes with oil font, restored chips   450-650 July 14, 1998 Sold for $300

3905. Weller Sicard vase, gold and purple iridescent glaze with stylized flowers and leaves, signed on side, 5"h, mint   500-700   July 13, 1998 Sold for $475

3906. Lessell vase, white with gold stylized trees, marked, signed Lessell, 9.5"h, mint   300-500   July 13, 1998 Sold for $375

3907. Weller vase, probably experimental, green top to burnt orange, two groups of holly leaves, marked and incised initials NC, 5.75"h, mint   500-700   July 13, 1998 Sold for $950

3908. Owens opalescent ewer, hi-glaze and standard floral decoration, 5.5"h, mint   150-250   July 13, 1998 Sold for $260

3909. Weller Aurelian vase, standard glaze with silver overlay, decoration of roses with roses in silver, marked, artist signed Dorothy England, 3.5"h, minor flaws to silver   600-800   July 13, 1998 Sold for $450

3910. Weller Hudson vase, blue flowers, marked, signed Sarah Timberlake, 10.75"h, mint   700-900 July 13, 1998 Sold for $800

3911. Weller Besline vase, etched leaves and berries, 7.75"h, mint   100-200   July 13, 1998 Sold for $190

3912. Weller Matt vase, maroon with lighter maroon flowers, 8"w x 12"h, mint   800-1100   July 13, 1998 Sold for $1000

3913. Weller Matt Scenic vase, orange with black stylized trees, marked, 13.5"h, mint   800-1100   July 13, 1998 Sold for $2500

3914. Weller Hudson Pictorial vase, gray and tan ground with portrait of queen holding staff, marked, 8.75"h, mint   1000-1500   July 13, 1998 Sold for $1600

3915. Weller Hudson vase, blue with flowers, signed Pillsbury, 11.5"h, mint   900-1200   July 13, 1998 Sold for $1600

3916. Weller Matt vase, peach with leaves and berries, signed L.J. Burgess, 14"h, mint   700-900   July 13, 1998 Sold for $1000

3917. Weller Matt ewer, purple with embossed decoration, marked, 6"w x 9"h, crack   200-300   July 13, 1998 Sold for $110

3918. Weller Blue Louwelsa vase, floral decoration, 6.5"h, mint   500-700   July 13, 1998 Sold for $650

3919. Weller Dickensware vase, dark blue with fish and seaweed, marked, 9.25"h, mint   900-1200 July 13, 1998 Sold for $850

3920. RV Rozane Royal cardholder, gray with playing cards, 3.5"h, mint   200-300   July 13, 1998 Sold for $375

3921. Weller Blue and Decorated vase in blue with bird and flowers, 8.5"h, hairlines   400-500   July 13, 1998 Sold for $500

3922. Weller Sicard vase, gold and purple with stylized flowers, marked on side, 6"h, hairline   200-300 July 13, 1998 Sold for $200

Not Pictured:

3923. Weller Dickensware vase, carved and painted decoration of blue, yellow and orange mums on a ground shading from brown to blue, impressed mark, artist signed Farrell, 13"h, minor chip to lip   500-700 June 7, 1998 Sold for $550

3924. Weller Marvo vase, blue and green matt glaze, 9.5"h, mint   400-600   July 15, 1998 Sold for $325

243

3925. Weller Bonito vase, floral decoration, incised mark, artist initialed, 11"h, mint 200-300 July 16, 1997 Sold for $150

3926. Weller Silvertone basket, molded grapes against a multicolored ground, ink mark, 12.5"h, mint 250-350 July 16, 1997 Sold for $375

3927. Weller Forest teapot, hi-glaze, impressed mark, 5"h, crazed, mint 200-300 July 16, 1997 Sold for $180

3928. Weller Forest pitcher, hi-glaze, unmarked, 5.5"h, mint 150-250 July 16, 1997 Sold for $150

3929. Weller Warwick basket, ink mark, 7"h, mint 100-200 July 16, 1997 Sold for $110

3930. Weller Baldin vase, brown, impressed mark, 5.5"h, mint 200-300 July 16, 1997 Sold for $150

3931. Weller Forest jardiniere, unmarked, 8.5"h, mint 350-450 July 16, 1997 Sold for $550

3932. Weller Malvern strawberry pot, unmarked, 5"h, mint 150-250 July 16, 1997 Sold for $120

3933. Weller Sabrinian ewer, stamp mark, 11"h, mint 250-350 July 16, 1997 Sold for $375

3934. Weller Forest jardinere, unmarked, 7"h, mint 250-350 July 16, 1997 Sold for $300

3935. Weller Bonito vase, floral decoration, incised mark, artist initials, 9"h, mint 200-300 July 16, 1997 Sold for $120

3936. Weller Etna vase, cameo jewel, artist initialed, 12"h, mint 350-450 July 16, 1997 Sold for $350

3937. Weller Jap Birdimal vase with swans, green ground, impressed marks, signed H.R., 8"h, mint 500-700 July 16, 1997 Sold for $500

3938. Weller Eocean vase, red and green pansy decoration on a green to cream ground, unsigned, 12"h, mint 350-450 July 16, 1997 Sold for $425

3939. **Weller Burntwood** jardiniere, children playing under trees, impressed mark, 6"h, mint   200-300
July 16, 1997   Sold for $350

3940. **Weller Bonita** vase, floral decoration, incised mark, artist initialed, 7.5"h, mint   150-250   July 16, 1997
Sold for $110

3941. **Weller Bonito** vase, floral decoration, incised mark, artist initials, 9"h, mint   150-250   July 16, 1997
Sold for $80

3942. **Weller Louella** vase, floral, impressed mark, 7"h, mint   100-150   July 16, 1997   Sold for $60

3943. **Weller Chase** vase, white hunter on horseback and hound on dark blue ground, marked, 8"h, mint   300-400
July 16, 1997   Sold for $300

3944. **Weller Chase** vase, white cameo of jumper on dark blue, marked, 6.5"h, mint   250-350   July 16, 1997
Sold for $240

3945. **Weller Klyro** bud vase, floral, good color, 8.5"h, mint   150-250   July 16, 1997   Sold for $210

3946. **Weller Etched Matt** vase, leaf and berry design in panels, dark brown with green, impressed mark, 9"h, mint   150-250   July 16, 1997   Sold for $300

3947. **Weller Roma** vase, birds and trees in red and yellow against a deep blue ground, not marked, 8"h, mint   350-550   July 16, 1997   Sold for $260

3948. **Weller Matt** vase, Art Nouveau floral design in peach on green, impressed mark, 8.75"h, mint   250-350
July 16, 1997   Sold for $175

3949. **Weller Blue Drapery** vase, roses on a blue ground, impressed mark, 11.5", mint   200-300   July 16, 1997
Sold for $125

3950. **Weller White and Decorated** vase, two painted birds in multicolored floral decoration on a cream ground, impressed mark, 8.5"h, mint   900-1200
July 16, 1997   Sold for $1400

3951. **Weller Hudson** vase, white flowers with yellow centers and green leaves on a lavender ground, incised mark, signed H. Pillsbury, 5.5"h, mint   350-450
July 16, 1997   Sold for $350

3952. **Weller Hudson** vase, pink and red floral decoration with green leaves, artist signed S. Timberlake, incised mark, 8"h, mint   400-600   July 16, 1997   Sold for $475

245

3953. Art Pottery vase, orange glaze with black highlights, 9"h, mint   150-250   July 16, 1997   Sold for $50

3954. Weller vase, modeled, incised and painted floral decoration in blue on green matt ground, 5.5"w x 3.5"h, mint   400-600   July 16, 1997   Sold for $160

3955. Weller Etched Matt vase, purple blossoms on green branch with incised black outlines on a cream ground, incised mark, 8"h, chip to lip   100-200   July 16, 1997   Sold for $230

3956. Weller Ivory vase, raised and molded design with light green and gold tint under ivory glaze, incised mark, 10"h, mint   150-250   July 16, 1997   Sold for $70

3957. Weller Silvertone vase, red and purple poppies with blue and yellow butterflies, green leaves and stems on multicolored ground, ink mark, 12"h, mint 350-450   July 16, 1997   Sold for $475

3958. Weller Hudson vase, irises in ivory, pink and yellow on broad green stems and leaves against a light purple to ivory ground, impressed mark, 11.5"h, mint   250-350 July 16, 1997   Sold for $400

3959. Weller Bronzeware lamp base, red metallic glaze, indention at foot for lamp cord, stamp mark, 9"h, small flake at top   250-350   July 16, 1997   Sold for $150

3960. Weller Hudson vase, dogwood in purple and yellow with green leaves on black branches, ground shades from pink to pale green to yellow, impressed Weller, 9"h, mint   450-650   July 16, 1997   Sold for $650

3961. Weller Marbleized vase, cream, green and brown swirls, impressed mark, 9.5"h, mint   250-350 July 16, 1997   Sold for $100

3962. Weller Eocean vase, floral decoration of green and red against a green to pink ground, unmarked, 10.5"h, some glaze scratches, mint   250-350 July 16, 1997   Sold for $250

3963. Weller Eocean mug, portrait of a bull dog in gray and white on gray to white ground, incised marks, signed E. Blake, 5"h, mint   900-1200 July 16, 1997   Sold for $1600

3964. Weller Eocean tankard, dark purple cherries, artist signed, incised mark, 13.25", mint   500-700 July 16, 1997   Sold for $425

3965. Zaneware bowl, blue, green and cream matt, not marked, 8"dia. x 2.75", mint 100-150 June 8, 1997 Sold for $80

3966. Weller Klyro wallpocket, impressed mark, 7"l, mint 100-200 June 8, 1997 Sold for $350

3967. Weller Glendale vase, partial sticker on base, 11.5"h, mint 500-700 June 8, 1997 Sold for $550

3968. Weller Wood Rose wallpocket, stamp mark, 6.75"l, minor flakes 100-150 June 8, 1997 Sold for $60

3969. Weller Woodcraft flower frog, log with three branches, not marked, 4" x 3.5", minor flakes 100-150 June 8, 1997 Sold for $100

3970. Weller Forest jardiniere, 4.75", mint 150-250 June 8, 1997 Sold for $120

3971. Weller Woodcraft vase, owl figural on side with flower frog holes in top, 15.25"h, small flake that appears to be in making 1000-1500 June 8, 1997 Sold for $900

3972. Weller Glendale vase, not marked, 4"h, mint 150-250 June 8, 1997 Sold for $160

3973. Weller Forest vase, impressed mark, 10"h, mint 250-350 June 8, 1997 Sold for $190

3974. Weller Wood Rose wallpocket, numbered, 10.25"l, mint 200-300 June 8, 1997 Sold for $200

3975. Weller Glendale vase, impressed mark, 6.5"h, mint 250-350 June 8, 1997 Sold for $500

3976. Zaneware vase, green, blue and brown, impressed mark, 8.25"h, mint 100-200 June 8, 1997 Sold for $50

3977. Weller Forest hanging basket, not marked, 7.75" x 3.25", crack 100-150 June 8, 1997 Sold for $60

3978. Weller Hudson vase, green lily pads with white and pink flowers, blue to pink ground, artist signed McLaughlin, incised mark, 9.5"h, mint 600-800 June 8, 1997 Sold for $475

3979. Weller Perfecto vase, lavender and pink peony with green leaves, pink to ivory ground, artist signed England, impressed mark, 9.5"h, tight line on top inside, doesn't appear to go through 700-900 June 8, 1997 Sold for $350

3980. Weller Hudson vase, pink and white dogwood, blue to cream ground, artist signed M. Timberlake, 9"h, mint 600-800 June 8, 1997 Sold for $375

247

3982. Weller Glendale wallpocket, marked, 7.5"w x 7"h, mint 300-500 June 8, 1997 Sold for $450

3983. Weller Forest vase, green, brown and gray matt glaze, 12"h, mint 250-350 June 8, 1997 Sold for $190

3984. Weller Glendale vase, marked, 8"h, mint 300-400 June 8, 1997 Sold for $425

3985. Weller Glendale vase, marked, 8.25"dia. x 8.75"h, mint 600-800 June 8, 1997 Sold for $900

3986. Weller wallpocket, blue with oak leaves and berries, 7"l, mint 100-200 June 8, 1997 Sold for $110

3987. Weller jar with lid, squirrel figural on top as handle, impressed mark, 8"h, good repair to squirrel ear 250-350 June 8, 1997 Sold for $400

3988. Weller candlestick with owl faces, marked, 12.5"h, repair to chip at top 300-400 June 8, 1997 Sold for $200

3989. Weller Forest vase, impressed mark, 10"h, mint 250-350 June 8, 1997 Sold for $240

3990. Weller Glendale vase, not marked, 5"h, mint 150-250 June 8, 1997 Sold for $200

3991. Weller hanging basket, fox and apple, with chains, 8.5"dia. x 4.5"h, mint 400-600 June 8, 1997 Sold for $280

3992. Weller wallpocket, not marked, 7.75"l, mint 100-200 June 8, 1997 Sold for $100

3993. Weller Woodcraft jardiniere, great color and mold, marked, 11"dia. x 8"h, tight line at rim 300-400 June 8, 1997 Sold for $425

3994. Weller Aurelian candlestick, yellow and brown roses with green leaves on a yellow to dark brown ground, impressed mark, 8"h, repaired 100-200 June 8, 1997 Sold for $80

3995. Weller Louwelsa vase, yellow rose with green and brown leaves and brown branches, ground shades from yellow, green to brown, impressed mark, artist initialed, 17"h, repaired top 250-350 June 8, 1997 Sold for $325

3996. Weller Louwelsa mug, cherry decoration with green leaves on an orange to brown ground, impressed marks, artist L.M., 6.25"h, small chip to base 100-150 June 8, 1997 Sold for $60

3997. Weller Louwelsa vase, yellow, green and brown roses and buds with green leaves on a dark brown ground, impressed mark, 18.5"h, repaired 300-500 June 8, 1997 Sold for $300

3998. **Weller Muskota** bowl with squirrel on the side, impressed mark, 7"dia. x 5"h, mint 300-400 July 15, 1997 Sold for $240

3999. **Weller Hobart** figurine, attribution, girl with goose in ivory hi-glaze, incised mark, 9"h, mint 250-350 July 15, 1997 Sold for $325

4000. **Weller Brighton** flower frog, two bluebirds, unmarked, 4"h, minor repair 200-300 July 15, 1997 Sold for $150

4001. **Weller Muskota** figural, nude with a swan, not marked, 7.5"l x 7"h, mint 450-650 July 15, 1997 Sold for $700

4002. **Weller Muskota** flower frog, turtle, 5"dia., unsigned, mint 150-250 July 15, 1997 Sold for $170

4003. **Weller Knifewood** bowl, molded swans, matt glaze, no mark, 3.5"h, mint 250-350 July 15, 1997 Sold for $200

4004. **Weller Muskota** fishing boy flower frog, 7"h, couple of minute flakes 350-450 July 15, 1997 Sold for $190

4005. **Weller Owl** figural, unusual Art Deco design with blue matt glaze, signed, 9"h, mint 600-800 July 15, 1997 Not Sold

4006. **Weller Muskota** swan flower frog, unsigned, 6"l, repaired chip 150-250 July 15, 1997 Sold for $150

4007. **Weller Patricia** bowl, swan heads form two handles, white, unsigned, 8"dia. x 5"h, hairline to top 100-150 July 15, 1997 Sold for $70

4008. **Weller Muskota** Gate with cats candleholder, 7.5"h, unsigned, possibly minor chip repair 500-700 July 15, 1997 Sold for $650

4009. **Weller Patricia** bowl, swan heads form two handles, green and brown, 10"l x 6.5"h, mint 150-200 July 15, 1997 Sold for $160

4010. **Weller Cactus** figural, pan with lily, incised mark, 5"h, mint 100-150 July 15, 1997 Sold for $100

4011. **Weller Eocean** tankard, red cherry, unsigned, 10"h, mint 300-400 July 15, 1997 Sold for $425

4012. **Weller Eocean** cup, attribution, green fish on light green ground, impressed mark, 3.5"h, mint 250-350 July 15, 1997 Sold for $130

4013. **Weller Eocean** vase, colorful floral decoration with red berries and red and green leaves, incised mark, 10.5"h, mint 450-650 July 15, 1997 Sold for $650

249

4014. Art Pottery Dog planter with three heads, green hi-glaze, 7"h, mint   100-150   July 15, 1997   Sold for $60

4015. Weller Novelty ashtray, dachshund, impressed mark, 6"l x 3"h, mint   100-150   July 15, 1997   Sold for $50

4016. Weller Mammy teapot, impressed mark, 7"h, mint 300-400   July 15, 1997   Sold for $500

4017. Weller Forest wallpocket with squirrel, not marked, 9", mint   150-250   July 15, 1997   Sold for $250

4018. Weller Muskota Kingfisher, marked, 6.5"h, mint 250-350   July 15, 1997   Sold for $400

4019. Weller Cactus Camel figural, yellow hi-glaze, incised mark, 4"h, mint   100-150   July 15, 1997   Sold for $80

4020. Weller duck and rabbit planter, attribution, yellow hi-glaze, not marked, 6.5"h, mint   100-200   July 15, 1997 Sold for $60

4021. Weller Pop-eyed dog, black ground, signed, 4"h, minor flake at nose   300-400   July 15, 1997   Sold for $425

4022. Weller Cactus Elephant figural, green hi-glaze with painted eye, marked, 4"h, mint   100-150 July 15, 1997   Sold for $170

4023. Weller Muskota dog figurine, impressed mark, 6"h, mint   400-600   July 15, 1997   Sold for $600

4024. Weller Muskota woman, impressed mark, 6"h, mint 350-550   July 15, 1997   Sold for $300

4025. Weller Patricia vase, swan heads form handles, white, incised mark, 4"h, roughness around top   50-100 July 15, 1997   Sold for $30

4026. Weller Woodcraft mug, three foxes, impressed mark, 6"h, mint 150-250 July 15, 1997 Sold for $240

4027. Parrot flower frog, white parrot, not marked, 8.5"h, mint   50-100   July 15, 1997   Sold for $50

4028. Weller Cactus duck figural, yellow hi-glaze, incised mark, 5"h, mint   100-150   July 15, 1997 Sold for $150

4029. Weller Hudson vase, yellow and green daffodils and leaves on a gray to green ground, impressed mark, 9.5"h, mint 250-350 July 15, 1997   Sold for $350

4030. Weller Hudson Pictoral vase, landscape with three houses and a picket fence along a road with stand of trees, artist signed McLaughlin, 9.5"h, mint   1000-1500   July 15, 1997 Sold for $2700

4031. Weller White and Decorated Hudson vase, multicolored flowers on multicolored band, marked, 10"h, mint   300-400   July 15, 1997 Sold for $350

4032. Weller Hobart girl flower frog, nude reclining on a rock in white matt, not marked, 6"h, mint   250-350
July 15, 1997 Sold for $190

4033. Weller Patricia flower bowl, three swans on side all in blue matt, not marked, 6.5"h, minute flake   300-400
July 15, 1997 Sold for $170

4034. Weller Hobart bowl with nude, blue matt glaze, not marked, 6.5"h, tiny flake   200-300 July 15, 1997
Sold for $160

4035. Weller Novelty seal ashtray, black gloss glaze, incised mark, 5.5"l, mint   150-200 July 15, 1997 Sold for $90

4036. Art Pottery Dog planter with three heads, green hi-glaze, 7"h, mint   100-150 July 15, 1997 Sold for $50

4037. Weller Muskota figural, boy with a metal fishing pole and fish on a stump base with goldfish bowl, earth tones, excellent detail, 12"l x 9"h, mint   800-1100
July 15, 1997 Sold for $700

4038. Weller ashtray with dog howling, green hi-glaze, impressed mark, 5.5"h, mint   200-300
July 15, 1997 Sold for $140

4039. Weller Lorber dove flower frog, pink hi-glaze, stamp mark, 7.5"h, mint   150-250 July 15, 1997
Sold for $120

4040. Weller duck and rabbit planter, attribution, yellow hi-glaze, not marked, 6.5"h, mint   100-200 July 15, 1997
Sold for $50

4041. Weller Patricia bowl, green and brown crystalline glaze, four swan heads circle bowl, marked, 7"dia. x 3.5"h, mint   200-250 July 15, 1997 Sold for $140

4042. Weller figural, owl on book, cream with brown highlights, not marked, 7"h, mint   250-350
July 15, 1997 Sold for $600

4043. Weller Hobart flower frog, cherub holding grapes, blue/green matt glaze, impressed mark, 7.5"h, mint
250-350 July 15, 1997 Sold for $120

4044. Weller Hudson vase, white and pink dogwood on a pink to gray ground, marked, signed H. Pillsbury, 10.5"h, mint   500-700
June 8, 1997 Sold for $550

4045. Weller White and Decorated Hudson vase, two birds on cream ground, impressed mark, 13"h, mint   800-1100 June 8, 1997
Sold for $1500

4046. Weller Hudson Delta vase, iris decoration, marked and KKT, 7.5"h, tight hairline to top and chip on bottom   300-400 June 8, 1997
Sold for $400

4047. **Weller Oak Leaf** basket, orange with acorn design and top, marked, 10"h, mint   100-200   July 15, 1997 Sold for $120

4048. **Weller Roma** wallpocket, floral design against cream and green ground, not marked, 7.5"h, mint   100-200 July 15, 1997 Sold for $140

4049. **Weller Blue Ware** wallpocket, female with grapes and floral design on blue ground, incised mark, 10", tiny chip to back edge   150-250   July 15, 1997 Sold for $300

4050. **Weller Lebanon** vase, Egyptian designs circle the vase with line designs top and bottom, impressed mark, 6.5"h, mint   250-350   July 15, 1997   Sold for $700

4051. **Weller Woodcraft** wallpocket, slender tree branch shape with pink flowers, stamp mark, 9", mint 150-250   July 15, 1997 Sold for $180

4052. **Weller** vase, footed shape with three branch handles around top, white dogwood decoration on an orange ground, 7.5"h, mint 100-150   July 15, 1997 Sold for $70

4053. **Weller Hobart** wallpocket, female holding skirt in lavender and light green, impressed mark, 11.5"l, mint 250-350   July 15, 1997 Sold for $375

4054. **Weller** vase, turquoise with silver deposit in ornate designs, two handles, marked, 8.5"h, mint   150-250 July 15, 1997 Sold for $190

4055. **Weller Warwick** wallpocket, cherry and leaf decoration on tree ground, 11", mint   150-250   July 15, 1997 Sold for $170

4056. **Weller Silvertone** wallpocket, yellow floral design on lavender ground, stamp mark, 10", mint   150-250 July 15, 1997 Sold for $650

4057. **Weller** vase, matt glaze scenic in green and brown on a light blue ground, impressed mark, 6"h, mint   100-200 July 15, 1997 Sold for $110

4058. **Weller Blue Drapery** wallpocket, red roses on blue ground, not marked, 7.5"l, mint   150-250 July 15, 1997 Sold for $140

4059. **Weller Lustre** basket with lid, attribution, purple glaze, not marked, 7.5"h, some wear to glaze, mint   200-300 July 15, 1997 Sold for $70

4060. **Weller Eocean** vase, dark and light pink leaves and berries on a green to pink ground, marked, 16.25"h, tiny flake at top 400-600   July 15, 1997   Sold for $750

4061. **Weller Rochelle** vase, pink cherries and green leaves on gray to pink and black ground, not marked, 8.5"h, mint 250-350   July 15, 1997   Sold for $220

4062. **Weller Floretta** tankard, Art Nouveau pink flowers form top edge with green trailing leaves, green/gray to pink ground, marked, 12.5"h, mint   300-400 July 15, 1997 Sold for $325

4063. Weller Novelty teapot wallpocket, white hi-glaze, incised script mark, 8", mint   100-200   July 15, 1997   Sold for $140

4064. Weller Greora vase, two handles, unmarked, 10"h, a few minute flakes at rim   250-350   July 15, 1997   Sold for $200

4065. Weller Atlas vase, star shaped vase in blue hi-glaze, impressed mark, 7"h, mint   150-200   July 15, 1997   Sold for $80

4066. Weller Roma wallpocket, floral basket with green and cream ground, marked, 8", mint   100-200   July 15, 1997   Sold for $120

4067. Weller Geode vase, blue with white stars and comets, marked and signed T.M., 6"h, mint   250-350   July 15, 1997   Sold for $950

4068. Weller Novelty wallpocket, pitcher shape in green hi-glaze, marked, paper label, 7.5"h, mint   100-200   July 15, 1997   Sold for $170

4069. Weller Atlas dish, star shape in blue and yellow hi-glaze, impressed mark, 2.5"h, mint   100-150   July 15, 1997   Sold for $50

4070. Weller Roma wallpocket, Dupont motif, unmarked, 10", water deposits   100-200   July 15, 1997   Sold for $140

4071. Weller Roma wallpocket, bee flying over red roses, black and cream lattice ground, impressed mark, 7", hairline to top   100-200   July 15, 1997   Sold for $140

4072. Weller Atlas vase, star shape in blue and yellow hi-glaze, impressed mark, 5.5"h, mint   150-200   July 15, 1997   Sold for $110

4073. Weller vase, undecorated vase with blue ground, probably intended to be a decorated Hudson, incised mark, 11.5"h, mint   200-300   July 15, 1997   Sold for $150

4074. Weller Souevo wallpocket, Indian, not marked, 8"l, mint   100-200   July 15, 1997   Sold for $210

4075. Weller Florala wallpocket, impressed mark, 10"l, mint   150-250   July 15, 1997   Sold for $290

4076. Weller Louwelsa mantle clock, floral decoration with berries, impressed mark, 11"h, mint   1200-1700   July 15, 1997   Sold for $1200

4077. RV Rozane Ware vase, yellow and orange floral on dark brown ground, wafer mark, signed Pillsbury, 4.5"w x 3.5"h, small flakes on top   200-300   July 15, 1997   Sold for $260

4078. Weller Louwelsa vase, attribution, orange mum on an orange to brown ground, excellent decoration, signed Ferrell on side, 11"h, mint   300-400   July 15, 1997   Sold for $600

253

4079. Weller Hudson vase, yellow, blue and pink berries with yellow, blue and green leaves on a green to blue ground, artist signed M. Ansel, 7"h, mint   350-450
July 15, 1997   Sold for $475

4080. Weller Hudson vase, cardinal on a lavender, green and ivory ground, impressed mark, 7", mint   900-1200
July 15, 1997   Sold for $1300

4081. Weller White and Decorated vase, red and yellow flowers at top with green leaves and vines on a cream ground, impressed mark, 9.5"h, mint   250-350
July 15, 1997   Sold for $260

4082. Weller Sicard vase, three-sided form with floral design, under green, gold and red iridescent glaze, signed, 4"h, a few scratches   450-650   July 15, 1997   Sold for $240

4083. Weller LaSa vase, single evergreen tree on shore of lake, hills and mountain in ground, iridescent green, red and gold glaze, paper label, signed, 3.5"h, mint 350-450
July 15, 1997   Sold for $250

4084. Weller Sicard vase, three-sided form with floral design, under green, gold and red iridescent glaze, signed, 3.5"h, a few minor flakes inside lip   300-500   July 15, 1997
Sold for $220

4085. Weller Sicard vase, three-sided form with molded design of corn under brilliant blue, red and green iridescent glaze, signed 5"h, mint   550-750
July 15, 1997   Sold for $750

4086. Weller Sicard vase, four-sided form with iridescent decoration of stylized leaves and flowers in green, purple and red, signed, 8"h, mint   650-850
July 15, 1997   Sold for $650

4087. Weller LaSa vase, landscape, signed on side, 9.5"h, mint   500-700   July 15, 1997   Sold for $300

4088. Weller LaSa vase, landscape scene, not marked, 3.5"h, mint   300-400   July 15, 1997   Sold for $400

4089. Weller Marengo vase, deep purple, orange to green ground with gold trees, marked, 8.25"h, mint   500-700   July 15, 1997   Sold for $300

4090. Weller Sicard vase, poppy decoration with circles in ground, red, green and gold lustre, impressed numbers, 12.25", mint   1200-1700   July 15, 1997   Sold for $1900

4091. Weller Sicard vase, gold iridescent fleur-de-lis design against a dotted ground of green, purple and gold, signed, impressed mark, 9"h, mint   1200-1700   July 15, 1997   Sold for $1100

4092. Weller Sicard vase, floral decoration in green and gold iridescent glaze, signed, 5", mint   400-600   July 15, 1997   Sold for $300

4093. Weller Sicard vase, leaf and berry decoration in purple green and gold iridescence, signed, 5", mint   600-800   July 15, 1997   Sold for $475

4094. Weller LaSa vase, palm tree decoration against gold, red and purple iridescent ground, signed, 12", scratches to surface, mint   700-900   July 15, 1997   Sold for $425

255

4095. Weller Woodcraft vase, three foxes, marked, 5.5"h, mint   350-450   July 15, 1997 Sold for $250

4096. Weller Muskota swan bowl, impressed mark, 10"w x 4.5"h, mint   700-900   July 15, 1997 Sold for $500

4097. Weller Woodcraft flower frog, Bee on top, impressed mark, 3.5"dia. x 2.5"h, mint   150-250   July 15, 1997 Sold for $160

4098. Weller Lustre bowl with frog of cupid, blue hi-glaze, impressed mark in bowl, frog unmarked, 9.5"dia. x 6"h, lines to both   200-300   July 15, 1997 Sold for $70

4099. Weller Florenzo flower vase, pierced top with water lily design, marked, 6.5"h, mint   250-350   July 15, 1997 Sold for $170

4100. Weller Novelty frog figurine, green hi-glaze, unmarked, 4"h, mint   200-300   July 15, 1997 Sold for $130

4101. Weller Patricia bowl, three geese on top edge, white hi-glaze, incised mark, 7.5"h, mint   400-600   July 15, 1997 Sold for $180

4102. Weller Muskota powder jar, purple ground, 7"h, head reglued   100-200   July 15, 1997 Sold for $170

4103. Weller Knifewood smoking set, scene of fox with chickens, impressed mark, 3.5"h, mint   350-550   July 15, 1997 Sold for $425

4104. Weller Cactus figural, yellow hi-glaze, incised mark, 3.5"h, chip to top   100-150   July 15, 1997 Sold for $40

4105. Weller Woodcraft jardiniere with woodpecker on the side, impressed mark, 6"h, mint   350-450   July 15, 1997 Sold for $375

4106. Weller Muskota Kingfisher, impressed mark, 8.5"h, minor flakes   250-350   July 15, 1997 Sold for $180

4107. Weller Woodcraft vase, three foxes, impressed mark, 8"dia., mint   350-450   July 15, 1997 Sold for $250

Not Pictured:

4108. Weller Rochelle vase, berries on a black, blue and gray ground, 11"h, mint   700-900   July 15, 1997 Sold for $800

4109. Weller Rochelle candleholders, multicolored floral decoration, unmarked, 8"h, mint   300-400   July 15, 1997   Sold for $325

4110. Weller Louwelsa vase, mums, 4"h, mint   200-300   July 15, 1997   Sold for $250

4111. Weller Louwelsa pitcher, decoration of boysenberries, signed, 6", minor scratches, mint   150-250   July 15, 1997   Sold for $250

4112. Weller Louwelsa ewer, green, signed, 8.5"h, mint   300-400   July 15, 1997   Sold for $450

4113. Weller Ivory vase, floral design with figures, cream with orange highlights, impressed mark, 13"h, mint   200-300   July 15, 1997   Sold for $350

4114. Weller Forest basket, stamp mark, 8.5"h, mint   250-350   July 15, 1997   Sold for $260

4115. Weller Dickens tankard, fish handle and decoration on both sides, fish swimming in waves, green, marked, 13"h, chip to top   250-350   July 15, 1997   Sold for $325

4116. Weller Rosemont vase, black with blue bird on green stems with yellow flowers, impressed mark, 9.5"h, mint   350-450   July 15, 1997   Sold for $325

4117. Weller Coppertone vase, incised mark, 6.5"h, mint   250-350   July 15, 1997   Sold for $250

4118. Weller Glendale vase, forest scene, bird and nest, stamp mark, 8"h, mint   300-400   July 15, 1997   Sold for $325

4119. Weller L'Art Nouveau tankard, ornate flowers, lady and grape design in peach on a green ground, flower form top edge, not marked, 15.25"h, mint   400-600   July 15, 1997   Sold for $350

4120. Weller Woodcraft tankard, three foxes, marked, 12.5"h, mint   500-750   July 16, 1997   Sold for $600

4121. Weller Hobart bowl and flower frog of boy with swan, blue matt glaze, 9.5"dia. x 7"h, mint   350-450   July 16, 1997 Sold for $450

4122. Weller Muskota powder jar, yellow ground, 7"h, mint   300-500   July 16, 1997   Sold for $220

4123. Weller Muskota robin, impressed mark, 5"h, mint   250-350   July 16, 1997   Sold for $600

4124. Weller Muskota flower frog, butterfly, 4", minor flake; with **Muskota** flower holder, unsigned, 2.5"dia., both mint   200-300   July 16, 1997   Sold for $150

4125. Weller Hobart flower frog, two nudes in waves, stamp mark, 7"h, mint   300-400   July 16, 1997   Sold for $400

4126. Weller Muskota frog, unmarked, 4.5"h, mint   250-350 July 16, 1997   Sold for $130

4127. Weller Woodcraft bowl, molded squirrels, no mark, 3.5", mint   150-250   July 16, 1997   Sold for $90

4128. Weller Muskota swan, impressed mark, 5.25"h, minute flake on bill   250-350   July 16, 1997   Sold for $200

4129. Weller Muskota bowl with squirrel on the edge, not marked, 7.5"dia. x 5.5"h, mint   250-350   July 16, 1997 Sold for $160

4130. Weller Muskota girl flower holder, 7.5"h, unsigned, mint   350-550   July 16, 1997   Sold for $375

4131. Weller Mammy pitcher, impressed mark, 7"h, mint 350-550   July 16, 1997   Sold for $500

4132. Weller Muskota chicks, not marked, 5"h, mint 300-400   July 16, 1997   Sold for $260

4133. Weller Patricia planter, duck in green and brown crystalline glaze, impressed mark, 6.5"h, mint   150-250 July 16, 1997   Sold for $50

4134. Weller Muskota Egret flower frog, ink mark, 6"h, mint 500-700   July 16, 1997   Sold for $240

4135. Weller Muskota bird, 6"h, impressed mark, mint 250-350   July 16, 1997   Sold for $150

4136. Weller Hobart flower holder, pink, 6"h, unsigned, mint 250-350   July 16, 1997   Sold for $150

4137. Weller Muskota flower frog with lizard, marked, 4.5", mint   150-250   July 16, 1997   Sold for $160

Not Pictured:

4138. Weller Pierre objects, cookie jar, green, 10"; cookie jar, pink, 10"; creamer, 5"; Tea pot, 8"; sugar, 2"; three piece tea set, all signed, some with flaws   350-450 July 16, 1997   Sold for $270

4139. Weller Zona dinner ware, six bowls, two tea cups, three plates, three pitchers, one pot, one mug, some marked, some with minor flaws   300-400   July 16, 1997 Sold for $200

4140. Weller jardiniere, incised red flowers with green leaves on a brown ground, impressed mark, 7"h, mint   300-400 July 16, 1997   Sold for $230

4141. Weller Zona pitcher, Kingfisher with greenery, white golden rod in panels bordered by bands of floral design, green handle and spout, hi-glaze, stamp mark, 8"h, mint 150-250   June 8, 1997   Sold for $425

4142. Weller Silvertone vase, two handles, marked, 9"h, mint 150-250   June 8, 1997   Sold for $325

4143. Weller Louwelsa Aladdin lamp, pansies, signed, 5"h, mint   250-350   July 15, 1997   Sold for $350

4144. Weller Aurelian vase, ivy leaves, 7"h, chip to base 300-400   July 15, 1997   Sold for $210

4145. Weller Woodcraft jardiniere, woodpecker, impressed mark, 6"h, mint   350-450   July 16, 1997   Sold for $375

4146. Weller Woodcraft candle holder, owl on top between two candle openings, unmarked, 13"h, mint   500-700 July 16, 1997   Sold for $400

4147. Weller Roma vase with pinecone decoration, impressed mark, 10", mint   200-300   July 15, 1997   Sold for $300

4148. Weller Clinton Ivory vase with nudes, 10", mint 150-250   July 15, 1997   Sold for $280

4149. Weller Claywood vase with lions and scarabs, 6", mint 100-200   July 15, 1997   Sold for $240

4150. Weller Kingfisher centerpiece, multi-color kingfisher, 7"w x 8.75"h, hairline to base   150-250   July 14, 1998 Sold for $230

4151. Weller Roma jardinere, molded floral design, incised, 17.5"dia. x 12"h, mint   450-650   July 14, 1999 Sold for $550

4152. Weller Granite Ware fish, unglazed, 17", fish has chips 1500-2500   July 13, 1999   Sold for $1600

4153. Weller Brighton Parrot, macaw on scroll base with wings closed, impressed mark, 12.5"h, repair to beak 800-1100   July 15, 1997   Sold for $1200

4154. Weller Brighton Pheasant, green and yellow bird, impressed mark, 11.5"l x 7"h, tail repaired   700-900 July 15, 1997   Sold for $375

4155. Weller Brighton Kingfisher, small, bird on stump, openings for flowers, impressed mark, 5.5"h, mint 300-400   July 15, 1997   Sold for $210

4156. Weller Brighton flower frog, two ducks, white and green, no mark, 5.5"h, mint   350-450   July 15, 1997 Sold for $150

4157. Weller Brighton Kingfisher wall vase, two openings, no mark, 12"l, damage to beak and one opening 500-700   July 15, 1997   Sold for $230

4158. Weller Brighton Parrot on stand, macaw on stand, impressed mark, 8"h, mint   600-800   July 15, 1997 Sold for $425

4159. Weller Brighton flower frog of two Robins, not marked, 5.5"h, restored   250-350   July 15, 1997 Sold for $120

4160. Weller Brighton Blue Bird on Baldin stand, impressed mark, 8"h, wing repaired   600-800   July 15, 1997 Sold for $225

4161. Weller Brighton Parrot on hanging stand, multicolored parrot on stand, no mark, 13"l, wing and tail repaired 800-1100   July 15, 1997   Sold for $500

Not Pictured:

4162. Weller Ivory vase, cylinder shape with two molded female figures, cream with brown highlights, not marked, 15"h, mint   200-300   July 16, 1997 Sold for $260

4163. Weller Muskota flower frog, nude seated on green base, impressed mark, 7.5"h, mint   300-400 July 15, 1998   Sold for $475

4164. Weller Eocean vase, pink and green dogwood, lavender to green ground, impressed mark, 8", mint   600-800 July 15, 1997   Sold for $290

4165. Weller Rochelle vase, four-sided form with floral decoration, 10"h, line on interior, doesn't appear to go through 250-350   July 15, 1997   Sold for $180

4166. Weller Art Nouveau vase with nude, two-handled form, green and tan matt glaze, impressed mark, 9", mint   600-800 July 15, 1997   Sold for $400

4167. Weller Etna vase, pink and red flowers on a blue and gray ground, impressed mark, 6.5", mint   200-300   July 15, 1997 Sold for $130

4168. Weller Hudson vase, blue grapes with red and green leaves, painted in an unusual style against a blue to yellow ground, artist signed by Timberlake, incised mark, 9.5", mint   800-1100 July 15, 1997 Sold for $1100

4169. Weller Brighton Parrot on Stand, macaw with wings open, impressed mark, 14"h, wings and tail repaired 900-1200   July 15, 1997   Sold for $650

4170. Weller Brighton Kingfisher, bird on stump flower holder, impressed mark, 9"h, mint   350-450 July 15, 1997   Sold for $300

4171. Weller Brighton Kingfisher, bird on stump with openings for flowers, impressed mark, 5.5"h, mint 300-400   July 15, 1997   Sold for $180

4172. Weller Brighton Cardinal on Stand, red and pink bird on green and brown stump, 5.5"h, mint   400-600 July 15, 1997   Sold for $325

4173. Weller Brighton Cardinal on sprinkler can, green and red, 8"w x 6.5"h, mint   450-650   July 15, 1997 Sold for $1100

4174. Weller Brighton Canary with base, attribution, small yellow and green, 4"h, mint   150-250   July 15, 1997 Sold for $60

4175. Weller Brighton Pheasant, brown and blue bird, 7"l x 5", tail and neck repaired   350-450   July 15, 1997 Sold for $200

4176. Weller Brighton Penguin flower frog, two blue, white and black penguins on rocks, not marked, 5"h, mint 600-800   July 15, 1997   Sold for $325

4177. Weller Brighton double Parakeets, birds on branch, impressed mark, 8.5"h, wings and tail repaired   600-800 July 15, 1997   Sold for $260

4178. Weller Brighton lamp base, bird on stand mounted to metal lamp base with flower, ceramic 6.5"h, with shade, repaired beak   600-800   July 15, 1997   Sold for $650

4179. Weller 2nd line Dickensware vase, cowboy on bucking horse, light colors, impressed mark, signed C.A. Dusenbery, 11"h, mint   800-1100 July 15, 1997   Sold for $900

4180. Weller White and Decorated Hudson vase, lavender, purple and black small flowers on black branches with green leaves on a cream ground, impressed mark, 8.5"h, hairline to top 100-150   July 15, 1997   Sold for $150

4181. Weller vase, possibly experimental, yellow with black and green swirling leaf design, marked, 8.5"h, mint   200-300   July 15, 1997 Sold for $210

4182. Weller Dresden vase, landscape with windmills and sailing ships, predominately green with blue decoration, incised marks and LJB, 15.75"h, mint   600-800   July 15, 1997   Sold for $700

259

For more details please call:
(513) 321-6742

4183. Weller Cloudburst vase, orange, pink, black and cream lustre glaze, not marked, 11"h, mint   350-550 June 8, 1997   Sold for $450

4184. Weller Matt Louwelsa vase, impressed mark, strawberries in green tones, signed H.W., 6"h, mint   400-600 June 8, 1997   Sold for $750

4185. Weller Eocean vase, pink flower and green leaves, green to white ground, marked, 4.75"h, mint 150-250   June 8, 1997   Sold for $130

4186. Weller Dickensware mug with Elk, impressed mark, 6"h, mint   250-350   June 8, 1997   Sold for $160

4187. Weller Dickensware mug, man with large bow tie, small hat and monocle, two handles, lavender and pink hi-glaze, impressed mark and numbers, 3.5"h, mint 250-350   June 8, 1997   Sold for $230

4188. Weller Dickensware pillow vase with leaping stag between two trees, incised E.W., impressed mark, 7"h, mint   500-700   June 8, 1997   Sold for $300

4189. Weller Etna vase, pink thistles and green leaves on gray to lavender ground, impressed mark and signed on side, 8.5"h, mint   250-350   June 8, 1997   Sold for $210

4190. Weller Dickensware pitcher, Indian brave in full headdress on dark green ground, not marked, 4.5"h, mint   300-400   June 8, 1997   Sold for $210

4191. Weller Eocean vase, red rose on green to gray ground, not marked, 6"h, mint   200-300   June 8, 1997 Sold for $200

4192. Weller Etna mug, molded and painted floral, impressed mark, 5.5"h, mint   100-200   June 8, 1997   Sold for $90

4193. Weller Burntwood vase, cream cork-like finish with birds and flowers, not marked, 11.5"h, mint   200-300 June 8, 1997   Sold for $200

4194. Weller Art Nouveau vase, embossed maiden with flowers and fruit, peach and green glaze, impressed mark, 15"h, harmless flakes   500-700   June 8, 1997 Sold for $600

4195. Weller Glossy Hudson vase, orchids in lavender and red with squeezebag decoration against a lavender to gray ground, impressed numbers, 8.5"h, lines in interior 800-1100   June 8, 1997   Sold for $750

4196. Weller Rochelle vase, four-sided form, floral decoration, blue, 5"h, mint   100-150   June 8, 1997 Sold for $110

4197. Weller Etna vase, molded red poppy on a gray to green ground, impressed mark, 10"h, mint   300-400 June 8, 1997   Sold for $300

4198. Weller Woodcraft figural with goldfish bowl, crane on a stump, 8"w x 11"h, mint   800-1100   June 8, 1997   Sold for $750

4199. Weller Hobart hunting dog flower frog, two dogs pointing in pink matt glaze, not marked, 5.5"h, mint   300-400   June 8, 1997   Sold for $400

4200. Weller Hobart box with flower frog lid, cherub on grapes on top, garlands around box, lavender matt glaze, not marked, 9.5"h, mint   300-400   June 8, 1997   Sold for $375

4201. Weller duck and rabbit planter, yellow hi-glaze, not marked, 6.5"h, mint   100-200   June 8, 1997   Sold for $40

4202. Frog planter, green with black eyes, unmarked, 5.5"l x 2.5"h, some water deposits   50-100   June 8, 1997   Sold for $30

4203. Weller Woodcraft wall plaque, trees branches with pink flowers and two birds with nest, 12"w x 14"h, one bird has broken tail   300-500   June 8, 1997   Sold for $650

4204. Weller Hobart bowl with nude, blue matt glaze, not marked, 6.5"h, mint   250-350   June 8, 1997   Sold for $240

4205. Weller Muskota girl figural flower frog, nude with leaf in white matt, not marked, 8.5"h, mint   200-300   June 8, 1997   Sold for $250

4206. Weller flower frog, young boy in tall grasses in a blue matt, marked, 6"h, chip   150-250   June 8, 1997   Sold for $100

4207. Weller Kingfisher flower frog, colorful hi-glaze, impressed mark, 9"h, mint   300-400   June 8, 1997   Sold for $325

4208. Weller Woodcraft candle holder, owl on top between two candle openings, marked, 13"h, broken top   500-700   June 8, 1997   Sold for $325

4209. Weller Novelty Line dish, monkey on a peanut, white hi-glaze, impressed mark, 7"l x 5"h, mint   100-200   June 8, 1997   Sold for $100

4210. Weller Blue Louwelsa vase, poppy in blue and white, impressed mark, 8"h, mint   800-1100   June 8, 1997   Sold for $950

4211. Weller Dickensware vase, cavalier in browns and white on a blue to green ground, hi-glaze, marked, 12"h, cracked   200-300   June 8, 1997   Sold for $160

4212. Weller Blue Louwelsa mug, blackberry decoration, impressed mark, 5"h, mint   300-400   June 8, 1997   Sold for $475

Not Pictured:

4213. Weller Blue Louwelsa vase, holly leaves with berry decoration around top, marked, 6"h, mint   500-700   July 15, 1997   Sold for $900

4214. Weller Blue Louwelsa vase, blue flowers on a cream, blue ground, impressed mark, 9.5"h, mint   800-1100   July 14, 1998   Sold for $1100

261

4215. Weller Muskota flower frog, lady in prone position, 7", unsigned, mint   500-700   July 15, 1997   Sold for $700

4216. Weller Coppertone bowl with frog on side, fish swimming on exterior, stamp mark, 10"l x 5"h, mint 600-800   July 15, 1997   Sold for $800

4217. Weller Hobart flower frog, nude figure sitting on a rock, blue hi-glaze, not marked, 8"h, mint   100-150   July 15, 1997   Sold for $150

4218. Weller Coppertone frog figural, good glaze, impressed mark, 2"h, small chip to foot   100-150   July 15, 1997   Sold for $60

4219. Van Briggle rabbit figurine, blue matt, incised mark, 2.5"h, crack in making, mint   150-250   July 15, 1997   Sold for $100

4220. Weller Coppertone bowl and flower frog, frog sitting on pad next to white flower, plain frog, stamp mark, 10.5"l x 4"h, mint   400-600   July 15, 1997   Sold for $475

4221. Weller Woodcraft wallpocket, owl, unmarked, 10"l, mint   200-300   July 15, 1997   Sold for $220

4222. Weller Coppertone figural frog, incised mark, 2"h, mint   150-250   July 15, 1997   Sold for $150

4223. Weller Novelty frog vase, frog holding flower all in orange hi-glaze, marked, 4"h, mint   250-350   July 15, 1997   Sold for $110

4224. Weller Coppertone bowl, frog on lily pad, stamp mark, 15.5"l x 3.5"h, mint   600-800   July 15, 1997   Sold for $450

4225. Weller Muskota turtle, impressed mark, 10"l, couple of minute flakes   300-500   July 15, 1997   Sold for $325

4226. Art Pottery figurine, white hi-glaze, 6"h, mint   50-100   July 15, 1997   Sold for $20

Not Pictured:

4227. Weller Coppertone planter, frog holding flower on lily pad, marked, 4"h, heavy water deposit   250-350   July 15, 1997   Sold for $200

4228. Weller Coppertone vase, frog on base, stamp mark, 9"h, mint   350-450   June 8, 1997   Sold for $350

4229. Weller Jap Birdimal vase, Geisha girl on front in black, green, gray and yellow on a deep green ground, incised mark and signed M.S., 14.5"h, repaired top   1200-1700   July 16, 1997   Sold for $900

Not Pictured:

4230. Weller Jap Birdimal vase, Geisha girl decoration in black, green, yellow and red, incised Weller Rhead Faience and artist signed LS on side, 10.5"h, mint   1500-2000   July 15, 1997   Sold for $1300

4231. **Weller Coppertone** turtle candlestick, green and brown matt, incised mark, 5"l, mint   250-350   July 15, 1997   Sold for $400

4232. **Weller Coppertone** console bowl, frog sits on lily pad, green and brown matt, with flower frog not pictured, ink mark, 10"l x 5.5"h, mint   500-700   July 15, 1997   Sold for $500

4233. **Weller Coppertone** fish, green and brown matt, 8"h, marked, minor flake to fin   500-700   July 15, 1997   Sold for $1100

4234. **Weller Coppertone** frog, green and brown matt, incised mark, 2.5"h, chip to foot   100-150   July 15, 1997   Sold for $70

4235. **Weller Coppertone** frog, green and brown matt, marked, 2.5"h, mint   150-250   July 15, 1997   Sold for $400

4236. **Weller Coppertone** console bowl with flower frog, frog and flower on side with lily pads, 10"l x 3.5"h, mint   500-700   July 15, 1997   Sold for $450

4237. **Weller Coppertone** vase, frog on edge of vase in green and dark gray matt glaze, initialed M.D., ink mark, 7"h, mint   600-800   July 15, 1997   Sold for $475

4238. **Weller Coppertone** turtle, green and brown matt, marked, 4", mint   250-350   July 15, 1997   Sold for $350

4239. **Weller Coppertone** bowl, green and brown matt glaze with darker brown, frog on pads with white lily, stamp mark and artist initialed, 10"l x 3.5"h, mint   500-700   July 15, 1997   Sold for $300

4240. **Weller Coppertone** console bowl with flower frog not pictured, green and brown matt, frog on side, 10"l x 5.5"h, mint   500-700   July 15, 1997   Sold for $500

4241. **Weller Coppertone** flower frog, green and brown matt, frog holding white lily, marked, 4"h, mint   250-350   July 15, 1997   Sold for $210

4242. **Weller Hudson** vase, blue ground with pink and brown Irises, artist signed McLaughlin, stamped mark, 13"h, mint   600-800   July 16, 1997   Sold for $1500

4243. **Weller Hudson** vase, Meadowlark on a tree branch on a blue to pink ground, artist signed L.B.M., 8.5"h, mint   1000-1500   July 16, 1997   Sold for $2600

4244. **Weller White and Decorated Hudson** vase, raspberries and flowers with green leaves against a blue band, cream ground, impressed mark, 11.5"h, mint   300-400   July 16, 1997   Sold for $425

4245. Weller vase, green and orange matt glaze on Patra form, no mark, 8"h, mint   150-250   July 15, 1997
Sold for $80

4246. Weller Forest bowl, four feet, shaded brown matt, no mark, 6.5"dia. x 3"h, flake to rim   100-200
July 15, 1997   Sold for $80

4247. Weller Woodcraft bud vase, green, brown and pink, impressed mark, 10"h, minute lines to base; with a **Weller Woodcraft** vase, tree supported by trunk and three branches, green, pink and brown matt, no mark, 9"h, hairlines   150-250   July 15, 1997   Sold for $160

4248. Weller Coppertone figural, frog holds lily, incised mark, 4"h, mint 250-350 July 15, 1997
Sold for $170

4249. Weller Wild Rose vase, in green, white and brown, incised mark, 11"h, line to base   100-200
July 15, 1997   Sold for $70

4250. Weller Woodcraft bowl, squirrel perches on edge, green and brown matt, no mark, 5.5"h, hidden chips to base   150-250   July 15, 1997   Sold for $130

4251. Weller Goldenglow vase, brown matt, incised mark, 11.5"h, mint   150-250   July 15, 1997   Sold for $160

4252. Weller Cornish vase, brown and black matt, incised mark, 3"h, mint   50-100   July 15, 1997   Sold for $150

4253. Weller Malvern vase, incised mark, 8"h, mint   100-200   July 15, 1997 Sold for $120

4254. Weller Forest vase, brown, cream and green matt, painted mark 16" x 4.5"; with a **Weller Greora** vase, green and brown matt, 5"h, both with flaws   200-300
July 15, 1997   Sold for $110

4255. Weller Aurelian floor vase, decoration of irises in yellow, orange, brown and green with large green and brown leaves, ground has the vibrant yellow, orange, green and brown, artist signed Charles J. Dibowski on side, incised marks on bottom, 24.5"h, harmless small flake on body   3500-5500   July 16, 1997
Sold for $1300

Not Pictured:

4256. Weller Aurelian vase, white bunches of grapes, stems of orange and green, ground in orange, yellow and green on an orange and dark brown ground, lobed top edge, marked and signed Ferrell, 11"h, mint 800-1100
July 15, 1997 Sold for $800

4257. Weller Roma vase, matt glaze with grapes on cream ground, no mark, 10"h, mint 150-250 July 16, 1997 Sold for $70

4258.Weller Burntwood jardiniere, chickens in brown matt, impressed mark, 9"dia. x 7"h, some wear to rim 150-250 July 16, 1997 Sold for $270

4259. Weller Woodcraft vase, owl on tree trunk, 15"h, repairs and lines to rim, small chip to base 250-350 July 16, 1997 Sold for $400

4260. Weller Claywood umbrella stand, tan and dark brown, no mark, 20"h, flakes to rim and base 450-650 July 16, 1997 Sold for $300

4261. Weller Dickensware vase, incised golfer in brown and white clothes, initialed by E. Pickens, impressed mark, 10.5"h, mint 900-1200 July 16, 1997 Sold for $950

4262. Weller Dickensware lamp, incised design of man seated near boy, initialed by artist, 11.5"h, hidden chips to top 350-550 July 16, 1997 Sold for $300

4263. Weller Forest jardiniere, green and brown, no mark, 8"dia. x 6.5"h, lines and flakes to rim 150-250 July 16, 1997 Sold for $70

4264. Weller Gloria vase, matt glaze with raised iris in cream, lavender and green on orange ground, incised mark, 12.5"h, mint 200-300 July 16, 1997 Sold for $110

Not Pictured:

4265. Weller Roma jardiniere and pedestal, pink flowers and green leaves on cream ground, no mark, 12.5"dia. x 10.5"h, all 29"h, repairs to jardiniere, pedestal is mint 700-900 July 16, 1997 Sold for $850

4266. Weller Louwelsa lamp, attribution, orange and brown blossoms with green leaves on brown and green ground, shade has same design, 12.5"dia., 17.5"h, flakes to body and edge of shade 700-900 July 16, 1997 Sold for $600

4267. Weller Louwelsa vase, large example with daisies, impressed mark, artist signed, 15"h, mint 1000-1500 June 6, 1999 Sold for $1200

4268. Weller Louwelsa vase, portrait of man with yellow and green striped shirt and orange hat against a dark brown, caramel, green and yellow ground, executed by Marie Rauchfuss, impressed mark, 15"h, repair to base and rim 2500-3500 July 16, 1997 Sold for $2700

Not Pictured:

4269. Weller Louwelsa floor vase, yellow blossoms and pointed leaves against a brown, green and yellow ground, signed by J. Herold, impressed mark, 21.5"h, flaking repair to rim, scratches to side, chips to base 900-1200 July 16, 1997 Sold for $800

265

4270. Weller Floretta mug, yellow and green molded grapes on an orange to brown ground, marked, 5"h, mint 100-150 July 16, 1997 Sold for $90

4271. Weller Louwelsa tankard, yellow, black and orange berry with leaves, marked and signed A. Haubrich, 12.5"h, crazed 150-250 July 16, 1997 Sold for $220

4272. Weller Floretta vase, small orange flowers on a dark brown ground, impressed, 5", mint 100-150 July 16, 1997 Sold for $40

4273. McCoy vase, standard glaze with orange pansy decoration, not marked, 12"h, mint 100-200 July 16, 1997 Sold for $70

4287. Weller Sicard vase, floral design in yellow, blue and green iridescence on a red ground with iridescent highlights, signed on side, 15"h, undetectable restoration to drill hole in bottom 3500-4500 July 16, 1997 Sold for $3750

4274. Weller Louwelsa pitcher, yellow and brown floral with green leaves, marked and signed F, 5"h, mint 150-250 July 16, 1997 Sold for $120

4275. Weller Louwelsa vase, orange flowers on dark brown ground, marked and incised L, 4"h, mint 100-200 July 16, 1997 Sold for $80

4276. RV Rozane vase, orange and yellow floral on a dark brown ground, marked, 4"h, mint 150-200 July 16, 1997 Sold for $100

4277. Weller 1st Line Dickensware jug, incised and painted ear of corn, impressed mark, 7"h, mint 250-300 July 16, 1997 Sold for $190

4278. Weller Louwelsa ewer, orange floral decoration, impressed mark, artist signed, 7"h, repaired lip 100-200 July 16, 1997 Sold for $90

4279. Weller Louwelsa floral vase, orange flowers and green leaves on brown, impressed mark, 4"h, mint 100-150 July 16, 1997 Sold for $70

4280. Weller Floretta vase, brown and orange with molded berry decoration, impressed mark, 8"h, mint 100-200 July 16, 1997 Sold for $100

4281. Weller Louwelsa ewer, yellow and orange pansy decoration, impressed mark, 9"h, mint 250-350 July 16, 1997 Sold for $220

4282. Weller Louwelsa ewer, yellow flowers with orange buds and green leaves, impressed mark, 7.5"h, mint 250-350 July 16, 1997 Sold for $200

4283. Weller Louwelsa vase, orange poppy decoration, signed Ferrell, 10.5"h, mint 200-300 July 16, 1997 Sold for $550

4284. Weller Louwelsa vase, orange flowers on brown ground, hi-glaze, impressed mark, 4"h, water deposits 100-150 July 16, 1997 Sold for $90

4285. Weller Louwelsa vase, orange and green floral on an orange to brown ground, not marked, 10.5"h, small chip 150-250 July 16, 1997 Sold for $160

4286. Owens Utopian vase, orange floral decoration on orange to brown ground, signed, 6"w x 4"h, mint 100-150 July 16, 1997 Sold for $100

4287. Weller vase, purple hi-glaze, incised Weller, 5.5"h, mint 250-350   June 8, 1997   Sold for $90

4288. Weller White and Decorated Hudson vase, floral decoration in red band around top, impressed mark, 12"h, mint   250-350   June 8, 1997   Sold for $260

4289. Weller Louwelsa vase, large yellow, orange and brown Iris decoration, artist signed Dibowski on side, impressed marks, 13"h, hairline to top   150-250 June 8, 1997   Sold for $220

4290. McCoy Rosewood pitcher, yellow fruit and leaf design, not marked, 6.5", factory flaws on rim, mint   100-200 June 8, 1997   Sold for $100

4291. Weller Louwelsa humidor, yellow and orange clover with green leaves, artist initialed, impressed marks, 5"dia. x 6"h, missing lid, surface scratches   150-200 June 8, 1997   Sold for $90

4292. Owens Utopian vase, orange and green flower and leaf decoration, painted by M. Timberlake, impressed marks, 8.5"w x 8"h, mint   250-350   June 8, 1997 Sold for $300

4293. Weller Woodcraft bowl, squirrel in forest scene in four panels, 3"h, mint   150-200   June 8, 1997 Sold for $160

4294. Loy-Nel Art vase, yellow and orange flowers with green leaves, 11"h, some roughness in making, mint 100-200   June 8, 1997   Sold for $80

4295. Weller Etna vase, modeled frog and snake in gray and white hi-glaze, marked, 7.5"h, good repair to frog's head 300-500   June 8, 1997   Sold for $300

4296. Weller Hudson vase, handles, blue, yellow and green floral decoration, signed Timberlake, 6", chip to foot 250-350   June 8, 1997   Sold for $210

4297. RV Rozane vase, orange and yellow floral, impressed marks, artist signed, 15.5"h, surface scratches   200-300 June 8, 1997   Sold for $200

4298. Weller Hudson vase, yellow, pink and blue floral decoration, signed S. Timberlake, 7.75"h, mint 250-350   June 8, 1997   Sold for $270

4299. Weller Hudson chandelier, red roses with green leaves on a brown matt ground, not marked, 20"dia. x 9"h, tight hairline   1000-1500   July 16, 1997   Sold for $350

267

4300. Owens Utopian vase, yellow and blue flowers with green leaves, impressed mark, 8"h, mint 200-300
July 15, 1997   Sold for $130

4301. RV Rozane vase, yellow and orange flowers, signed W. Meyers, wafer mark, tight hairline 75-150
July 15, 1997   Sold for $100

4302. RV Rozane Ware vase, yellow and orange flowers on a green an brown ground, impressed mark, 6.5"h, mint 150-250   July 15, 1997   Sold for $140

4303. RV Rozane Ware vase, orange flowers with green leaves, impressed mark, artist initialed, 3", mint 100-200   July 15, 1997   Sold for $100

4304. Weller Dickensware I jug, yellow daisies on a green and brown ground, artist initialed, impressed mark, 6"h, mint 200-300   July 15, 1997 Sold for $180

4305. Weller Dickensware vase, orange and yellow floral on brown ground, impressed mark, 3"h, mint 150-250   July 15, 1997   Sold for $110

4306. RV planter, squeezebag decoration of water lilies, 5"h, minor flakes 250-350   July 15, 1997   Sold for $150

4307. RV Rozane Ware pitcher, orange and yellow cherries, artist initialed, wafer mark, 10.5"h, small bruise to lip 150-250   July 15, 1997   Sold for $200

4308. Weller Dickensware vase, portrait of a man smoking a cigarette, marked and signed E.L. Pickens, 11.5"h, minor flaking at top rim 500-750   July 15, 1997
Sold for $650

4309. Weller Chengtu vase, large form in Chinese Red glaze, ink mark, 14"h, minute flakes to bottom 400-600
July 15, 1997   Sold for $400

4310. Weller Dickensware tankard, portrait of stag and tree, marked, 11.5"h, mint 400-600   July 15, 1997
Sold for $270

Not Pictured:

4311. Weller Dickensware jardiniere, portrait of man with curly hair, teal hat and suit with white collar against a blue ground, impressed mark, 11"dia. x 8.5"h, flaking repairs to base and rim; with a **Weller Dickensware** vase, gray and cream birds on gray branches against a blue and green ground, impressed marks, 9"h, flaking restoration 500-700   July 16, 1997   Sold for $400

268

4312. Weller Dickensware pitcher and tankard set, six pieces, landscape with elk on pitcher in brown, yellow and green, 13.5"h, all marked, all mint   1000-1500
July 15, 1997   Sold for $900

4313. McCoy Loy-Nel vase, attribution, orange iris decoration with green and yellow leaves on the front with small orange floral decoration on reverse on a dark brown ground, incised WLK, 14.5"h, mint   400-600
July 15, 1997   Sold for $350

4314. Clewell pitcher and mug set, seven pieces, copper clad pottery with hammered and rivet design, impressed marks, 10.5"h, pitcher and one mug have cracks in pottery   600-800   July 15, 1997   Sold for $325

Not Pictured:

4315. Weller Dickensware vase, bisque finish, incised and painted portrait of monk on a green, yellow to pink ground, impressed mark, 13"h, mint   450-650
July 15, 1997   Sold for $300

4316. Weller Dickensware vase, bisque finish, incised and painted decoration of a lady seated by a harp in green and brown on a blue, brown to green ground, incised mark, 16"h, hairline to top   400-600   July 15, 1997
Sold for $425

4317. Weller Dickensware vase, incised and painted Dickens scene of several people in orange, brown to green ground, inscription on reverse, impressed mark, 13.5"h, chip to top edge   400-600   July 15, 1997
Sold for $450

4318. Weller Dickensware vase, bisque glaze with farm scene with house and cattle and a couple meeting on a country road, brown, green, yellow, pink, blue and tan, impressed mark, artist signed H.S., 16"h, mint   900-1200
July 15, 1997   Sold for $2300

4319. Weller Dickensware vase, incised and painted tavern scene of men playing checkers with onlookers, multicolored browns, green, yellow, orange, blue and cream, not marked, 18"h, repaired bottom   1000-2000
July 15, 1997   Sold for $1700

269

4320. Weller Xenia vase, matt glaze with
purple grapes and brown curling vines
on green ground, impressed mark,
7"h, mint   700-900   July 16, 1997
Sold for $650

4321. Weller Matt vase, blue matt glaze
with raised design of bats, incised and
impressed Weller, 8.5"h, cracked
500-700   July 16, 1997
Sold for $600

4322. Weller Xenia vase, matt glaze with
stylized blossoms and swirl design in
purple, lavender and gray, impressed
mark, 8.5"h, minute lines to base
600-800   July 16, 1997
Sold for $850

Not Pictured:

4324. Weller Xenia vase, cream with pink floral decoration,
11"h, mint   200-300   June 12, 1995   Sold for $270

4325. Weller vase, molded wheat design in yellow to purple
matt with green drip, impressed mark, 12.5"h, crack to
top   150-250   July 16, 1997   Sold for $325

4326. Weller Lebanon vase, Wisemen on camels, impressed
mark, 9"h, minor roughness   200-300   July 15, 1997
Sold for $1300

4327. Weller Glendale double bud vase, bird between trees in
green, brown, blue, yellow and pink, ink mark, 7.5"w x
7.5"h, mint   250-350   June 2, 1996   Sold for $250

4328. Weller Louwelsa vase, attribution, head of cat in
yellow, green, black and brown, no mark, 15"h, repaired
chips and hairlines   1500-2500   July 16, 1997
Sold for $1900

4329. Weller Blue Louwelsa vase, hi-glaze with floral design,
all in blue, impressed mark, 11"h, mint   1200-1700
July 16, 1997   Sold for $1900

Not Pictured:

4330. Weller Fudzi vase, floral in brown, green and blue,
impressed mark, 8"h, mint   500-700   June 8, 1997
Sold for $600

270

4331. Weller Glossy Hudson vase, lavender and pink trumpet flowers with multicolored green leaves and stems, against a green to pink ground, artist signed Pillsbury on base, 12"w x 30"h, restoration to minor chips 3500-4500   July 16, 1997   Sold for $2100

Not Pictured:

4332. Weller Hudson vase, pink and white roses with yellow centers on brown branches and green leaves against a shaded blue ground, initialed by Hester Pillsbury, incised mark and paper label, 13"h, mint   700-900 June 2, 1996   Sold for $950

4333. Weller Hudson vase, pink and white roses with yellow centers on brown branches and green leaves against a shaded blue ground, initialed by Hester Pillsbury, incised mark, 13"h, mint   700-900   June 2, 1996 Sold for $950

4334. Weller Dickensware vase, incised and painted Dickens scene of several people in orange, brown and green on an brown to green ground, inscription on reverse, impressed mark, 13.5"h, chip to top edge   400-600 July 15, 1997   Sold for $450

4335. Weller Dickensware vase, bisque glaze with farm scene with house and cattle and a couple meeting on a country road, brown, green, yellow, pink, blue and tan, impressed mark, artist signed H.S., 16"h, mint   900-1200 July 15, 1997   Sold for $2300

4336. Weller Dickensware vase, incised and painted tavern scene of men playing checkers with onlookers, multicolored browns, green, yellow, orange, blue and cream, not marked, 18"h, repaired bottom   1000-2000 July 15, 1997   Sold for $1700

4337. Weller Hudson vase, blue ground with red and pink flowers and green leaves, artist signed Timberlake, stamped mark, 12.5"h, mint   700-900 July 16, 1997 Sold for $550

4338. Weller Hudson vase, peach, yellow, white and blue flowers with green leaves, impressed mark, 8.5"h, mint 300-500   July 16, 1997   Sold for $400

4339. Weller White and Decorated vase, eight-sided with floral decoration on cream ground, impressed mark, 9.5"h, harmless tight line to lip   250-350   July 16, 1997 Sold for $300

Not Pictured:

4340. Weller Hudson vase, gray and white dogwood on a blue to pink ground, signed S. Timberlake, impressed mark, 7"h, mint   400-500   July 15, 1997   Sold for $500

271

4341. Weller Sicard vase, wheat decoration with iridescent highlights in green, purple and gold on an octagon form, 9"h, mint   600-800   July 16, 1996   Sold for $850

4342. Weller Dresden vase, windmill and sailboat decoration, blue and green matt glaze, impressed mark, 7"h, mint 300-400   July 16, 1996   Sold for $500

4343. Owens Lotus vase, leaves and berries in green, purple, and blue matt glaze, impressed mark, 9"h, mint 300-400   July 16, 1996   Sold for $500

4344. Weller Hudson vase, pink blossoms and buds with mustard and brown centers atop light green stems and leaves against a shaded blue ground, 10"h, mint 500-700   July 16, 1996   Sold for $450

4345. Weller White and Decorated Hudson vase, floral decoration in red, blue and green, backed with an ivory matt glaze, impressed mark, 10"h, mint 250-350   July 16, 1996   Sold for $260

4346. Weller Hudson vase, floral decoration in green, blue, and cream, backed by a green and pink matt glaze, ink mark, signed Pillsbury on side, 7.5"h, mint   250-350 July 16, 1996   Sold for $475

4347. Clifton vase, cream colored crocus backed by a brown matt glaze, marked, 8.5"h, mint   300-400 July 16, 1996   Sold for $270

Not Pictured:

4348. Weller Sicard vase, poppies in gold, green, purple and lavender, signed Weller Sicard, 13.5"h, repair to top and drill hole in bottom   550-750   June 7, 1998 Sold for $750

4349. Weller Sicard vase, six sides, green and gold swirls against a deep red ground with blue highlights, signed, 8"dia. x 4.5"h, line to rim   400-600   July 15, 1997 Sold for $550

4350. Weller Sicard vase, floral decoration, gold and green on red, gold and platinum ground, signed on side, 6"h, mint 500-700   July 15, 1997   Sold for $425

4351. Weller Sicard vase, iridescent swirls of gold, purple and green, signed on side, 5"h, mint   400-500 July 16, 1996   Sold for $500

4352. Weller Sicard vase, iridescent flowers decorating a twisted form, in shades of gold, purple and green, impressed mark and signed on side, 10"h, small chips underneath   1000-1500   July 16, 1996 Sold for $950

4353. Weller Sicard vase, iridescent design with gold, green and purple hi-lights, signed on side, 5.75"h, mint   500-600   July 16, 1996   Sold for $425

4354. Weller LaMar vase, scenic decoration of tall trees and brush at edge of still water with sailing ships, windmill and mountains on far shore, all in shades of black and red, 8"h, slight wear to surface   300-400   July 16, 1996   Sold for $160

4355. Jap Birdimal mug, scene of Oriental woman in yellow dress with green sash seated at writing desk under stylized brown, green and cream trees, initialed L. S., 6"h, hairline to rim   250-350   July 16, 1996   Sold for $375

4356. RV Rozane Royal vase, broad-shouldered form with floral decoration of cream blossoms and leaves against a shaded green ground, signed M. Imlay, wafer mark, 8.5"h, minute flaw to surface   200-300   July 16, 1996   Sold for $475

4357. Weller vase, raised decoration of blossoms atop narrow stems, all in light green hi-glaze, impressed mark, 5.5"h, mint   200-300   July 16, 1996   Sold for $90

4358. Weller Eocean vase, narrow form with crane design in lavender, cream, gray, maroon and black, against a gray to cream ground, signed Chilicotte on side, incised mark, 12"h, mint   1000-1200   July 16, 1996   Sold for $1700

4359. Weller Dickensware vase, tapered form with figure of man with brown hair, pink shirt, blue trousers and black shoes, blue wafer on reverse reads "Smike Nicholas Nickleby" in white letters, incised mark, 5"h, hairlines   150-250   July 16, 1996   Sold for $180

4360. Weller Rochelle vase, mustard and cream blossoms atop tan stems and leaves against a pink, green, deep rose, gray, pale blue and black ground, 9"h, mint   250-350   July 16, 1996   Sold for $375

4361. Owens Sudanese vase, pale lavender and cream lily atop broad light green lilypad against a brown hi-glaze ground, impressed mark, 7"h, mint   400-500   July 16, 1996   Sold for $350

4362. La Moro jug, brown glaze with caramel and yellow berries on brown thorned branches and broad green leaves against a brown, caramel and green ground, impressed mark, 5.5"h, mint   100-200   July 16, 1996   Sold for $60

4363. Weller Blue Louwelsa vase, floral decoration in green and white against a blue hi-glaze ground, impressed mark, 8"h, mint   600-800   July 16, 1996   Sold for $500

4364. Weller Blue Louwelsa vase, white flowers backed by a blue hi-glaze, with formed open handle, impressed mark, 5.5"dia x 3"h, mint   400-500   July 16, 1996   Sold for $600

Not Pictured:

4365. Weller Blue Louwelsa vase, white and blue floral decoration, impressed mark, 10"h, mint   800-1100   June 7, 1998   Sold for $1400

4366. Weller Woodcraft wallpocket, owl peering from tree trunk in brown and green matt, ink mark, 11"h, mint 300-400 July 17, 1996 Sold for $240

4367. Weller Coppertone console bowl, frog perched on lily pad with budding lily in shades of green, cream and brown matt, ink mark, 11"dia. x 4"h, chip to rim; with a **Weller Coppertone** flower frog, green and brown in lily pad form, ink mark, 5"dia., mint 200-300 July 17, 1996 Sold for $270

4368. Weller Coppertone candlestick, pair, turtle on lily pad, lily forms cup, green, brown and cream, ink mark, 5"w x 3"h, mint 300-400 July 17, 1996 Sold for $250

4369. Weller Coppertone centerpiece bowl, frog, lily and lily pad design, green, brown and cream, incised mark, 15.5"l x 10"w x 3"h, mint 800-1100 July 17, 1996 Sold for $550

4370. Weller Woodcraft flower frog, overlapping branches in green and brown matt, no mark, 7"dia. x 4"h, mint 100-200 July 17, 1996 Sold for $250

4371. Weller Coppertone figural, garden frog in green and brown mottled glaze, no mark, 6"h, chip to base 400-600 July 17, 1996 Sold for $350

4372. Weller Coppertone flower frog, frog emerging from lily sitting on lily pad in green, brown and ivory, no mark, 5"dia. x 5"h, chip to lip 250-350 July 17, 1996 Sold for $160

Not Pictured:

4373. Weller Coppertone vase, impressed marks, 8.5"h, mint 200-300 July 15, 1997 Sold for $250

4374. Weller Coppertone vase, impressed marks, 8.5"h, mint 200-300 July 15, 1997 Sold for $250

4375. Weller vase, frog, lilypad and bud at side of vase, matt green glaze, impressed mark, 7"h, mint 500-700 July 17, 1996 Sold for $700

4376. Weller Coppertone figural, garden frog in green and brown mottled matt glaze, cement filled, no mark, 6"h, small hairline to lip and base 400-600 July 17, 1996 Sold for $500

4377. Weller vase, turtle clings to side, matt green glaze, impressed mark, 5"h, mint 900-1200 July 17, 1996 Sold for $1200

Not Pictured:

4378. Weller Coppertone figural, frog in green and brown matt, ink mark, 3.5"h, mint 250-350 July 17, 1996 Sold for $270

4379. **Weller Coppertone** vase, frog supports vase of rushes in green, cream and brown, ink mark, 8.5"h, mint 400-600 July 17, 1996 Sold for $550

4380. **Weller Woodcraft** figural, squirrel on edge of tree trunk, green and brown matt glaze, impressed mark, 4.5"h, minute chip 200-250 July 17, 1996 Sold for $425

4381. **Weller Forest** jardiniere, forest scene in green, brown, yellow and light blue, 8"dia. x 7"h, mint 300-400 July 17, 1996 Sold for $300

4382. **Zaneware** flower frog, attribution, frog design in mottled light blue and tan matt glaze, 5"w x 2.5"h, flakes to base 100-150 July 17, 1996 Sold for $30

4383. **Weller Woodcraft** flower frog, frog in open lily on swirling vines, 4"h, mint 300-400 July 17, 1996 Sold for $150

4384. **Weller Woodcraft** jardiniere, squirrel on side of oak tree with leaves and acorns in shades of green and brown matt, no mark, 11"dia. x 10.5"h, hairline 500-700 July 17, 1996 Sold for $300

4385. **Weller Coppertone** figural, frog in green with tan and black highlights, incised mark, 2"h, hairline to base 150-250 July 17, 1996 Sold for $210

4386. **Weller Coppertone** figural, frog in green and brown matt, ink mark, 3.5"h, mint 250-350 July 17, 1996 Sold for $550

4387. **Weller Coppertone** figural, frog holds lily on lily pad, in green, cream and brown, ink mark, 3.5"h, mint 300-400 July 17, 1996 Sold for $230

4388. **Weller Ivory** jardiniere, tree with birds and squirrels in ivory, brown and black, 8"dia. x 7"h, hairlines to rim 150-250 July 17, 1996 Sold for $40

4389. **Weller Coppertone** tray, frog rests on lily pad in green and brown mottled glaze, incised mark, 6"dia. x 2"h, mint 350-450 July 17, 1996 Sold for $240

4390. **Weller Coppertone** vase, frog supports vase of rushes in green, cream and brown, ink mark, 8.5"h, mint 400-600 July 17, 1996 Sold for $500

4391. **Weller Coppertone** vase, shades of green, ivory and brown matt, ink mark, 8"h, mint 800-1100 July 17, 1996 Sold for $950

4392. **Weller Coppertone** bowl, turtle rests on lily pad overlooking pond, with flower frog, in green and brown mottled glaze, incised mark, 17"l x 11"w x 5"h, hairline to side 600-800 July 17, 1996 Sold for $1100

4393. **Weller Coppertone** vase, two frogs sit on lily pad base, rushes form body, in green and gray with cream and brown highlights, incised mark, 10"w x 8.5"h, mint 900-1200 July 17, 1996 Sold for $1000

Not Pictured:

4394. **Weller Coppertone** flower frog, frog sits on lily pad in green, cream and brown, 4.5"h, mint 250-350 July 17, 1996 Sold for $425

275

4395. RV Aztec pitcher, blue with white and green squeeze-bag decoration, 5"h, mint 300-500 July 16, 1996 Sold for $375

4396. Peters and Reed vase, landscape decoration in shades of blue, green and brown, 7.5"h, mint 200-300 July 16, 1996 Sold for $350

4397. Weller Hudson vase, floral decoration in shades of blue, green, pink and ivory, artist signed Pillsbury, impressed mark, 9"h, mint 400-600 July 16, 1996 Sold for $650

4398. RV Rozane Woodland vase, twist form with floral decoration, in shades of yellow, green and tan, wafer mark, 7"h, restored 300-500 July 16, 1996 Sold for $389

4399. Weller Baldin vase, blue ground with shades of red, yellow, and green, impressed mark, 11.5"h, mint 400-600 July 16, 1996 Sold for $400

4400. Weller Windsor vase, blue with green leaf decoration, 5.25"h, mint 150-200 July 16, 1996 Sold for $190

4401. Weller Monticello vase, light-blue ground with white tan and green decoration, 7"h, mint 200-300 July 16, 1996 Sold for $400

4402. RV Windsor vase, geometric design in shades of green and yellow on blue ground, 6"h, mint 150-200 July 16, 1996 Sold for $260

4403. Weller Woodcraft mug, fox and oak tree decoration in shades of brown and green, impressed stamp, 6"h, mint 100-200 July 16, 1996 Sold for $180

Not Pictured:

4404. Weller Forest vase, forest scene in green, brown and light blue, impressed mark, 8"h, mint 250-350 July 17, 1996 Sold for $200

4405. Weller Woodcraft vase, owl peering from tree trunk in shades of green and brown matt, impressed mark, 13.5"h, mint 600-800 July 17, 1996 Sold for $475

4406. Weller Woodcraft basket, brown and green, impressed mark, 10"h, mint 150-250 July 17, 1996 Sold for $260

4407. Weller Woodcraft vase, green and brown with foxes, 7"w x 5"h, mint 200-300 July 17, 1996 Sold for $200

4408. Weller vase, hi-glaze with raised leaf design in brown, incised mark, 5.5"h, mint 200-300 July 16, 1996 Sold for $100

4409. Weller Aurelian vase, caramel, yellow, salmon and dark brown blossoms atop narrow green stems and leaves against a yellow, orange, pale green, caramel and dark brown ground, initialed by artist, 15.5"h, chip to rim 1200-1700 July 16, 1996 Sold for $1000

4410. Weller Hudson vase, large iris blossoms and buds in medium blue and pink with yellow and caramel centers atop light green leaves and stems, all outlined in black on a pale green to pink ground, signed Walch, 9.5"h, flake at base   400-600   July 15, 1996   Sold for $450

4411. Weller Hudson vase, yellow goldenrod and blue daisies with yellow and green centers on a gray to pink ground, initialed by Hester Pillsbury, 7"h, glaze imperfection, tight hairline   200-300   July 15, 1996   Sold for $180

4412. Weller Hudson vase, pink and white water lily with caramel and yellow center atop broad leaves of green and gray against a gray to pink ground, signed Kennedy, impressed mark, 10.5"h, mint   500-700   July 15, 1996   Sold for $375

4413. Weller Hudson vase, yellow goldenrod on blue and green stems and leaves against a medium blue to ivory ground, signed Pillsbury on side, 9.5"h, repaired base chip   400-600   July 15, 1996   Sold for $500

4414. Weller Hudson vase, roses in pale yellow, mustard, gray and cream on leaves of gray, olive and pale green on a gray to pale yellow ground, signed by D. England, 8.5"h, mint   300-500   July 15, 1996   Sold for $220

4415. Weller Hudson vase, violets in blue, pink and cream on broad dark green leaves against a green to pink ground, signed by L. Morris, ink mark, 7"h, mint   300-500   July 15, 1996   Sold for $260

4416. Weller Hudson vase, iris blossom and buds in cream and blue with pink and yellow highlights on blue leaves against a blue to violet to cream ground, signed Pillsbury, 10"h, mint   500-700   July 15, 1996   Sold for $450

4417. Weller Woodcraft floor vase, tree trunk form with owl and squirrel on side, branches form open handles, green and brown, impressed mark, 17"h, line to one handle   600-800   July 15, 1996   Sold for $700

4418. Weller Glendale vase, marsh scene of bird and nest among cattails in green, brown, tan and light blue, ink mark, 13"h, hairline and chip to base   700-900   July 15, 1996   Sold for $425

Not Pictured:

4419. Weller Knifewood bowl, hunting dogs in yellow against a gray and brown ground, impressed mark, 8"dia. x 3.5"h, mint   250-350   July 17, 1996   Sold for $450

4420. Weller letter holder, yellow and tan blossoms with brown centers among green leaves, 5"w x 2"d x 3.5"h, hairline   100-200   July 16, 1996   Sold for $90

4421. Weller Louwelsa vase, orange and mustard blossoms with brown centers atop narrow green stems, impressed mark, 9"h, mint   100-200   July 16, 1996   Sold for $220

4422. Owens Utopian vase, tan, cocoa and dark brown blossoms against a gray and tan matt ground, impressed marks, 4"h, chip to base   50-100   July 16, 1996   Sold for $50

4423. Rozane Royal vase, yellow, gray, white and caramel roses amid broad green leaves and thorned branches, signed by Imlay, 8"dia. x 6"h, mint   600-800   July 16, 1996   Sold for $500

4424. Weller Dickensware vase, town scene depicting boy with man wearing top hat and cane in foreground, in shades of green, tan, yellow, teal, black and white, impressed words read, Mr. Micawber Impressing the Names of Streets Upon Me That I Might Find My Way Back Early in The Morning—David Copperfield, impressed mark, 11"h, mint   600-800   July 16, 1996   Sold for $500

4425. La Moro vase, caramel and green leaves, impressed mark, 6"h, mint   100-200   July 16, 1996   Sold for $60

4426. Weller Matt vase, dogwood blossoms on narrow stems, all in burgundy matt glaze, incised mark, 7.5"dia. x 4.5"h, mint   400-600   July 16, 1996   Sold for $270

4427. Owens Utopian vase, broad caramel and tan leaves, impressed mark, 3.5"h, mint   100-150   July 16, 1996   Sold for $90

4428. Weller Louwelsa vase, yellow and caramel blossoms atop narrow green stems and leaves, initialed by Mary Gillie, impressed mark, 9.5"h, mint   200-250   July 16, 1996   Sold for $200

4429. Owens Utopian mug, orange and cream berries atop orange thorned stems and broad green leaves, initialed T. S. on side, impressed mark, 5"h, mint   100-200   July 16, 1996   Sold for $110

4430. Weller Hudson vase, pink, coral and lavender blossoms with yellow and mustard centers atop bowed white and green stems and leaves against a shaded blue ground, initialed by Hester Pillsbury, impressed mark, 10"h, mint   800-1100   July 16, 1996   Sold for $800

4431. Weller Hudson vase, pink and cream blossoms with yellow and dark brown centers atop narrow cream and green stems and leaves against a shaded blue ground, initialed by Hester Pillsbury, impressed mark, partial paper label, 10"h, mint   800-1100   July 16, 1996   Sold for $800

4432. Weller Brighton figural, pheasant in blue, gray, white and pink, impressed mark, 10"w x 7"h, mint   250-350   July 15, 1996   Sold for $400

4433. Weller Brighton wallpocket, woodpecker on branch in blue, gray, pink, green and black, 12"h, chips to bottom edge   300-400   July 15, 1996   Sold for $400

4434. Weller Brighton figural, woodpecker in blue, gray, green, orange and black, 5.5"h, chips to base and beak   150-250   July 15, 1996   Sold for $60

4435. Weller Brighton figurals, pair, small birds in gray, pink, yellow and black, 4"w x 2"h, minute chip to one beak, otherwise mint   200-300   July 15, 1996   Sold for $300

4436. Weller Brighton figural, parrot in pink, green, yellow, black and gray, impressed mark, 12.5"h, repairs to tail and wing tips   400-600   July 15, 1996   Sold for $550

4437. Weller Brighton wallpocket, crow on branch with grapes in black, green and violet, 15"h, several minute chips   500-700   July 15, 1996   Sold for $900

4438. Weller Brighton flower frog, kingfisher in blue, green, black, white and rust, impressed mark, 8.5"h, hairline to base   150-250   July 15, 1996   Sold for $170

4439. Weller Brighton flower frog, swan in white, black and green, 5.5"w x 5"h, mint   200-300   July 15, 1996   Sold for $290

4440. Weller Muskota flower frog, fish surround stump in green and caramel, impressed mark, 5"h, fin and tail repaired   150-250   July 15, 1996   Sold for $100

4441. Weller Brighton flower frog, canaries in yellow, green and brown, 4.5"h, chip to beak   150-250   July 15, 1996   Sold for $220

4442. Weller Kenova vase, raised floral decoration of roses and leaves on branches, branch forms two small open handles, in a gray/green and caramel matt glaze, impressed mark, 9.5"h, flake to rim   400-600   July 15, 1996   Sold for $300

4443. Weller Baldin vase, raised decoration of pink and yellow fruit, green and brown leaves and brown branches against a blue ground, two small closed handles, impressed mark, 10"h, hairline to base   200-300   July 15, 1996 Sold for $190

279

4444. Weller Coppertone bowl, frog on lily pad, green and brown matt, with flower frog not pictured, ink mark, 10"dia. x 5.5"h, mint 500-700 July 17, 1996 Sold for $450

4445. Weller Coppertone figural, frog in green and brown, incised mark, 2"h, mint 200-300 July 17, 1996 Sold for $160

4446. Weller Ivory jardiniere, tree and squirrel design in ivory and brown, 6"dia. x 5"h, mint 200-250 July 17, 1996 Sold for $130

4447. Weller Woodcraft wallpocket, owl on tree trunk in brown and green matt, no mark, 11"h, chip to side 200-300 July 17, 1996 Sold for $160

4448. Weller Ivory jardiniere, ivory and brown matt with animals among leaves and branches, 8"dia. x 7"h, mint 200-300 July 17, 1996 Sold for $100

4449. Weller Forest vase, forest scene in green and brown, 12"h, mint 400-600 July 17, 1996 Sold for $200

4450. Weller Woodcraft bowl, squirrel on branch among leaves in green and brown, initialed by artist, 6"dia. x 3"h, mint 300-400 July 17, 1996 Sold for $200

4451. Weller Coppertone vase, frog handles in shades of green, ivory and brown mottled glaze, ink mark, 8"h, mint 800-1100 July 17, 1996 Sold for $1300

4452. Weller Woodcraft wallpocket, squirrel on branch eating acorn, brown and green matt, no mark, 9"h, mint 300-400 July 17, 1996 Sold for $250

4453. Weller Woodcraft covered jar, acorn design in green and brown matt, with squirrel and oak leaves on lid, impressed mark, 8"h, mint 400-500 July 17, 1996 Sold for $650

4454. Weller Forest vase, green, brown, caramel and light blue matt glaze, ink mark, 4.5"h, mint 200-250 July 17, 1996 Sold for $275

4455. Weller Etna umbrella stand, hi-glaze with peacock with long trailing feathers in blue, gray, red, yellow, green and white, large pink blossoms with yellow centers on green stems on reverse, all against a shaded green and white ground, 22"h, small bubbles to glaze, mint 1200-1700 July 17, 1996   Sold for $1200

4456. Weller Besline vase, three-handled orange hi-glaze with grape vine matt, 9.5"h, hairline   100-200   July 16, 1996 Sold for $70

4457. RV Aztec vase, blue and white squeezebag decoration on green ground, 10"h, hairline   200-300   July 16, 1996 Sold for $90

4458. Swastika Keramos pitcher, green broad leaf decoration on gold hi-glaze, wafer mark 704-L, 10"h, minor flake to base   200-300   July 16, 1996 Sold for $180

4459. Weller Turada bowl, white lace decoration atop a green raised leaf form, 5"dia. x 3"h, minor flake to decoration 200-300   July 16, 1996 Sold for $80

4460. Weller White and Decorated vase, white rose on ivory and gray ground, impressed mark, 13.5"h, mint 300-400   July 16, 1996 Sold for $475

4461. Weller Lasa vase, landscape decoration in shades of gold, red and green, not signed, 6"h, mint   250-350 July 16, 1996   Sold for $210

4462. Weller Lamar vase, landscape with windmill decoration in shades of red and black, partial paper label, 10.5"h, mint with scratches   250-350   July 16, 1996 Sold for $110

4463. Avon vase, grape vine in shades of blue and brown with lime green ground, incised mark 1902, 9"h, mint 400-600   July 16, 1996 Sold for $850

4464. Weller Marengo vase, tree decoration in shades of pink and red, no mark, 7"h, mint   300-400   July 16, 1996 Sold for $300

4465. Weller Louwelsa vase, portrait of Native American chief with headdress of cream and brown wrapped in brown leather, breast plate of bones and beads in ivory and brown and fringed leather jacket with beaded decoration in ivory and tan with rich aqua highlights, Chief Hollow Horn Bear, Sioux, initialed by W.A. Long, 17"h, restoration   3000-4000   July 15, 1996 Sold for $ 2700

Not Pictured:

4466. Weller Dickensware vase, incised portrait of "Little Wound Chief" with headdress in white, blue, tan, gray and yellow against a caramel and green ground, bisque finish, initialed by Charles Upjohn, impressed mark, 12"h, mint   900-1200   July 15, 1996   Sold for $1600

4467. **Weller Cactus** figural tray, swan in aqua matt, incised mark, 6.5"w x 3.5"h, mint   100-200   July 17, 1996 Sold for $50

4468. **Weller Hobart** flower frog, swan and boy in tall grass, mint green matt glaze, impressed mark, 6"h, mint 100-200   July 17, 1996 Sold for $140

4469. **Weller Cactus** figural dish, dachshund in brown and pink matt, incised mark, 5.5"w x 3"h, mint   100-200 July 17, 1996 Sold for $50

4470. **Weller Burntwood** charger, design of fish in brown and tan matt, 11"dia., repair to rim   150-200   July 17, 1996 Sold for $250

4471. **Weller** figural, bumblebee in black, gray, yellow, green and pink hi-glaze, 2"w, mint   100-200   July 17, 1996 Sold for $200

4472. **Weller** figural, butterfly in gray, pink, black, brown and green hi-glaze, 2.5"w, mint   100-200   July 17, 1996 Sold for $120

4473. **Weller** figural, bird in blue and yellow hi-glaze, 4"w, flake to beak   100-200   July 17, 1996   Sold for $150

4474. **Weller** figural, bird in blue, black and cream hi-glaze, 3.25"w, mint   100-200   July 17, 1996   Sold for $150

4475. **Weller Cactus** figural tray, seal in black, incised mark, 3.5"h, mint   100-200   July 17, 1996   Sold for $80

4476. **Weller Hobart** flower frog, child holding grapes, aqua matt, 6.5"h, mint   150-250   July 17, 1996 Sold for $140

4477. **Weller Hobart** flower frog, girl and duck near rock, no mark, 5"h, mint   100-200   July 17, 1996 Sold for $140

4478. **Weller Hudson** vase, white blossoms with green, black and yellow centers atop rose branches against a pink, green and blue ground, 9.5"h, small chip at base   200-300   July 17, 1996 Sold for $240

4479. **Weller Hudson** vase, blossoms in pink, yellow and gray with centers of mustard, black, blue and red atop stems with broad, curled leaves of gray, green and cream all outlined in black on a medium blue to pink ground, signed Leffler, Weller Ware ink mark, 11.5"h, mint   800-1100 July 17, 1996   Sold for $1200

4480. **Weller Dresden** vase, Dutchman in billowing pants, wooden shoes, jacket and cap standing on rolling ground backed by a small cottage among large windmills and distant sailboats on a body of water, all in shades of blue and blue/gray with white highlights, incised Weller Matt, artist's initials LGB, impressed, 9"h, mint   400-600 July 17, 1996   Sold for $750

4481. Weller Woodcraft flower frog, squirrel atop leaves in green, gray and brown matt, impressed mark, 3.5"h, repairs   200-300   July 17, 1996 Sold for $140

4482. Weller Woodcraft hanging basket, fruit and owl design in green, brown and deep rose, 10"dia. x 5"h, hairlines to rim   250-350   July 17, 1996 Sold for $160

4483. Weller Coppertone tray, frog sits at edge of dish in lily pad design, ink mark, 6"w x 2"h, mint   300-400 July 17, 1996 Sold for $400

4484. Weller Woodcraft candlestick, owls perch on top of twisting vines in shades of tan and green matt glaze, red berries, no mark, 14"h, drilled hole in base   400-600 July 17, 1996 Sold for $230

4485. Weller Woodcraft console bowl, squirrel atop branches and leaves with acorns, in brown and green matt, no mark, 10"dia. x 6"h, mint   400-500   July 17, 1996 Sold for $400

4486. Weller Knifewood jardiniere, animals and birds among leaves and branches in muted shades of green, brown, gray and purple, impressed mark, 9"dia. x 8"h, mint 400-500   July 17, 1996 Sold for $500

4487. Weller Woodcraft candlestick, owls perched on a tree, with twisting vines, leaves and berries, in a brown, green and red matt glaze, impressed mark, 14"h, mint 600-800   July 17, 1996 Sold for $750

4488. Weller Coppertone figural, frog in green, tan and gray matt, ink mark, 3.5"h, mint   300-400   July 17, 1996 Sold for $425

4489. Weller Woodcraft planter, with original liner, green and brown with black and lavender highlights, 8"dia. x 3.5"h, mint   300-400   July 17, 1996 Sold for $170

4490. Weller Coppertone flower frog, frog atop lily pad protruding from budding lily, with six openings, in green, cream and brown mottled glaze, ink mark, 4"dia. x 4"h, mint   300-400   July 17, 1996 Sold for $600

4491. Weller Hudson vase, yellow, blue and caramel blossoms on green branches and leaves, all outlined in dark green, against a blue to tan ground, signed Timberlake, impressed mark, 12.5"h, mint   600-800 July 17, 1996   Sold for $1100

4492. Weller Hudson vase, maroon and dark pink blossoms atop narrow stems and leaves on a deep purple matt ground, incised mark, 8"h, mint   700-900 July 17, 1996   Sold for $1000

283

4493. Weller Forest floor vase, large, form in green, brown and blue, 13"h, minor hidden flakes to base   800-1100 June 2, 1996   Sold for $700

4494. Weller Forest jardiniere and pedestal, brown, green and blue, 30"h, minor flakes to jardiniere, pedestal mint 800-1100   June 2, 1996   Sold for $950

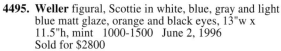

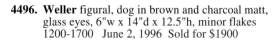

4495. Weller figural, Scottie in white, blue, gray and light blue matt glaze, orange and black eyes, 13"w x 11.5"h, mint   1000-1500   June 2, 1996 Sold for $2800

4496. Weller figural, dog in brown and charcoal matt, glass eyes, 6"w x 14"d x 12.5"h, minor flakes 1200-1700   June 2, 1996 Sold for $1900

4497. Weller Blue Louwelsa vase, floral decoration of rounded blossoms on narrow stems, all in shades of blue, impressed mark, 7"h, minute chip to base 400-500   June 2, 1996 Sold for $700

4498. Weller Blue Louwelsa vase, decoration of cherries and broad leaves on narrow stems, all in shades of blue, impressed mark, 7"h, minute chip to base   400-500 June 2, 1996 Sold for $475

4499. Weller Art Nouveau floor vase, raised decoration of pink woman with yellow hair in blue dress between pink blossoms against a shaded green and pink ground, pink rose on reverse, bisque finish, impressed mark, 21.5"h, minute flakes to base   700-900   July 15, 1996 Sold for $750

4500. Weller Ivory umbrella stand, Art Nouveau design of sinuous leaves and blossoms, with cutouts, ivory with rust highlights, 10.5"w x 8.5"d x 23"h, hairlines to base 600-800   July 15, 1996   Sold for $270

4501. RV Rozane jardiniere, red, yellow, blue and purple against a cream ground, 9"h, mint   200-300 July 17, 1996   Sold for $180

4502. Weller Jewel jardiniere, green to cream with blue and green jewels, 32"h, jardiniere with repaired flakes to body, hairline, pedestal with minor flakes   700-900 July 17, 1996   Sold for $400

4503. RV Rozane Woodland vase, blossoms, buds and stems in caramel, brown and green on a perforated ground of bisque finish, 8.5"h, repaired chips   400-600 July 16, 1996   Sold for $250

4504. Weller Louwelsa vase, floral in yellow, green and brown, impressed mark, artist signed, 16"h, mint 700-900   July 16, 1996   Sold for $1200

4505. Weller Hudson vase, pictorial landscape in green and ivory, incised mark, artist signed Timberlake, 9"h, hairlines   700-900   July 16, 1996   Sold for $1600

4506.Weller Hudson vase, pink and lavender blossoms against blue, cream, light and medium green leaves outlined in black, all against a shaded blue ground, signed D. England on side, ink mark, 7.5"dia. x 8"h, hairline   400-600   July 16, 1996 Sold for $375

4507. Weller Hudson vase, white, pink, blue and lavender blossoms with brown and yellow centers, all atop light and dark green stems and leaves against a gray to pink ground, initialed by Hester Pillsbury, impressed mark, 10"h, mint   600-800   July 16, 1996 Sold for $700

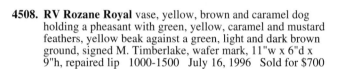

4508. RV Rozane Royal vase, yellow, brown and caramel dog holding a pheasant with green, yellow, caramel and mustard feathers, yellow beak against a green, light and dark brown ground, signed M. Timberlake, wafer mark, 11"w x 6"d x 9"h, repaired lip   1000-1500   July 16, 1996   Sold for $700

4509. Weller Louwelsa kerosene lamp, green iris with yellow center on green stems and broad green and brown leaves on green and dark brown ground, copper rim to hold font, impressed marks, pottery 24.5"h, with font 29"h, globe missing, minute flake to base, minor scratches   2500-3500 July 16, 1996   Sold for $1400

4510. Weller Louwelsa vase, brown, cream, caramel and shaded green clusters of grapes with narrow shaded brown and green branches and broad leaves against a green, caramel, rust and dark brown ground, signed by artist on side, impressed marks, 16.5"h, flakes to rim and side   1200-1700   July 16, 1996 Sold for $700

4511. Weller Louwelsa vase, rose blossoms and buds in yellow, gray, cream, caramel and orange with detailed centers of dark brown and tan atop thorned stems of green and brown and veined leaves of mint green and cream against a dark brown ground with caramel and green highlights, impressed marks, 24"h, mint 900-1200   July 16, 1996   Sold for $2000

4512. Weller Louwelsa vase, caramel, light and dark yellow blossoms atop caramel and green stems and leaves against a shaded brown ground, signed by H. Pillsbury, impressed marks, 13"h, mint   300-500   June 2, 1996   Sold for $350

4513. Owens vase, fruit and leaves in yellow, caramel, orange and green initialed by artist, impressed mark, 10.5"h, minute flake to base   150-250   June 2, 1996   Sold for $200

Not Pictured:

4514. Weller Louwelsa pitcher, peach and pink blossoms and green stems against a peach, lavender and gray ground in bisque finish, initialed by Ferrell, impressed mark, 12"h, mint   300-400   July 15, 1996   Sold for $325

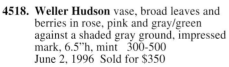

4515. Weller Hudson vase, pink apple blossoms, ground of green to pink, signed by M. Ansel, 6.5"h, mint   350-450   July 15, 1996   Sold for $425

4516. Weller vase, ivory, pink and lavender blossoms and buds atop against a pink and light green ground, signed McLaughlin, impressed mark, 12"h, minute hairline to rim   600-800   July 15, 1996   Sold for $260

4517. Weller Perfecto vase, pink blossoms in blue, pink and green against a pink to lavender ground, initialed by Hester Pillsbury, impressed mark, 6"dia. x 5.5"h, mint   250-350   July 15, 1996   Sold for $280

4518. Weller Hudson vase, broad leaves and berries in rose, pink and gray/green against a shaded gray ground, impressed mark, 6.5"h, mint   300-500   June 2, 1996   Sold for $350

4519. Weller Hudson vase, two-handled form with flowers in blue and green against a gray/green ground, artist signed Leffler, ink mark, 9.5"dia. x 9.5"h, mint   800-1100   June 2, 1996   Sold for $1200

4520. Weller Hudson vase, iris decoration in blue, tan, caramel and lavender with muted green leaves against a blue to pink ground, artist signed J. England, impressed mark, ink mark, 9.5"h, mint   500-700   June 2, 1996   Sold for $900

4521. RV Rozane vase, hi-glaze with design of thistles in cream and green against a green and cream ground, signed Pillsbury on side, wafer mark, 9.5"h, chips to wafer mark, otherwise mint   350-550   July 17, 1996 Sold for $270

4522. Weller Rhead pitcher, scene of windmills and trees in blue against a tan ground, signed by F.H. Rhead, 4.5"h, hairline to rim   200-300 July 17, 1996 Sold for $260

4523. Weller Eocean vase, hi-glaze with design of berries and large broad leaves in lavender, pale green and light blue against a light blue to white ground, incised mark, 9.5"h, flake to base 400-600   July 17, 1996 Sold for $325

4524. Weller Sicard vase, swirling blossoms, leaves and vines in caramel and green against a purple and green ground with blue highlights, signed Weller Sicard, 9"h, mint   1500-2000   July 15, 1996   Sold for $1700

4525.Weller Sicard vase, peacock feather in golden yellow and green over a deep rose metallic ground, signed Weller Sicard, 8.5"h, minute flakes to rim   800-1100 July 15, 1996   Sold for $400

4526. Weller Sicard vase, twisted form with gold and violet blossoms and leaves against a green, purple, blue and violet ground, raised mark 11.5"h, mint   1500-2000 July 15, 1996   Sold for $1700

4527. Weller Hudson Perfecto vase, pink and yellow blossoms on brown branches with green leaves, all outlined in brown, against a white to green ground, incised mark, 13"h, mint   600-800   July 17, 1996 Sold for $600

4528. Weller Hudson Perfecto vase, purple blossoms on green stems and leaves, all outlined in brown, against a white to green ground, initialed by Hester Pillsbury, incised mark, 13"h, mint   600-800   July 17, 1996 Sold for $600

4529.Weller LaSa vase, trees, rocks and brush backed by water and distant mountains under clouds in sunset sky, in pink, gold, green, purple, orange, red and black, 6.5"h, mint 350-450 July 17, 1996 Sold for $350

4530. Weller LaSa vase, pine trees backed by water and distant mountains under clouds, all in gold and black with green, purple and red highlights, signed on side, 11"h, hole in base, some wear 400-500 July 17, 1996 Sold for $650

4531.Weller LaSa vase, pine trees backed by water and distant mountains under clouds in sunset sky, all in pink, gold, green, purple and black, 6.5"h, mint 350-450 July 17, 1996 Sold for $425

4532. Weller Hudson vase, waterlily decoration in white and pink against a gray, mauve and cream ground, artist signed, impressed mark, 10.5"h, mint 400-600 July 17, 1996 Sold for $500

4533. Weller Hudson vase, charcoal gray ground with gray and white flowers and green leaves, no marks, 5"h, mint 250-350 July 17, 1996 Sold for $260

4534. Weller Louwelsa tankard, green and rust grapes on brown and green branch with green and rust leaves against an orange, caramel, green and brown ground, signed M. Lybarger, impressed marks, 14"h, repair to lip 150-250 July 16, 1996 Sold for $200

4535. RV Rozane Royal vase, yellow, caramel, green and dark brown iris blossoms and buds atop green, yellow and tan leaves on a green, caramel and brown ground, signed M. Timberlake, wafer mark, 21"h, minute flakes 2500-3500 July 16, 1996 Sold for $1900

289

4536. Weller dragonfly, green body and gray wings with blue, pink and orange highlights, 3"w, repair to tail 150-200 July 15, 1996 Sold for $80

4537. Weller butterfly, green body with cream, tan and green wings, 4"w, hairline to wing 150-200 July 15, 1996 Sold for $60

4538. Weller dragonfly, green body and gray wings with blue, pink and orange highlights, 3"w, hairline to wing 150-200 July 15, 1996 Sold for $170

4539. Weller butterfly, brown body with pink and black wings, 2.5"w, hairline 150-250 July 15, 1996 Sold for $70

4540. Weller bumblebee, green and white body with gray wings, 2"w, mint 200-300 July 15, 1996 Sold for $220

4541. Weller butterfly, green body and caramel wings with pink and black highlights, 3"w, flakes to edges 150-250 July 15, 1996 Sold for $80

4542. Weller butterfly, black body with black, white and rose wings, 3"w, mint 250-350 July 15, 1996 Sold for $110

4543. Weller dragonfly, green body and gray wings with blue, pink and orange highlights, 3"w, repair to tail 150-250 July 15, 1996 Sold for $80

4544. Weller butterfly, green body and yellow wings with black and blue highlights, 3.5"w, chips to wings 150-250 July 15, 1996 Sold for $100

4545. Weller butterfly, gray with green, rose and black highlights, 3"w, mint 250-350 July 15, 1996 Sold for $150

4546. Weller Matt vase, large frog with black eyes clings to shoulder atop lily pad and bud with long, trailing stem, all in a rich dark brown and green matt glaze, impressed Weller, 6.5"h, mint 200-900 July 15, 1996 Sold for $325

4547. Weller Sicard vase, floral decoration of blossoms with long tentacles in iridescent glaze of deep wine, blue, violet and green, 5.5"h, mint 400-600 July 15, 1996 Sold for $450

4548. Weller Sicard vase, decoration of broad blossoms on twisting stems in gold with violet and blue iridescence on a deep wine ground, signed Weller Sicard, 9"h, mint 900-1200 July 15, 1996 Sold for $1100

290

4549. Weller Pearl vase, pink, green, lavender and black on white hi-glaze ground, impressed mark, 6"h, mint 70-150   July 17, 1996 Sold for $70

4550. Weller Eocean vase, cluster of purple, lavender and cream grapes on curling green vines with broad leaves against a dark green to white ground, signed L. Mitchell, incised mark, 8"h, mint   500-700   July 17, 1996 Sold for $800

4551. Weller Eocean vase, deep red, pink and cream blossoms atop narrow green stems and broad leaves against a dark gray to white ground, initialed M.L., incised mark, ink mark, 10"h, mint   400-600   July 17, 1996 Sold for $500

4552. Owens Sudenese vase, pink, white and yellow blossoms and green leaves against a black hi-glaze ground, impressed mark, 4.5"h, mint   250-350   July 17, 1996 Sold for $300

4553. Weller White and Decorated vase, matt glaze with jonquils in yellow and white atop broad pale green stems and leaves, impressed mark, 12"h, mint   250-350 July 17, 1996 Sold for $270

4554. Weller Rosemont vase, blue, green and deep rose on black ground, impressed mark, 10.25"h, chip to base in making, mint   300-500   July 17, 1996 Sold for $240

4555. Weller Dickensware mug, green and tan leaves on thorned brown branches against a dark blue and green ground, raised artist mark on side, impressed mark, 5"h, mint   150-200   July 17, 1996 Sold for $130

4556. Weller White and Decorated vase, muted red, pink, purple and blue blossoms on black branches with green leaves against a cream ground, impressed mark, 7"h, mint   100-200   July 17, 1996 Sold for $160

4557. Weller Hudson vase, yellow, pink, white, blue and brown blossoms among green leaves against a gray to pink ground, initialed by Hester Pillsbury, incised mark, 6"h, mint   350-550   July 17, 1996   Sold for $475

4558. Weller Rochelle vase, pink and yellow rose blossoms atop thorned branches and green leaves against a mottled purple and blue hi-glaze ground, 12.5"h, mint   900-1200 July 17, 1996 Sold for $1100

291

4559. Weller Aurelian vase, green, black and ivory grapes on green and brown branches and leaves against an ground of brown, green and yellow, signed by Frank Ferrell, impressed marks, 14"h, minute chips to rim   400-600 June 2, 1996   Sold for $550

4560. Weller Louwelsa clock, yellow and rust blossoms and buds on round green leaves and narrow stems against a caramel and brown ground, 12.5"w x 5"d x 11"h, chips to rear of one foot, minor chips to edge of bevel on face 600-800   June 2, 1996   Sold for $650

Not Pictured:

4561. Weller Aurelian vase, standard glaze, dragon in fire, marked and signed Edward Abel, 5"w x 12.5"h, mint 250-450   July 13, 1998   Sold for $600

4562. Weller Aurelian ewer, nasturtiums, marked, artist signed Helen Smith, 6.25"w x 9"h, minor flakes to rim 100-200   July 13, 1998   Sold for $220

4563. Weller Etna vase, poppy decoration in pink, yellow and green on an olive to gray ground, incised Weller on side, impressed mark, 10"h, mint   200-300   June 2, 1996 Sold for $350

4564. Weller Coppertone vase, frog sits on lily pad, in green, brown and ivory matt, with large flower frog, ink mark, 10"dia. x 5.5"h, mint   700-900   July 17, 1996 Sold for $550

4565. Weller Coppertone vase, stylized decoration of lily pads and blossoms, frog heads at base, in green, cream and brown, ink mark, 11.5"h, minor chips to base 600-800   July 17, 1996   Sold for $950

4566. Weller Coppertone vase, frog ascends raised lily pads, in brown and green mottled glaze, ink mark, 7.5"h, hairline to base   400-500   July 17, 1996   Sold for $500

Not Pictured:

4567. Weller Coppertone candleholders, pair, turtle design, stamp mark, 5.5"dia. x 3"h, mint   550-650 June 8, 1997   Sold for $600

4568. Weller Jap Birdimal pitcher, duck and tree decoration in dark green, brown, cream, yellow and gray/green hi-glaze, 6"h, mint 250-350 June 2, 1996 Sold for $350

4569. Weller Jap Birdimal vase, butterflies in dark olive, black, cream and blue hi-glaze, artist signed, 6"h, mint 500-700 June 2, 1996 Sold for $650

4570. Weller Jap Birdimal vase, duck and tree decoration in yellow, brown and shades of green hi-glaze, 4"h, mint 250-350 June 2, 1996 Sold for $450

Not Pictured:

4571. Weller Forest basket, forest scene in green, brown and blue, impressed mark, basket 6"dia. x 4"h, mint 200-300 July 17, 1996 Sold for $300

4572. Weller Barcelona vase, stylized decoration in yellow, rose, blue and caramel, ink mark, 9"h, mint 200-300 July 16, 1996 Sold for $325

4573. Weller wallpocket, attribution, leaf decoration in brown, yellow, caramel, green and tan, 6"h, mint 200-300 June 2, 1996 Sold for $325

4574. Weller Chase vase, silver overlay decoration of chase scene, aqua matt glaze ground, reads Sterling, 6.5"h, mint 150-250 June 2, 1996 Sold for $325

4575. Weller Sicard covered bowl, decoration of gray, green and gold dots, swirling blossoms and vines, deep burgundy ground, signed Sicard, 4"dia. x 3"h, mint 700-900 July 15, 1996 Sold for $750

4576. Weller Sicard hair receiver, three-footed hair receiver with blue swirl decoration, decoration of gray, green and gold dots, swirling blossoms and vines, deep burgundy ground, 5"dia. x 3.5"h, chips to base in making, mint 600-800 July 15, 1996 Sold for $800

4577. Weller Blue Louwelsa vase, cherries, 7.5", mint
1000-1500   June 6, 1999   Sold for $1000

4578. Weller Eocean vase, painted floral decoration, signed by Leffler, incised mark, 16"h, mint   1000-1500
June 6, 1999   Sold for $1300

4579. Weller Blue Louwelsa jug, cherries, 5.5"h, mint
1000-1500   June 6, 1999   Sold for $1200

Not Pictured:

4580. Weller Woodcraft mug, foxes peer out of tree trunk form in tan, brown and green, impressed mark, 6"h, mint
200-300   June 12, 1995   Sold for $325

4581. Weller Coppertone bowl and flower frog, frog sits on lily pad green and brown mottled glaze, incised marks, bowl 15.5"w x 3.5"h, mint   700-900   June 12, 1995
Sold for $475

4582. Weller Coppertone candlesticks, pair, turtles atop oval lily pads in green and brown mottled glaze, ink mark, 5"dia. x 3"h, one with base flake, one mint   300-500
June 12, 1995   Sold for $350

4583. Weller Coppertone bowl and flower frog, frog sits on lily pad, green and brown mottled glaze, incised marks, bowl 15.5"w x 3.5"h, mint   700-900   June 12, 1995
Sold for $650

4584. Weller Louwelsa pitcher, portrait of elk in brown, tan, salmon, cream, gray and green on a pink to green ground, signed A. Haubrich on side, impressed mark, 17"h, mint   900-1200   June 12, 1995   Sold for $1200

4585. Weller Louwelsa pitcher, portrait of spaniel in brown, salmon, ivory, tan and blue on a beige to green ground, signed A. Haubrich on side, impressed marks, 12.5"h, repaired chips   500-700   June 12, 1995   Sold for $475

4586. Weller Hudson vase, white dogwood blossoms with yellow centers on brown branch with green leaves on a shaded blue ground, artist's initials DL, marked, 7"h, mint 300-400 June 12, 1995 Sold for $325

4587. Weller Hudson vase, white and pale blue blossoms on swirling green, blue and pink leaves and stems on a blue to pink ground, signed Pillsbury, script mark, 9"h, mint 350-450 June 12, 1995 Sold for $700

4588. Weller Hudson vase, white dogwood blossoms with yellow centers on brown and green branch with green leaves on a shaded blue ground, script mark, 7"h, mint 300-400 June 12, 1995 Sold for $300

4589. Weller Matt vase, large blossoms in peach, tan, blue, green and brown on dark green stems and leaves against a caramel ground, impressed mark, 12.5"h, mint 400-600 June 12, 1995 Sold for $550

4590. Weller Hudson vase, yellow, brown, pink and ivory iris blossom on green stems and leaves on a blue ground, artist's initials DL, script mark, 6"h, mint 300-400 June 12, 1995 Sold for $550

4591. Weller Blue & Decorated vase, pink, white and burgundy blossoms with yellow and black centers on leaves and stems in gray/green and pale blue, impressed mark, 9.5"h, base chip 200-300 June 12, 1995 Sold for $160

4592. Lonhuda vase, angel with wings and legs crossed seated atop clouds backed by a round moon, all in shades of muted yellow, gray and black against a tobacco brown, yellow and gray ground, impressed shield mark, 300, 5.5"h, mint 800-1100 June 12, 1995 Sold for $1000

4593. Owens Utopian vase, sterling silver overlay, caramel and yellow blossoms on olive and brown stems and leaves against a dark brown to muted yellow ground, overlay in design of stylized swirling leaves and stems, impressed marks, sterling not marked, 9"h, mint 1200-1700 June 12, 1995 Sold for $1400

4594. Weller Blossom vase, pink, yellow and green, two-handled form, script mark, 8"h, mint 100-150
June 12, 1995 Sold for $80

4595. Weller Baldin vase, apples in red and yellow on brown and green ground, 5.5"h, mint 250-350
June 12, 1995 Sold for $160

4596. Weller Woodcraft vase, owl peers from hole in tree trunk, yellow/green and brown matt glaze, 13.5"h, mint 500-700 June 12, 1995 Sold for $550

4597. Weller Warwick, vase floral decoration wrapped around tree trunk body, 9"h, mint 100-200
June 12, 1995 Sold for $100

4598. Weller Baldin vase, apples in red and yellow on brown and green ground, 10.5"h, mint 500-700
June 12, 1995 Sold for $475

4599. Weller Baldin vase, apples in red and yellow on brown and green ground, 10"dia. x 6"h, mint 300-400
June 12, 1995 Sold for $270

4600. Weller Louella covered jar, daffodil in mustard and pale yellow with green leaves on a pink and black ground, 9"h, mint 250-350 June 12, 1995
Sold for $220

4601. Weller Aurelian vase, iris blossom with yellow, tan, caramel, green and brown petals on olive, yellow and brown stems and leaves on an ground of dark brown, yellow, caramel and green, incised artist's initials, impressed Weller, 10.5"h, mint 1200-1700
June 12, 1995 Sold for $1300

4602. Weller Aurelian vase, iris blossoms with yellow, tan, orange, caramel, green, teal and brown petals atop long stems and leaves of olive, green and caramel against an ground of brown, yellow, orange and green, artist signed MP, impressed mark, 17"h, minor scratches to side, hairline in bottom 1200-1700 June 12, 1995
Sold for $1000

Not Pictured:

4603. Weller Aurelian vase, iris and leaves in green against a yellow, green, caramel and brown ground, initialed by M. Hurst, incised mark, 7"h, minor scratches, mint 400-600 July 16, 1997 Sold for $280

4604. Weller Eocean vase, blossom in wine and pink with green center atop gray/green stems and leaves on a green to gray ground, incised mark, 6.5"h, mint 200-300 June 12, 1995 Sold for $220

4605. Weller Eocean vase, blossoms and buds in wine and pink atop gray/green leaves and stems on a brown, green and ivory ground, raised marks, 12"h, mint 400-600 June 12, 1995 Sold for $270

4606. Weller Eocean vase, large berries in wine and pink on thorny stems and leaves of green and gray/green against a olive, ivory and pink ground, incised script mark, 5.5"h, minute chip to side 200-300 June 12, 1995 Sold for $160

4607. Weller Eocean vase, single large blossom in wine, rose and ivory atop leaves and stems in green against a olive to pale green ground, impressed and incised marks, 6"dia. x 3"h, mint 200-300 June 12, 1995 Sold for $160

4608. Weller Etna vase, pink and white rose blossoms on thorny gray stems with dark green and ivory leaves against a gray, ivory and gray ground, impressed marks, 14"h, mint 400-600 June 12, 1995 Sold for $450

4609. Weller Etna vase, three pansies, pink and white, yellow and cream and violet, lavender and yellow, all with caramel centers against a gray to ivory ground, impressed marks, 8"dia. x 4"h, mint 200-300 June 12, 1995 Sold for $160

4610. Weller Rochelle vase, yellow, pink and caramel blossoms on leaves of green, blue and teal against a swirled ground of lavender, black, rose, pink and yellow, 8.5"h, flake at base 200-300 June 12, 1995 Sold for $275

4611. Weller Eocean vase, jonquil with wine and rose center surrounded by white petals atop leaves and stems of green and white against a green to ivory ground, 8"h, mint 200-300 June 12, 1995 Sold for $325

4612. Weller Louwelsa clock, mustard and yellow blossoms on olive stems and leaves against a shaded dark brown ground, impressed mark, 11.5"w x 4.5"d x 10"h, mint 600-800 June 12, 1995 Sold for $1200

Not Pictured:

4613. Weller Louwelsa clock, orange and green floral decoration on an orange to brown ground, signed, 12.5"w x 11"h, mint 900-1200 July 15, 1997 Sold for $1300

4614. Weller Louwelsa clock, yellow, orange and green floral decoration, 10"h, mint 700-900 June 12, 1995 Sold for $700

297

4615. Peters and Reed Chromal vase, stylized landscape in rose, blue, ivory and tan matt glaze, 7.5"h, mint 200-250   June 12, 1995   Sold for $250

4616. Weller Dickensware vase, incised scene of monk kneeling at altar in gray, yellow, blue, caramel and black against a rich chocolate brown ground, impressed marks, incised W, 11"h, mint   700-900   June 12, 1995 Sold for $1500

4617. Weller Art Nouveau vase, peach and caramel poppies with yellow and green centers against a pale peach and green ground, impressed mark, 13"h, small scratch to side   400-600   June 12, 1995   Sold for $200

4618. Weller Dickensware vase, incised Native American chief with feathered headdress and breast plate in white, cocoa, brown, yellow, pink and teal against a tan, green and brown ground, incised Ghost Bull on side, impressed marks, 7.5"h, mint   500-700   June 12, 1995 Sold for $475

4619. Owens vase, large pink, white, caramel and gray blossoms atop brown branches with broad gray/green leaves on a ivory ground, impressed mark, 20"h, crack to spout, base flakes   250-350   June 12, 1995 Sold for $240

4620. Weller vase, two Oriental woman in long robes of lavender, pale blue, white, gray/green and tan on a red clay ground, 5"h, mint   500-700   June 12, 1995 Sold for $475

4621. Weller Art Nouveau vase, light to dark green bisque finish with peach roses on slender stems in an Art Nouveau style, impressed block mark, 11"h, mint 300-500   June 12, 1995   Sold for $260

4622. Owens Henri Deux vase, stylized Art Nouveau decoration in caramel, gold and dark brown, 9.5"dia. x 6.5"h, base chips   250-350   June 12, 1995 Sold for $160

4623. Weller Sicard vase, floral design with strong pink, green, blue and purple iridescent highlights, signed at base and side, 12"h, mint   2000-2500   June 10, 1995 Sold for $2200

4624. Weller Sicard vase, floral design on a deep red ground with purple and gold highlights, no mark, 4.5"h, mint 600-800   June 10, 1995   Sold for $750

4625. Weller Glendale vase, birds and nest in treetop, yellow, blue, pink and green, ink mark, 8"h, mint   300-400   June 12, 1995   Sold for $425

4626. Weller Rosemont jardinere, blue birds among pink blossoms and pale green branches against a black ground, impressed mark, 8.5"dia. x 7"h, mint   300-400   June 12, 1995   Sold for $270

4627. Weller Glendale vase, birds and nest in treetop, caramel, pink, green and blue, ink mark, 7.5"h, hairline   150-250   June 12, 1995   Sold for $200

4628. Weller Greenbriar vase, large form covered in a gray, violet and vivid green matt glaze, 15.5"h, mint   300-500   June 12, 1995   Sold for $325

4629. Weller Rosemont vase, cockatoos in lavender, rose and ivory on black ground, 9"h, minor scratches to side   300-400   June 12, 1995   Sold for $375

4630. Weller Matt vase, school of fish swimming among bubbles and seaweed in teal matt glaze, impressed mark, 5"h, minute flakes   400-600   June 12, 1995   Sold for $250

4631. Weller Glendale vase, birds and nest in treetop, caramel, pink and green, partial paper label, 8"h, mint   300-400   June 12, 1995   Sold for $375

4632. Weller Jap Birdimal vase, geisha in brown robe with black and white floral design, blue and black sash and brown, black and white umbrella among large butterflies, dragonflies and beetles in ivory, yellow, black and caramel against a teal ground, incised Weller Rhead Faience, 7"h, repair to rim   500-700   June 12, 1995   Sold for $400

4633. Weller Jap Birdimal vase, geisha in blue, mustard, black and white hat and robe carrying black stringed instrument white daisies with yellow centers on a caramel ground, overlapping olive and white circles surrounds rim, artist's initials VMH, 5, 13"h, mint   1700-2200   June 12, 1995   Sold for $2200

4634. Weller Jap Birdimal vase, Asian girl in blue and tan with squeezebag highlights in orange and black against a green ground, artist's initials VMH, 5, 6.5"h, mint   700-900   June 12, 1995   Sold for $600

4635. Weller Lotus mug, horseshoe and blossoms in blue, orange and yellow on a green ground, impressed marks, 5.5"h, mint   250-350   June 12, 1995   Sold for $300

4636. Weller Blue and Decorated lamp, blossoms in pink, rose, white, yellow and black on green, white and black leaves against a deep blue ground impressed Weller, pottery 12"h, mint   250-350   June 12, 1995 Sold for $240

4637. Weller Dickensware vase, incised portrait of Cavalier in shades of blue against a blue ground, impressed marks, 14.5"h, mint   500-700   June 12, 1995 Sold for $650

4638. Weller LaSa vase, tall pines atop rolling ground against large, billowing clouds in an iridescent lustre glaze, 10"h, minor wear to lustre finish   250-350 June 12, 1995   Sold for $170

4639. Weller Chase vase, hunt scene in ivory on a dark blue ground, script mark, 12"h, mint   600-800 June 12, 1995   Sold for $550

4640. Weller Hudson vase, pansies in rose, pink, white and yellow with green leaves and stems on a blue to ivory ground, initialed JL, incised mark, 6"h, mint   250-350 June 12, 1995   Sold for $325

4641. Weller Woodcraft vase, tree trunk with owl looking from inside and squirrel on side, earth tones in matt glaze, 18"h, mint   900-1200   June 12, 1995 Sold for $1000

4642. Weller Woodcraft dish, fox and cubs on side, earth tones in matt glaze, 5"h, mint   250-350   June 12, 1995 Sold for $290

Not Pictured:

4643. Weller Woodcraft pitcher, three foxes, 12.5"h, minute chip to top   300-400   June 6, 1999   Sold for $400

4644. Weller Woodcraft pitcher, three fox heads on tree trunk form, 12.5"h, minor flakes   300-400   June 7, 1998 Sold for $500

4645. Weller Knifewood vase, yellow daisies and blue butterflies, impressed mark, 4.5"h, minute chip 100-150   June 12, 1995   Sold for $80

4646. Weller Knifewood jardinere, blue and yellow birds atop branches with cherries, 6"h, mint   200-300 June 12, 1995   Sold for $350

4647. Weller Hudson vase, octagonal shape, cream to lavender with white and pink dogwood decoration, impressed mark, 10"h, hairline   100-150   June 12, 1995 Sold for $80

4648. Weller Rochelle bowl, dark blue to gray around top with floral decoration and gray bottom with red highlights, 9"dia. x 3"h, mint   200-300   June 12, 1995 Sold for $140

4649. Weller Cheng Tu vase, bright orange glaze, 13"h, mint 150-250   June 12, 1995   Sold for $210

4650. Weller Hudson vase, gray to blue with colorful iris, signed by Timberlake, 9.5"h, repaired   150-250 June 12, 1995   Sold for $110

4651. Weller Rochelle candlestick, gray to black with small red and yellow floral decoration, 3"h, mint   100-150 June 12, 1995   Sold for $60

4652. Weller Brentwood vase, design of children playing among stylized trees, 6.5"h, mint   400-500 June 12, 1995   Sold for $290

4653. Weller Rhead Faience vase, carved yellow ducks with teal hats and bows on a brown ground, incised Weller Rhead Faience, 7"h, glaze flaws   500-700 June 12, 1995   Sold for $425

4654. Weller Dresden vase, light to darker blue with windmills and boats, 10.5"h, mint   300-500   June 12, 1995 Sold for $650

4655. Weller Hudson White and Decorated vase, light colors with raspberry clover decoration, 5"h, mint 100-200   June 12, 1995   Sold for $170

301

4656. Weller Novelty woodpecker flower frog, attribution, light aqua matt glaze, unmarked, 7"h, mint 100-200 June 12, 1995 Sold for $70

4657. Weller Brighton woodpecker, impressed mark, 9"h, mint 150-250 June 12, 1995 Sold for $290

4658. Weller Novelty camel, green hi-glaze, 4"h, mint 100-150 June 12, 1995 Sold for $90

4659. Weller Novelty flower frog, nude, white matt, 8.5"h, mint 100-150 June 12, 1995 Sold for $210

4660. Weller Woodcraft candle lamp, owl perched between two branches, impressed Weller, 8"w x 13.5"h, mint 400-600 June 12, 1995 Sold for $400

4661. Fulper flower frog, draped nude with green flowers around her skirt and base, vertical mark, 9"h, minute flake 250-350 June 12, 1995 Sold for $300

4662. Weller Hobart pelican, green matt glaze, script mark, 5.5"h, mint 100-150 June 12, 1995 Sold for $80

4663. Weller Brighton parrot, green, pink and yellow bird on earth tone stand, impressed block mark, 8"h, mint 200-300 June 12, 1995 Sold for $700

4664. Weller Brighton bird flower frog, attribution, colorful bird on earth tone base, unmarked, 6"h, mint 200-300 June 12, 1995 Sold for $160

4665. Weller White and Decorated Hudson vase, banded design around top in deep blue to lavender flowers and green leaves, 9"h, mint 200-300 June 12, 1995 Sold for $350

4666. Weller Hudson vase, blue with light to dark blue floral decoration and green leaves all outlined in black, artist signed MT, 7"h, minute glaze flake 300-400 June 12, 1995 Sold for $350

Not Pictured:

4667. Weller Blue and Decorated vase, black grapes and vines on a yellow, pink and pale blue wide band, dark blue ground, impressed mark, 9.5"h, mint 200-250 June 10, 1995 Sold for $200

4668. Weller Hudson vase, yellow, pink, blue, brown and lavender blossoms on pale green leaves, black berries and outlining on pink to blue ground, impressed and ink marks, 6"h, base chip 150-250 June 10, 1995 Sold for $210

4669. Weller Eocean vase, jonquil blossoms in white, pink and green on white, green and brown stems and leaves against a pale gray ground with rose highlights, impressed mark, 8.5"h, mint   300-400   June 12, 1995 Sold for $375

4670. Weller Eocean vase, berries and blossoms in wine and white on branches of green, white and rose on a green, white and pink ground, incised marks, 10"h, mint 300-400   June 12, 1995   Sold for $550

4671. Weller Eocean vase, six open handles with a bunch of grapes in purple, lavender and white backed by olive, gray/green and white grapes on green and lavender stems with large leaves on a green to ivory ground, signed Ferrell, wafer marks, 14.5"h, mint   700-900 June 12, 1995   Sold for $1700

4672. Owens Lotus vase, green and white toadstools on a white to gray ground, impressed mark, 5"h, mint 250-350   June 12, 1995   Sold for $325

4673. Weller Eocean vase, blossoms in blue, and violet with centers of orange and rose atop vertical stems and leaves of gray and green on a green to ivory ground, incised marks, 10.5"h, mint   400-600   June 12, 1995 Sold for $750

4674. Weller Louwelsa vase, in yellow and peach pansies, impressed mark, 10"h, mint   300-400   June 12, 1995 Sold for $325

4675. Weller Louwelsa vase, Native American chief with long hair, two-feathered headdress and necklace of claws and beads all in shades of brown, caramel, yellow and tan with gray/green accents, dark brown ground, artist's initials on side, impressed marks, 13"h, mint 2500-3500   June 12, 1995   Sold for $1800

Not Pictured:

4676. Weller Louwelsa vase, yellow and tan blossoms on olive, brown and caramel leaves and stems against a brown and olive ground, impressed mark, 10.5"h, mint 250-350   June 12, 1995   Sold for $300

303

4677. Weller Dickensware mug, incised Native American chief with feathers in hair and large bow at collar in brown, pink, caramel, deep teal and white, incised Fox Tail, initialed FS, impressed marks, 5.5"h, mint
400-500   June 12, 1995   Sold for $350

4678. Weller Silvertone vase, calla lilies in white and blue with caramel centers on green stems and leaves, mottled lavender and blue ground, ink mark, 12"h, mint
200-300   June 12, 1995   Sold for $325

4679. Weller White and Decorated Hudson vase, floral design in wine, cream, gray, ivory, green and blue on an ivory ground, impressed Weller, 8"h, mint
250-300   June 12, 1995   Sold for $230

4680. Weller Coppertone cigarette holder, frog on lily pad in vivid green and brown mottled glaze, 4.5"w x 4"h, mint
150-250   June 12, 1995   Sold for $425

4681. Weller Dickensware Monk vase, incised monk singing and playing a lute in brown, tan, white, black and pink on a brown and olive ground, impressed marks, incised artist's initials, 11"h, mint   500-700   June 12, 1995 Sold for $400

4682. Weller Coppertone candlesticks, turtle on lily pad in mottled green and brown glaze, ink mark, one with partial paper label, 4.5"w x 3"h, both mint   250-350
June 12, 1995   Sold for $425

4683. Weller White and Decorated Hudson vase, blossoms in wine, pink, green and gray on black branches against an ivory ground, impressed mark, 7.5"h, mint   250-350
June 12, 1995   Sold for $300

4684. Peters and Reed vase, chromal scenic in brown, blue, tan and yellow, 10"h, mint   200-300   June 12, 1995
Sold for $270

4685. Owens vase, three-handled form in matt glaze with floral decoration in peach, pink and pale blue, impressed marks, 7"h, minor flakes, scratch to side   200-300
June 12, 1995   Sold for $250

4686. Weller Flemish jardinere and pedestal, green ground with colorful floral decoration and blue parrots on top and bottom, 31"h overall, mint   1500-2500
June 12, 1995   Sold for $1900

Not Pictured:

4687. Weller Flemish jardinere and pedestal, cream with red stylized roses, 30"h, mint   500-700   June 11, 1994
Sold for $475

4688. Weller Flemish umbrella stand, earth tones with greenery and red apples, 22"h, mint   300-500
June 11, 1994   Sold for $280

4689. Weller Hudson Perfecto vase, lavender to green floral decoration with ground showing through, signed England, impressed mark, 6"h, mint   250-350 June 12, 1995   Sold for $140

4690. Weller Hudson vase, daffodils in yellow, caramel, brown and white atop green and teal stems and leaves against a blue ground, impressed Weller, 8.5"h, mint 300-500   June 12, 1995   Sold for $650

4691. Weller Hudson vase, muted yellow rose blossoms with white centers on green and white stems and leaves against a blue to cream ground, impressed mark, 7.5"h, mint   150-250   June 12, 1995   Sold for $200

4692. Weller vase, carved leaves and branches with round berries, geometric design surrounds base topped by a carved spider web all covered in a violet hi-glaze, incised Weller, 6"h, mint   400-600   June 12, 1995 Sold for $270

4693. Weller Hudson jardinere, blossoms in pink, blue, yellow, rose, ivory and black atop leaves of dark and light green against a blue to yellow ground, impressed Weller, 10"dia. x 7"h, mint   600-800   June 12, 1995 Sold for $475

4694. Weller vase, carved stylized trumpet blossoms among overlapping leaves and stems covered in a violet and aqua hi-glaze, incised mark, 4.5"h, mint   600-800 June 12, 1995   Sold for $325

4695. Weller Hudson vase, decoration of white lily of the valley blossoms with mustard yellow centers on green stems and broad leaves against a blue to cream ground, impressed mark, 7"h, mint   150-250   June 12, 1995 Sold for $200

4696. Weller Hudson vase, mustard, pink, olive, ivory, caramel, blue, lavender and brown daisies on stems and leaves of green, teal, yellow and gray against a pink, yellow and blue ground, signed Pillsbury, impressed marks, 8"h, mint   250-350   June 12, 1995 Sold for $300

4697. Weller Hudson vase, ivory water lily and buds with yellow and brown center atop gray lily pad against a light gray ground, impressed mark, 6.5"h, mint 300-400   June 12, 1995   Sold for $300

4698. Weller Aurelian vase, rose blossoms in yellow, caramel, peach and tan atop thorned stems and leaves in dark and light green, brown, olive and ivory against an abstract ground of dark brown, orange, mustard, green, yellow and caramel, signature of Hattie Mitchell '99, incised Weller Aurelian, 40"h, glaze flakes and minor base roughness   9,000-12,000   June 10, 1995 Sold for $14,000

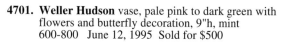

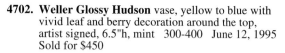

4699. Weller Hudson vase, blue, peach, yellow, ivory and pink blossoms on green and cream stems and leaves against a dark blue to pale pink ground, signed Timberlake on side, impressed Weller, 9"h, mint   300-500   June 10, 1995 Sold for $450

4700. Weller Hudson vase, clumps of violet, lavender, white, yellow and rose blossoms atop gray/green and pale green leaves, all outlined in black on a pink to pale green ground, signed Pillsbury on side, 12.5"h, mint   600-800 June 10, 1995   Sold for $650

4701. Weller Hudson vase, pale pink to dark green with flowers and butterfly decoration, 9"h, mint 600-800   June 12, 1995 Sold for $500

4702. Weller Glossy Hudson vase, yellow to blue with vivid leaf and berry decoration around the top, artist signed, 6.5"h, mint   300-400   June 12, 1995 Sold for $450

4703. Weller Sicard vase, iridescent glaze of purple, green and blue, fleur-de-lis design in green and rose, signed on side and base, 10"h, mint   1700-2200   June 10, 1995 Sold for $1500

4704. Weller Sicard vase, twisted form with four prominent ribs, deep red ground with floral design in blue, green and gold, 4.5"h, mint   600-800   June 10, 1995 Sold for $600

4705. Owens vase, hi-glaze single iris blossom in white and purple with green leaves against a ground that shades from pale green to cream, incised mark, artist signed, 8"h, mint   700-900   June 12, 1995 Sold for $500

4706. Owens vase, stylized leaf design of green against a ground shading from pale green to tan to buff, impressed mark, 7"h, mint 400-600   June 12, 1995 Sold for $325

4707. Weller Sicard vase, flaring form with iridescent glaze of floral decoration in a wide range of colors, excellent definition to glaze, signed on side, 7.5"h, mint 1200-1700   June 12, 1995   Sold for $1000

Not Pictured:

4708. Weller Sicard vase, twisted form with purple, green and blue iridescent ground behind gold and rose circular decoration, signed Weller Sicard, 5"h, mint   400-600 July 13, 1993   Sold for $600

4709. Weller Hudson vase, white and gray blossoms with rose highlights atop brown branches with green and white leaves against a blue ground, initialed HP, incised Weller, 10.5"h, mint   600-800   June 10, 1995 Sold for $650

4710. Weller Hudson vase, pink and white blossoms and buds with yellow and caramel centers on green and white branches with, curled leaves against a ground of pink to green, signed McLaughlin, impressed Weller, 13"h, mint 600-800   June 10, 1995   Sold for $500

4711. Weller Hudson vase, iris blossom and bud in yellow, ivory, pink, blue and caramel atop green stems and leaves, blue to yellow ground, signed Timberlake, impressed Weller, 10"h, mint   500-700   June 10, 1995 Sold for $800

307

4712. Weller Marvo bowl, rust floral design, 6.5"h, mint 100-150   June 11, 1994   Sold for $20

4713. Weller Chase vase, dark blue with white hunt scene, 9"h, mint   200-300   June 11, 1994   Sold for $240

4714. Weller Silvertone vase, multi-color floral vase, 8"h, mint   150-250   June 11, 1994   Sold for $190

4715. Weller Blueware vase, blue ground with light color dancing lady with floral highlights, 10.5"h, mint 200-300   June 11, 1994   Sold for $130

4716. Weller Sabrinian vase, shell design in lavender and green, 7"h, glaze chip to interior   100-200   June 11, 1994   Sold for $95

4717. Weller vase, pale aqua with silver overlay, unmarked, 9"h, mint   150-250   June 11, 1994   Sold for $300

4718. Weller Blueware jardinere, female figures on dark blue ground bordered by floral design, 7.5"h, chip to foot 200-300   June 11, 1994   Sold for $200

Not Pictured:

4719. Weller L'Art Nouveau vase, green bisque female figure in flowing gown, poppies around top, 15.5"h, mint 300-500   June 11, 1994   Sold for $650

4720. Weller L'Art Nouveau vases, two, green bisque finish with Art Nouveau women, flowers around top, 8.5"h, mint   250-350   June 11, 1994   Sold for $500

4721. Weller Sylvan jardiniere, design of fox and rabbits in brown tones, 9"dia. x 7.5"h, mint   150-250 June 11, 1994   Sold for $300

4722. Weller Forest vase, 10.5"h, mint   150-250 June 11, 1994   Sold for $100

4723. Weller Roma compote, ivory and brown, 7"d x 5"h, mint   50-100   June 11, 1994   Sold for $30

4724. Weller Baldin vase, blue with red apples, 10.25"h, mint 250-350   June 11, 1994   Sold for $525

4725. Weller Flemish jardiniere, brown and green with floral design, 7"dia. x 9"h, mint   150-250   June 11, 1994 Sold for $70

4726. Weller Woodcraft compote, brown and green with stems, leaves and fruit, 10"h, mint   150-250 June 11, 1994   Sold for $180

4727. Weller Baldin vase, brown with red apples, 6"dia. x 6"h, mint   100-200   June 11, 1994   Sold for $135

4728. Weller Sicard vase, iridescent floral design, signed, 5"h, mint 400-600 June 11, 1994 Sold for $375

4729. Weller Sicard vase, iridescent floral design, signed, 5"h, mint 500-700 June 11, 1994 Sold for $450

4730. Weller LaSa vase, landscape design, signed, 8.5"h, mint 350-550 June 11, 1994 Sold for $450

4731. Weller Sicard box, iridescent floral design, 2.5"h, damaged 400-600 June 11, 1994 Sold for $140

4732. Weller Lasa vase, landscape, 14"h, surface scratches, mint 500-700 June 11, 1994 Sold for $1100

4733. Weller Sicard vase, iridescent flower, leaf and dot design, signed Weller and Sicard, 11"h, mint 500-700 June 11, 1994 Sold for $2500

4734. Weller Sicard vase, iridescent floral decoration, signed, 6.5"h, mint 500-700 June 11, 1994 Sold for $475

4735. Weller LaSa bud vase, landscape design, signed, 6.5"h, mint 250-350 June 11, 1994 Sold for $150

4736. RV Velmoss Schroll vase, white with red and green stylized floral decoration, 6"h, mint 100-150 June 11, 1994 Sold for $105

4737. Weller Lotus jardinere, green matt with leaf design, 6.5"dia., mint 150-250 June 11, 1994 Sold for $220

4738. Weller Dickensware ewer, 2nd line, carved mermaids on green to blue ground, 11"h, mint 300-500 June 11, 1994 Sold for $550

4739. RV Egypto vase, green matt, 9"h, mint 300-500 June 11, 1994 Sold for $400

4740. Weller Floretta ewer, matt green and purple, 10.5"h, mint 300-400 June 11, 1994 Sold for $220

4741. Weller Dickensware I jardinere, green hi-glaze with yellow floral, 8"dia. x 6.5"h, mint 250-350 June 11, 1994 Sold for $160

4742. RV Gold Trace candleholder, cream with green and purple decoration, 9"h, mint 150-250 June 11, 1994 Sold for $170

309

4743. **Weller Marvo** vase, molded leaf and berry design covered in a tan to green matt glaze, unmarked, 8.5"h, hairline   50-100   July 13, 1994   Sold for $30

4744. **Weller Woodcraft** vase, squirrel on trunk and the owl looking out, 18"h, mint   600-800   July 13, 1994 Sold for $1200

4745. **Weller Baldin** vase, bulbous shape with apples, 11"h, two minute flakes   250-350   July 13, 1994 Sold for $250

4746. **Weller Flemish** vase, artist signed, 18"h, mint   250-350 July 13, 1994   Sold for $375

4747. **Weller Forest** vase, scene in earth tones with blue in water and sky, 8"h, tiny flake on foot   50-100 July 13, 1994   Sold for $80

Not Pictured:

4748. **Weller Burntwood** jardinere, cream and dark brown with etched design of birds flying over waves, 10"dia. x 9"h, mint   150-250   June 11, 1994   Sold for $275

4749. **Weller Coppertone** vase, open handles, 6.5" x 8.5", mint   200-300   July 10, 1994   Sold for $325

4750. **Weller Selma** vase, with peacocks, impressed mark, 12", mint   250-350   July 10, 1994   Sold for $375

4751. **Weller Coppertone** vase, closed handles, 6.5" x 9", mint   250-350   July 10, 1994   Sold for $425

4752. **Weller Blue and Decorated** vase, blue jay in blue, pink, rose, black and white perched on a brown branch surrounded by narrow leaves of green, yellow and pink on a blue matt ground, impressed Weller, 13.5"h, several tiny flakes   July 13, 1994   Sold for $700

4753. **Weller** vase, branch handle, brown and green branches are molded onto body and support green and pink leaves and red and yellow blossoms, artist signed D. England, kiln mark, 12"h, mint   900-1200   July 13, 1994 Sold for $1100

4754. Weller Hudson Perfecto vase, lavender to green with
outlined floral decoration, signed England, impressed
mark, 6"h, mint   250-350   July 13, 1994   Sold for $200

4755. Weller Blue and Decorated vase, blue ground with
gray to pink around top, slip floral in blue, pink and
yellow with dark green branches and leaves, impressed
mark, 9"h, mint   200-300   July 13, 1994   Sold for $275

4756. Weller Hudson vase, white and gray roses with pale
green leaves and centers on a gray to green to cream
ground, impressed mark, 7"h, mint   150-250
July 13, 1994   Sold for $220

4757. Weller Hudson vase, blue to yellow ground with light
and dark blue and pink flowers, green leaves, signed
McLaughlin, Weller mark, 12"h, mint   600-800
July 13, 1994   Sold for $900

4758. Weller vase, yellow centered white and black flowers
with gray, impressed mark, 6.5"h, mint   300-500
July 13, 1994   Sold for $475

4749. Weller Hudson vase, blue and pink floral with green
leaves and vines, unmarked, 7"h, hairline   100-200
July 13, 1994   Sold for $140

Not Pictured:

4750. Weller Blueware jardinere, blue ground with winged
figures and floral decoration in ivory, 10"dia., two small
flakes   300-500   June 11, 1994   Sold for $450

4751. Weller Matt vase, carved blue butterflies and flower
blossoms surrounded by green leaves, blue ground,
impressed Weller, 12"h, mint   800-1100   July 13, 1994
Sold for $850

4752. Radford Thera vase, pink and lavender blossoms with
yellow centers on brown branches with green, brown
and white leaves on a matt green ground, 12.5"h, mint
700-900   July 13, 1994   Sold for $350

4753. Weller Dickensware vase, bisque finish in brown and green with incised portrait of Ghost Bull, impressed mark, 9.5"h, mint 700-900
July 13, 1994 Sold for $475

4754. Weller Dickensware Turk tobacco jar, incised Dickens Weller on lid, 7.5"h, mint 500-700 July 13, 1994 Sold for $425

4755. Weller Dickensware Chinaman tobacco jar, impressed Dickens Weller on lid, 6"h, hairline crack in front 300-500 July 13, 1994 Sold for $240

4756. Weller Dickensware Captain tobacco jar, incised Dickens Weller on lid, 6.5"h, mint 500-700
July 13, 1994 Sold for $600

4757. Weller Dickensware Irishman tobacco jar, blue-green bisque finish with brown, lid incised Dickens Weller, 6"w x 6"h, repaired chip on lid 500-700 July 13, 1994 Sold for $300

4758. Weller Dickensware vase, green to brown background with incised deer with antlers, artist initials, impressed Weller Dickensware, 6.5"h, unchipped chip on handle 300-500 July 13, 1994 Sold for $140

4759. Weller Lustre vase, mirror glaze with purple, green and gold highlights, unmarked, 8.5"h, mint 100-200
July 13, 1994 Sold for $120

4760. Weller Sicard vase, flowers in purple, blue and green, Weller Sicard signature, 8.5"h, mint 800-1100
July 13, 1994 Sold for $1000

4761. Weller Sicard vase, dark iridescent green, purple and blue highlights with gold, unsigned, 9"h, mint 800-1100 July 13, 1994 Sold for $650

4762. Weller Sicard vase, bud vase, deep green with purple and gold highlights, golden berry and leaf decoration, signed Weller Sicard, 7"h, mint 500-700
July 13, 1994 Sold for $475

4763. Weller Lamar vase, landscape with mountains in the background, trees in the foreground, light and dark pink with metallic gray, unmarked, 8"h, some wear, mint 250-350 July 13, 1994 Sold for $200

4764. Weller Lasa bud vase, landscape in brilliant metallic colors, signed Weller Lasa on side, x'd on bottom, 7.5"h, mint 250-450 July 13, 1994 Sold for $375

4765. Weller Dickensware vase, green to brown with etched female golfer, impressed Weller Dickensware, 7.5"h, mint 600-800 July 13, 1994 Sold for $900

4766. Weller Dickensware vase, green ground with brown behind incised portrait of gentleman with white hat, vine with dark red flowers on each side, impressed mark, 10.5"h, mint 500-700 July 13, 1994 Sold for $325

4767. Weller Dickensware vase, green, yellow to lavender bisque ground with incised portrait of monk, impressed mark and raised, 13"h, mint 600-800 July 13, 1994 Sold for $450

4768. Weller Dickensware pitcher, etched Dutch lady with milk pails and cow in foreground, grassy landscape etched overall and windmills in the background, green bisque background, signature of C.A. Busenbery, impressed Weller, 12.5"h, restored handle 300-500 July 13, 1994 Sold for $450

4769. Weller Dickensware vase, green to brown background with etched female golfer, #855, 7.5"h, mint 600-800 July 13, 1994 Sold for $900

4770. Weller Dickensware II mug, incised and painted in blue with fish and fish handle, 5"h, mint 200-300 July 13, 1994 Sold for $200

4771. Weller Dickensware vase, incised portrait of monk with bottle in one hand and glass in the other, impressed mark, 6.5"h, mint 400-600 July 13, 1994 Sold for $250

4772. Weller Dickensware vase, incised Dutch girl in blue dress with white hat, shiny flower and vine design running down sides, impressed marks and 8"h, chips to top 300-500 July 13, 1994 Sold for $250

4773. Weller Dickensware II jug, incised and painted with Indian in headdress, marked Blue Hawk, 6"h, mint 700-900 July 13, 1994 Sold for $450

4774. Weller Dickensware II mug, incised and painted with monk drinking ale, 6"h, mint 250-350 July 13, 1994 Sold for $140

Not Pictured:

4775. Weller Dickensware vase, incised decoration of monk, blue to yellow and brown ground, 7.5"h, mint 300-500 June 12, 1995 Sold for $220

4776. RV Rozane Aztec pitcher, light blue with squeezebag decoration, unmarked, 5.5", mint 300-500
July 13, 1994 Sold for $260

4777. Weller Dickensware vase, yellow/brown ground with incised stylized design in a dark brown outlined in orange, impressed Dickensware Weller, 10.5"h, mint 300-500 July 13, 1994 Sold for $275

4778. RV Rozane vase, standard glaze with decoration of carnations, Rozane RPCo. mark, 9.5"h, mint 150-250
July 13, 1994 Sold for $170

4779. Weller Crocus vase, green ground with blue floral decoration with yellow beaded highlights and green leaves in an Art Nouveau design, unmarked, 9.5"h, chip to bottom 300-400 July 13, 1994 Sold for $275

4780. RV Rozane vase, standard glaze with crocus decoration, Rozane Ware wafer mark, 6"h, mint 150-250
July 13, 1994 Sold for $170

4781. Weller LaSa vase, iridescent ground with poppy and pods and trailing vines over striped band all in golden tones, unmarked, 9"h, some wear, mint 250-350
July 13, 1994 Sold for $325

4782. Weller Sicard vase, iridescent green to purple ground with gold and green circles over body, unsigned, impressed mark on bottom, 4.5"h, mint 400-600
July 13, 1994 Sold for $325

4783. Weller Perfecto vase, cream with blue top and bottom with watercolor style painted decoration of purple and green berries with orange and pink leaves all outlined in black, impressed mark, 6"dia. x 6"h, mint 500-700
July 13, 1994 Sold for $400

4784. Weller Dickensware vase, carved and painted portrait of Indian with headdress in white, light blue, brown and orange on brown and green ground, artist signed J. Daugherty, incised name of Indian "Ghost Bull", impressed mark, 8.5"h, mint 900-1200
July 13, 1994 Sold for $1100

4785. Owens vase, black, brown, white and gray kitten with green eyes and pink nose on a dark brown, golden brown and gray ground, marked J.B. Owens, 8"h, mint 2000-3000
July 13, 1994 Sold for $2800

4786. C.B. Upjohn dish, advertising item for the Y Bridge in Zanesville, red clay with raised scene of bridge at sunset and inscription, impressed C.B. Upjohn, 4.5"dia., mint 50-100   July 13, 1994 Sold for $80

4787. Weller vase, pink and blue vertical leaves and stems, black matt ground, script signature, 6"h, mint   300-500 July 13, 1994 Sold for $260

4788. Weller Matt Louwelsa vase, gray matt glaze with three circles of incised floral design in white and pink, impressed mark, 4.5"h, mint   250-350   July 13, 1994 Sold for $350

4789. Weller vase, gunmetal bisque finish with enameled floral in orange to yellow and pink, impressed mark, 6.5"h, mint   500-700   July 13, 1994 Sold for $475

4790. Weller Jap Birdimal creamer, green hi-glaze with cream squeeze bag quote, unmarked, 4"h, mint 200-300   July 13, 1994 Sold for $260

4791. Weller Lessell vase, landscape design of golden lustre trees, mountains and foreground trimmed in white, pale yellow water and sky, signed Lessell, 6"h, mint 250-350   July 13, 1994 Sold for $230

4792. Weller Lessell lamp base, landscape of golden trees, mountain and foreground trimmed in white, deep cream water and sky with black highlights, signed Lessell, 8"h, mint   200-300   July 13, 1994 Sold for $200

Not Pictured:

4793. Weller Matt Louwelsa vase, pink grapes with green leaves on beige and green stems, artist signed M. Lybarger, ground of light green to beige, 14"h, mint 800-1100   July 13, 1993 Sold for $750

4794. Weller Lessell vase, metallic glaze with trees and clouds above mountain range, painted signature, minor scratches, 8"h, mint   600-800   July 14, 1998 Sold for $600

4795. Weller Sicard vase, leaf and berry design in purple and green, signed on side, 7.5"h, mint   700-900 June 10, 1995 Sold for $850

4796. Weller Sicard vase, floral design with iridescent glaze, twisted handles at top, signed Sicard Weller, 5"h, mint 600-800   June 10, 1995   Sold for $600

Not Pictured:

4797. Weller Sicard vase, three lobe form, impressed mark, signed Sicard, 4"h, mint   600-800   July 14, 1998 Sold for $1000

4798. Weller Sicard vase, four-sided form, floral decoration in gold, purple and rose, signed Weller Sicard, 5.5"h, mint 550-750   July 14, 1998 Sold for $500

4799. Weller Sicard vase, twisted form with floral decoration in gold, green and blue, gold, blue and purple, signed Weller Sicard, 12"h, mint   1500-2500   July 14, 1998 Sold for $1900

4800. Weller Etna pitcher, hi-glaze, red clover decoration with green leaves on a dark to light gray ground, impressed block mark, 7"h, mint 100-150 July 13, 1994 Sold for $120

4801. Weller Jap Birdimal vase, squeezebag decoration of three fish in blue, black and white against a gray/green ground, impressed mark, artist's initials LS, 6"h, mint 700-900 July 13, 1994 Sold for $850

4802. Weller Eocean vase, pansies in pink, gray and white with brown and yellow centers on a dark to pale gray ground, incised Eocean Weller, artist's signature L.J. Burgess, 10.5" mint 500-700 July 13, 1994 Sold for $350

4803. Owens Lotus vase, white and pink blooms, gray and green stems and leaves on a pale gray to white ground, artist signature, script Owens, 10.5"h, repair to lip 200-300 July 13, 1994 Sold for $200

4804. Owens Lotus vase, white and gray toadstools on a ground of brilliant lavender to gray, impressed Owens Lotus, 7.5"dia. x 5"h, mint 400-600 July 13, 1994 Sold for $350

4805. Weller Jap Birdimal vase, green hi-glaze with painted white goose in flight, 9.5"h, mint 600-800 July 13, 1994 Sold for $650

Not Pictured:

4806. Weller Eocean vase, purple and white iris with green leaves, incised mark, 10"h, mint 500-700 July 13, 1993 Sold for $700

4807. Weller Eocean vase with pansy decoration, red, white and yellow on dark green to white ground, 8", hairline at rim 100-150 July 18, 1990 Sold for $200

4808. Weller Eocean vase, burgundy cherries, cylindrical form, 16", mint 600-800 July 18, 1990 Sold for $450

4809. Weller Eocean vase, two white, rose, pink and lavender storks with red/brown beaks and legs in preparation for landing, ground of dark to light gray to a creamy lavender, signed Chilcote, Eocean Weller in script, 10.5"h, mint 2000-3000 July 13, 1994 Sold for $3000

4810. Weller Rochelle vase, pink and lavender flowers with green and yellow leaves on a black, gray and green to cream ground, impressed mark, 7"h, mint   75-150 July 13, 1994 Sold for $200

4811. Weller Floretta vase, pink flower with green stem on a light to dark gray ground, impressed mark, 5.5"h, mint 75-150   July 13, 1994 Sold for $100

4812. Weller Rochelle candlestick, pink, red, white and yellow flowers with black and gray against a black, green, yellow and pink bottom, unmarked, 12"h, mint 150-250   July 13, 1994 Sold for $150

4813. Weller Etna vase, red flowers with yellow centers and stems on a dark to lighter gray ground with pink around bottom, impressed marks, 4.5"h, mint   100-200 July 13, 1994 Sold for $250

4814. Weller Etna vase, pink roses and green stems on gray ground, unsigned, 13"h, mint   600-800   July 13, 1994 Sold for $375

4815. Weller Etna vase, pink thistles with gray pods and stems on light to dark gray ground, impressed mark, 8.5"h, mint   150-250   July 13, 1994 Sold for $170

4816. Weller Etna vase, , pink and white grapes with green stems on light to dark gray ground, impressed signature, 6"h, mint   150-250   July 13, 1994 Sold for $140

Not Pictured:

4817. Weller Etna vase, rose decoration with pink petals on green stems and leaves against a gray to white to lavender ground, 12"h, mint   600-800   July 13, 1993 Sold for $375

4818. Weller Jap Birdimal vase, Geisha in robe holding parasol, butterflies flying over head and encircle the vase, white and yellow flowers are on the ground above green, artist's initials incised Weller Rhead Faience, 13"h, mint 1500-2500   July 13, 1994 Sold for $2800

4819. RV Rozane Woodland vase, gray/beige ground in bisque finish with incised and hi-glaze mistletoe decoration of green and white, wafer mark, 8.5"h, restored base   500-700   July 13, 1994 Sold for $300

4820. Weller Art Nouveau vase, orange poppies with green stems and swirling leaves on a tan ground, impressed signature, 9.5"h, mint   250-350   July 13, 1994 Sold for $325

4821. Owens Utopian matt vase, tan, brown and white blossoms with green, white and pale green leaves and stems on a ground of brown, orange and green, impressed J.B. Owens, impressed artist's initials DH, 3.5"h, mint   200-300   July 13, 1994 Sold for $150

4822. RV Rozane Woodland vase, cream bisque ground, incised floral in each section in hi-glaze yellow and brown, wafer mark, 10.5"h, mint   800-1100 July 13, 1994 Sold for $950

4823. Weller Art Nouveau vase, green bisque finish with applied frog on top with banded design of peach flowers, impressed mark, 4"h, small chip   150-250 July 13, 1994 Sold for $350

4824. Weller Art Nouveau vase, green bisque finish with peach roses with slender stems, impressed block mark, 11"h, mint   300-500   July 13, 1994 Sold for $200

4825. RV Rozane Woodland bud vase, bisque finish with orange and brown mums with pale green leaves, wafer mark, 8"h, glaze flake to top   700-900   July 13, 1994 Sold for $600

4826. Owens vase, iris blossoms and leaves in white, blue and tan matt on a ground of blue to gray, unmarked, 8.5"dia. x 13"h, mint   400-600 July 13, 1994   Sold for $750

4827. Owens Utopian vase, brown, orange to yellow ground with large orange and green poppy decoration, impressed mark, 13"h, mint 300-500   July 13, 1994   Sold for $400

4828. RV Rozane Woodland vase, orange and brown floral decoration, wafer mark, 8.5"h, restored bottom 600-800   July 13, 1994   Sold for $300

4829. RV Rozane Woodland vase, orange and brown floral decoration against beige cork style ground, wafer mark, 6.5"h, glaze rub at base   300-500   July 13, 1994 Sold for $225

4830. Weller Matt vase, stylized design of green and blue leaves, impressed Weller, 12"h, mint   800-1100 July 13, 1994   Sold for $1000

4831. Weller Art Nouveau vase, light to dark green bisque finish with orange flowers at top, 13.5"h, mint   500-700 July 13, 1994   Sold for $750

4832. Owens Matt vase, floral design in cocoa and cream with gray/green leaves on a green and brown ground, artist signed, impressed mark, 4.5"h, mint   150-200 July 13, 1994   Sold for $250

4833. RV Rozane Woodland vase, leaf decoration in dark brown, orange to yellow against a beige cork style ground, wafer mark, 10.5"h, small flake to side 700-900   July 13, 1994   Sold for $475

4834. Owens Utopian matt vase, carved and painted profile of woman with swirling hair in pale pink, cocoa, medium brown and white on a beige ground, impressed Utopian Owens, 6"h, mint   1000-1500   July 13, 1994 Sold for $1400

4835. Weller Louwelsa vase, grapes in blue, yellow and orange with green and orange leaves and branches against a dark orange to brown ground, artist signed J. Imlay, 9"dia. x 15.5"h, mint   1000-1500   July 13, 1994 Sold for $850

4836. Weller Louwelsa vase, silver overlay, light and dark orange rose decoration on a bright orange to dark brown ground framed in silver overlay with shield on reverse for monogram, impressed mark, artist signature covered by silver, 10"h, mint   1500-2500   July 13, 1994 Sold for $1500

Not Pictured:

4837. Weller Louwelsa vase, three swallows in flight, three handles, marked, signed Abel, 4.5"h, mint; with a **Owens** mug, standard glaze, yellow flowers, marked, 5"h, hairline   300-400   July 13, 1998 Sold for $425

4838. Weller vase, raised gray, white and blue jewels hanging from yellow band around top, impressed mark, 5.5"h, mint 100-150 July 13, 1994 Sold for $160

4839. Weller Eocean vase, scene of man with couple behind bar, two medallions of dark blue with white bust of man and name David Copperfield, ground is dark to light green with, raised Weller mark 12"h, top missing, mint 700-900 July 13, 1994 Sold for $600

4840. Weller Jap Birdimal pitcher, green/blue ground with blue leaves and trees with squeezebag outlining, painted Rhead on bottom, 4"h, mint 200-300 July 13, 1994 Sold for $700

4841. Weller Turada bowl, orange and blue floral decoration, impressed Weller, 4.5"dia. x 2.5"h, mint 200-300 July 13, 1994 Sold for $150

4842. Weller Jap Birdimal mug, blue ground with dark blue landscape with windmills, painted Rhead on bottom, 3.5"h, mint 200-300 July 13, 1994 Sold for $325

4843. Weller Jap Birdimal pitcher, blue with stylized white squeezebag floral decoration, signed LP, Weller block mark, 11"h, chip to spout and lid missing 400-600 July 13, 1994 Sold for $200

4844. Owens Lotus vase, light and dark gray mushrooms on a light to dark gray ground, impressed mark, 3"h, mint 200-300 July 13, 1994 Sold for $210

4845. Weller Eocean vase, white flowers with green and pink leaves on a light green ground, hi-glaze, artist signed L.J.B., script Eocean Weller, 6"h, mint 200-300 July 13, 1994 Sold for $450

4846. Owens Lotus vase, violet, lavender, yellow and white iris blossoms atop gray/green leaves and stems on a light gray to white ground, artist signature, script Owens, 7.5"h, mint 900-1200 July 13, 1994 Sold for $700

4847. Weller Eocean vase, pale pink, rose and gray toadstools, ground of dark gray to cream, script Eocean Weller, 5"h, mint 300-400 July 13, 1994 Sold for $400

4848. Weller Etna vase, molded frog at shoulder covered in a gray, to lavender to white hi-glaze, incised Etna, impressed Weller, 4"h, mint 200-300 July 13, 1994 Sold for $500

Not Pictured:

4849. Weller Eocean vase, pink clover blossoms with green leaves against a green to pink ground, decorated by Charles Fouts, incised marks, 9.5"h, mint 350-550 July 16, 1997 Sold for $400

4850. Weller Lustre vase, cranberry glaze with metallic luster, black Weller stamp, 6"h, mint 150-250 July 13, 1994 Sold for $90

4851. Weller Sicard vase, silver swirl design with fuchsia design and some crystal effects, signed Sicardo, 8"h, mint 600-800 July 13, 1994 Sold for $650

4852. Weller LaSa vase, forest landscape in iridescent glaze, 10"h, mint 600-800 July 13, 1994 Sold for $300

4853. Weller Sicard vase, lustrous silver/pink hues, signed Sicardo, 8"h, mint 400-600 July 13, 1994 Sold for $450

4854. Weller Sicard bowl, Art Nouveau molded design in vibrant floral colors, signed Sicardo, 4"dia. x 8"h, mint 800-1100 July 213, 1994 Sold for $600

4855. Weller LaSa vase, ocean landscape with mountains and palm trees, iridescent glaze, 5"h, mint 300-500 July 13, 1994 Sold for $400

4856. Weller Sicard vase, floral design, signature on side, blue, silver and red iridescent glaze, 7"h, mint 700-900 July 13, 1994 Sold for $500

4857. Weller Sicard vase, stylized blossoms, leaves and stems in iridescent purple, blue and green, script Weller Sicardo, 9"h, mint 800-1100 July 13, 1994 Sold for $650

4858. Weller Sicard vase, tapered, ribbed form, stylized stems and leaves surrounded by tiny dots in green and pink iridescence on a deep purple iridescent ground, signed Weller Sicardo, 7.5"h, mint 1500-2000 July 13, 1994 Sold for $1800

4859. Weller Sicard vase, stylized green and pink iridescent blossoms and stems, ground of iridescent blue, purple and rose, signed Weller Sicardo, 9"h, mint 1200-1700 July 13, 1994 Sold for $2200

4860. Weller Sicard vase, wide form decorated cyclamen design, signature on side, blue, silver and red iridescent glaze, 7"h, mint 700-900 July 13, 1994 Sold for $600

4861. Weller Etna vase, floral on gray to white ground, 7"h, mint 100-200 July 13, 1994 Sold for $120

4862. Weller Eocean Rose vase, roses and stems over front and side, signed by Wm. Stemm,, 13"h, mint 500-700 July 13, 1994 Sold for $900

4863. Weller Eocean vase, white, black, green and pink fish under white swirls of water, gray, green sea grasses, artist initials ER, impressed Weller, 8"h, mint 800-1100 July 13, 1994 Sold for $1100

4864. Weller Eocean vase, burgundy, lavender and pink blossoms with yellow centers, green leaves on a lavender ground, incised script Weller, 10"h, mint 600-800 July 13, 1994 Sold for $400

4865. Weller Eocean vase, gray, pink and rose toadstools on a gray, brown to cream ground, script signature Eocean Weller, 5.5"h, mint 400-600 July 13, 1994 Sold for $325

4866. Weller Etna vase, floral decoration, white to gray ground, 6"h, mint 100-200 July 13, 1994 Sold for $130

Not Pictured:

4867. Weller Eocean vase, with red nasturtiums, signed A. Haubrich, 17"h, mint 500-750 July 18, 1990 Sold for $750

4868. Weller Eocean vase, lavender to blue ground with pink lilies, signed A. Haubrich, 17"h, mint 500-750 July 18, 1990 Sold for $650

4869. Weller Sicard vase, floral decoration in an iridescent glaze, red, blue and green tones with platinum high-lights, signed on side and bottom, 11"h, mint 3000-4000 June 10, 1995 Sold for $2400

Not Pictured:

4870. Weller Sicard vase, cylindrical form with gold and silver iris decoration against a rose ground, signed Weller Sicard, 10"h, minute bruise on bottom edge 700-900 July 13, 1993 Sold for $1200

4871. Weller Sicard covered vessel, four-lobed form with a floral decoration in gold, green and blue iridescence against a purple, rose, gold and green ground, signed Sicard Weller, 9"w x 5.5"h, restored chip to lid 700-900 July 13, 1993 Sold for $800

4872. Weller Dickensware vase, etched design of male golfer, impressed mark, 10"h, minor flake to bottom 900-1200   July 13, 1994   Sold for $1400

4873. Weller Hudson vase, of blue blossoms with yellow, white and brown centers on green leaves and stems on a gray to lavender ground, initialed by Pillsbury, script mark, 6"h, mint   250-350   July 13, 1994
Sold for $290

4874. Weller Hudson vase, of yellow, orange, cream, lavender and blue iris blossoms atop stems and leaves of green and blue on a gray to beige ground, artist signed, impressed mark, paper label, 15"h, mint   1500-2000
July 13, 1994   Sold for $1600

4875. Weller Hudson vase, white lilies with pink, yellow and green centers on vertical stems and leaves of green and white on a gray to lavender ground, initialed by Pillsbury, script mark, 10"h, mint   400-600
July 13, 1994   Sold for $700

4876. Weller Louwelsa ewer, form, standard glaze with floral decoration, artist signed, no mark, 10"h, mint   150-250
July 13, 1994   Sold for $250

4877. Weller Louwelsa vase, orange poppies in light to dark orange and green stems and leaves wrapping around one side of front and over opposite side, against green, orange to dark standard glaze, artist signed C Leffler, 12"dia. x 20"h, mint   1200-1700   July 13, 1994
Sold for $1900

4878. **Weller Frosted Matt** vase, volcanic type glaze of light gray and black, iridescent highlights, 12.5"h, mint 300-500   July 10, 1994   Sold for $210

4879. **Weller Hudson** vase, white and gray decorated with yellow daffodils, 12.5"h, mint   400-600   July 10, 1994   Sold for $325

4880. **Weller Dickensware** vase, incised scene with lady in field of flowers in the foreground, mountains and buildings in background, brown, green, orange and yellow, impressed mark, 17"h, drill hole, glaze flakes 600-800   July 10, 1994   Sold for $550

4881. **RV Rozane Woodland** vase, cream bisque finish, wafer mark, 11"h, small chip repair   600-800   July 10, 1994   Sold for $275

4882. **Weller Louwelsa** pitcher, purple grapes, green leaves and orange stems, signed Ferrell, 16.5"h, restored 200-300   July 10, 1994   Sold for $210

4883. **Weller Louwelsa** vase, orange and yellow mums with slender green and yellow stems, ground shades from dark brown, orange to green, signed A. Haubrich on side, impressed circular mark, 16"h, mint   1000-1500 July 13, 1994   Sold for $1500

Not Pictured:

4884. **Weller Louwelsa** vase, brown hi-glaze, wild roses, impressed mark, artist signed Mae Timberlake, 9.5"h, minor bruise to lip   200-300   June 7, 1998 Sold for $270

4885. **Weller Louwelsa** vase, brown glaze with poppies, 10.5"h, mint   150-250   July 13, 1998 Sold for $300

4886. **Weller Louwelsa** umbrella stand, yellow and brown daffodils, impressed Maril, 20"h, mint   400-600 July 13, 1993   Sold for $550

4887. **Weller Louwelsa** bowl, orange flowers and green leaves and stems on mahogany and green ground, artist's initials T.S., 8"dia. x 4"h, mint   250-350   July 13, 1993 Sold for $325

4888. Weller Hudson vase, pink and yellow flowers and green leaves on pale pink to green ground, artist signed Hood, impressed mark, 7"h, mint   250-350   July 10, 1994   Sold for $300

4889. Weller Blue & Decorated vase, blue, white, yellow and pink sprays of wild flowers with green leaves against a blue ground and pink rim, impressed mark, 11"h, mint   200-300   July 10, 1994   Sold for $290

4890. Weller Hudson vase, pink, blue and yellow iris blossom on yellow and green vertical leaves and stems on a blue and pale yellow ground, signed McLaughlin, black circular ink mark, 8.5"h, mint   400-600   July 10, 1994   Sold for $700

4891. Weller Hudson vase, of rose, pink and yellow buds and green stems against a dark blue to light blue ground, impressed mark, 7"h, mint   250-350   July 10, 1994   Sold for $375

4892. Weller Hudson Perfecto vase, floral under matt glaze , signed by Dorothy England, 6.5"h, minute flake on base   250-350   July 10, 1994   Sold for $300

4893. Weller Hudson vase, roses in yellow and white with green leaves and yellow stems on light blue and green ground, artist signed Pillsbury, stamp mark, 8"h, mint   300-400   July 10, 1994   Sold for $500

4894. Weller Aurelian vase, yellow, brown, green and orange birds on an abstract ground of dark brown, orange, yellow, tan and green, signed Ed Abel, incised Aurelian, impressed Weller, 11"h, mint   1200-1700   July 13, 1994   Sold for $1400

Not Pictured:

4895. Weller Aurelian charger, spaniel dog with collar, olive green ground, signed A. Haubrich, dated 1900, unmarked, 13"dia., scratch and chip on back   2000-3000   July 13, 1993   Sold for $1600

4896. Weller Hudson vase, lavender, pink, blue, white and black iris blossoms with tan centers on blue and green vertical leaves and stems, artist signed, impressed Weller, 8.5"h, mint 400-600 July 13, 1994 Sold for $425

4897. Weller White and Decorated Hudson vase, white and blue floral decoration, 10"h, mint 200-300 July 13, 1994 Sold for $240

4898. Weller Hudson vase, crocus flowers, signed by Dorothy England, 7.5"h, mint 300-500 July 13, 1994 Sold for $350

4899. J.B. Owens Utopian vase, dark brown bisque body with light green to orange highlights, orange and brown roses with green and brown leaves, artist signed S.T. impressed marks, 10.5"h, mint 200-300 July 13, 1994 Sold for $220

4900. Weller Blue and Decorated Hudson vase, floral decoration on blue ground, 8"h, mint 150-250 July 13, 1994 Sold for $170

4901. Weller Hudson Light vase, cream background with decoration of lavender Arts and Crafts style roses with green leaves draped around bottom section, impressed Weller, 6"h, mint 250-350 July 13, 1994 Sold for $375

4902. Weller Hudson vase, white, tan, gray, yellow and rust brown daisies and buds on vertical leaves and stems of gray, green and black on a pale blue to cream ground, artist signed, paper label, impressed Weller, 11"h, mint 600-800 July 13, 1994 Sold for $900

4903. Weller Hudson vase, pink, white, pale blue, rose, black and green blossoms with pale yellow centers against leaves of blue, green, yellow, black and white, on pink and brown stems, on a green and blue ground, artist signed, script mark, 12"h, small area of discolored crazing on back, mint 700-900 July 13, 1994 Sold for $850

4904. Weller Hudson vase, dogwood blossoms and buds in white, pink, yellow and rust on light gray and cream branches, with blue, green and gray leaves outlined in black on a ground of blue/gray, artist signed, paper label, impressed Weller, 13"h, mint 600-800 July 13,1994 Sold for $700

4905. Weller Aurelian vase, grapes and vines, ground with brown, orange, yellow and green, impressed signature, 11"h, minor flakes to top   600-800   July 10, 1994   Sold for $425

4906. Weller Aurelian jardinere, yellow and brown roses with green leaves, brown and green stems, ground in dark brown, orange, yellow and green, incised mark, 8.5"dia. x 7.5"h, mint   500-750   July 10, 1994   Sold for $200

4907. Weller Aurelian pitcher, orange and brown raspberries on green and brown stems and leaves on an dark brown, rust and yellow ground, artist initialed by Elizabeth Blake, incised mark, 11, 5"h, mint   200-300   July 10, 1994   Sold for $375

4908. Weller Aurelian vase, green iris and long leaves on an abstract ground of dark brown, carmel, yellow and light green, signed Madge Hurst, incised mark, K, #557, 3, 7"h, several flakes, minor scratches   400-600   July 10, 1994   Sold for $300

4909. RV Rozane vase, portrait of hunting dog with bird in mouth, artist signed, impressed mark, 11"dia. x 9"h, mint   1200-1700   July 13, 1994   Sold for $1000

4910. Owens Utopian vase, yellow and orange daffodil decoration with green leaves against a orange, green to brown ground, artist signature, impressed mark, 11"h, some glaze scratches but mint   250-350   July 13, 1994   Sold for $200

4911. Weller Louwelsa mug, portrait of monk, impressed mark, 6"h, some green glaze on portrait, mint   300-500   July 13, 1994   Sold for $220

Not Pictured:

4912. Weller Louwelsa jardiniere, rust and caramel blossoms atop green stems and green and white leaves, impressed mark, 12"dia. x 10"h, mint   250-350   July 17, 1996   Sold for $600

4913. Cambridge vase, poppies with yellow and carmel blossoms with dark brown and green centers on twisted stems of brown and pale green on a brown, carmel and deep mustard ground, artist signed by A. Williams, impressed Cambridge, 24"h, some minor chips 2000-3000 July 13, 1994 Sold for $1400

4914. Weller Hudson chandelier, matt glaze decoration of rose blossoms atop long thorny stems with curling leaves in rich caramel, cream and tan against a muted peach ground, impressed marks, 18"dia. x 6"h, excellent condition 1200-1700 June 12, 1995 Sold for $550

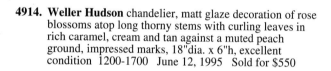

4915. Weller Louwelsa vase, rose blossom, buds and thorned stem in yellow and olive among hanging seed pods of caramel, tan and ivory, dark brown, olive and orange ground, artist's initials HM, impressed marks, 12"h, mint 500-700 June 10, 1995 Sold for $700

4916. Weller Aurelian vase, green iris and long leaves on an abstract ground of dark brown caramel, vivid yellow and light green, artist signed Madge Hurst, incised mark, D, 7"h, several flakes, minor scratches 400-600 June 10, 1995 Sold for $375

4917. Cambridge vase, portrait of young girl in yellow and brown with brown eyes and flowing shoulder length hair, wearing a green garment against a brown, orange and green ground, artist signed by A. Williams, impressed Cambridge, 24"h, some minor chips 5000-7000 July 13, 1994 Sold for $3750

4918. Weller Aurelian lamp, decoration of roses in yellow and brown against a ground of dark brown with yellow and green leaves and brown stems, artist signed E. Abel, 23"h overall, mint 500-700 June 12, 1995 Sold for $850

4919. Owens Utopian vase, bisque finish in orange to green with orange, cream and green clover decoration, artist signed, 11"h, mint 200-300 June 12, 1995 Sold for $250

4920. Owens Utopian vase, hi-glaze orange and green with cream and orange pansy decoration, 5"h, mint 100-200 June 12, 1995 Sold for $110

329

4921. Weller Etna vase, pink flowers on a ground shading from gray to pink bottom, impressed Weller Etna, 6.5"h, mint   100-150   July 13, 1993   Sold for $160

4922. Weller Camelot lamp base, green with incised Greek key and twisted line design in cream, incised Weller mark, 11.5"h, tiny chip   150-250   July 13, 1993   Sold for $250

4923. Weller LaSa bud vase, landscape in gold and brown with scene in gold, iridescent highlights in blue, green and pink, signed Weller LaSa, no wear, 5.5"h, mint   100-200   July 13, 1993   Sold for $200

4924. Weller Malvern vase, dark orange to brown with large green leaf design, Weller Pottery script signature, 8"dia. x 10"h, mint   100-200   July 13, 1993   Sold for $150

4925. Weller Etched Matt vase, incised portrait of a blonde lady on a mottled green to tan ground, hi-glaze, incised mark Weller Etched Matt, 5"h, mint   150-250   July 13, 1993   Sold for $160

4926. RV Egypto vase, Arts & Crafts design top and bottom, suspended green glaze, unmarked, 6"w x 16"h, glaze flakes   200-300   July 13, 1993   Sold for $300

4927. Weller Glossy Hudson, vase, orange floral design, impressed mark, signed Frank Dedonatis, 8"dia. x 9"h, mint   200-300   July 13, 1993   Sold for $425

4928. Weller Sicard vase, purple with iridescent green flowers around top and gold, blue and pink highlights overall, signed Sicard Weller, 6.5"h, mint   500-700   July 13, 1993   Sold for $500

4929. RV Aztec, vase, blue with yellow arrowroot design, unmarked, 11.5"h, restored   100-200   July 13, 1993   Sold for $280

4930. Weller Etna vase, gray on raised grape design with vines around grapes, dark gray around ruffled top shading to pale cream bottom, unmarked, 8"w x 7.5"h, small glaze flake on top   100-200   July 13, 1993   Sold for $80

4931. Weller Blue and Decorated vase, blue jay on a branch surrounded by narrow leaves, impressed Weller, 13.5"h, small flakes   700-900   June 12, 1995   Sold for $750

4932. Weller Hudson tile, seaside castle bordering choppy water with sail boat, signed Timberlake, 6"square, mint   1000-1500   June 12, 1995   Sold for $4500

4933. Weller Eocean vase, red raspberries with green and red leaves, ground shades from a dark green top to lavender, signed Weller Eocean, 6"w x 7.5"h, mint 250-350 July 13, 1993 Sold for $375

4934. Weller Etna pitcher, raised pink flowers with green leaves against a gray to pink ground, marked, 10.5"h, mint 150-250 July 13, 1993 Sold for $150

4935. Weller Eocean pitcher, light cream to lavender ground with yellow corn and cream husks, marked, 8.5"h, mint 150-250 July 13, 1993 Sold for $150

4936. RV Rozane Royal vase, green shading to yellow/green on base with two peach-colored open roses on long green stems, artist W. Myers, wafer mark, 3.5"dia. x 15"h, mint 700-900 July 13, 1993 Sold for $550

4937. RV Rozane Light vase, cream ground shading to gray at the bottom with yellow, white/gray roses and pale green leaves, signed J. Imlay, 8"w x 6"h, mint 400-600 July 13, 1993 Sold for $550

4938. Weller Eocean vase, dark purple floral with dark green leaves and stems against a dark green to pale green ground, impressed mark, incised Eocean mark, 9.5"h, mint 200-300 July 13, 1993 Sold for $230

4939. Weller Eocean tankard, of red berries and green leaves, long stems against a medium gray to cream ground, artist's initials W.S., 10.5"h, mint 200-300 July 13, 1993 Sold for $325

4940. Weller Eocean vase, cream and gray nasturtiums on gray ground shading to light gray and pink at the base, artist's initials, Weller Eocean in script, 5"w x 6.5"h, mint 200-300 July 13, 1993 Sold for $250

4941. Weller Dickensware vase, man and woman with hats and canes in violet, black, gray, peach and ivory on a gray to white ground, wafer mark, 4.5"h, lid may be missing, mint 200-300 June 10, 1995 Sold for $200

4942. Weller Jap Birdimal pitcher, geisha in robe of caramel with black, white and yellow highlights carries parasol of ivory and black backed by trees with brown trunks and green and white leaves on a light blue ground, incised Weller Faience, 11.5"h, mint 900-1200 June 10, 1995 Sold for $900

4943. Weller Dickensware, vase, Viking ship with incised rigging in black, yellow and white atop teal waves on a gray/green ground, impressed marks, 4"h, mint 300-500 June 10, 1995 Sold for $260

331

4944. Weller Hudson vase, pink, white, black and yellow daisies on green stems and leaves against a gray/green to lavender ground, initialed by Sarah Timberlake, 6.5"h, minute hidden chip to base   300-400   July 15, 1996   Sold for $300

4945. Weller White and Decorated Hudson vase, pink, gray black and tan blossoms on black and gray thorned branches on ivory ground, black band at shoulder, impressed mark, 7"h, unchipped chip to rim   100-200   July 15, 1996   Sold for $110

4946. Weller White and Decorated Hudson vase, pink, gray and yellow blossoms with light and dark green leaves and thorned stems against ivory and black ground, impressed mark, 10"h, cracked and repaired   100-200   July 15, 1996   Sold for $50

4947. Weller Hudson planter, floral decoration in mustard, olive and caramel against ivory and mustard ground, 8"square x 4"h, mint   500-700   July 15, 1996   Sold for $350

4948. Weller White and Decorated Hudson vase, floral decoration of burgundy, rose and pink blossoms with black and yellow centers on gray and brown branches with veined green leaves on ivory ground, band of green, gray and rose at shoulder, impressed mark, 9.5"h, hairline   100-200   July 15, 1996   Sold for $125

4949. Weller Hudson vase, yellow, dark and pale pink blossoms with black centers on narrow vines and broad leaves in green, yellow, brown and blue against a blue ground, signed Timberlake, ink mark, 7"h, mint   300-400   July 15, 1996   Sold for $425

4950. Weller Hudson Perfecto vase, pink and rust leaves among green, blue, purple and white, all outlined in black, against shaded teal, blue and cream ground, test glazes on bottom, initialed by Frank Dedonatis, incised mark, 6"h, mint   250-350   July 15, 1996   Sold for $425

Not Pictured:

4951. Weller White and Decorated Hudson vase, multicolored floral design at top on a cream ground, impressed mark, 8"h, mint   100-150   June 7, 1998   Sold for $220

4952. Weller Etna vase, pink and deep rose flowers with yellow highlights on green and gray stems and flowers against a white to dark gray ground, impressed mark, 13.5"h, mint   400-600   July 15, 1996   Sold for $375

4953. Weller Eocean vase, pink, lavender and deep rose hibiscus flowers and buds on gray/green stems and leaves against a pink to gray ground, incised mark, signed Leffler on side, 17.5"h, minor flake to base   900-1200   July 15, 1996   Sold for $1800

4954. Weller Louwelsa lamp base, yellow and orange daffodil, marked, artist initialed TS, 10"h, mint 100-200   July 13, 1993   Sold for $165

4955. Owens Utopian pitcher and mugs, blackberries in dark blue and orange, six mugs, all marked, pitcher 12"h, mugs 5"h, chip on one mug, all others mint   900-1200 July 13, 1993   Sold for $550

4956. Weller Louwelsa vase, green, yellow and brown grapes, orange, yellow and green stems and leaves, artist signed J. Imlay, 10"w x 16"h, mint   800-1100   July 13, 1993 Sold for $750

4957. Owens Utopian pitcher and mugs, orange and green leaves on pitcher, four mugs have different decorations, 12" pitcher marked Owens Utopian, 5" mugs, two marked, two unmarked, one mug has tiny chip, others mint   700-900   July 13, 1993   Sold for $425

4958. Weller Louwelsa vase, orange, yellow and green flowers with stems and thorns of brown to orange, artist signed Mitchell, impressed Weller Louwelsa, 12"h, mint 250-350   July 13, 1993   Sold for $325

Not Pictured:

4959. Weller Louwelsa vase, Cavalier, signed and numbered, 8"w x 7"h, minute flake   400-500   July 13, 1993 Sold for $325

4960. Weller Louwelsa vase, large brown glaze with yellow, orange and green daffodils, 17"h, repair to chips at top 200-300   July 17, 1996   Sold for $300

4961. Weller Sicard vase, iridescent glaze on dark purple and green with pink and green highlights, acorns, leaves and dots encircle vase in gold iridescence, signed, 9.5"h, hairline   300-400   July 13, 1993   Sold for $650

4962. Weller Dickensware vase, carved portrait of Native American chief with large feathered head dress and breast plate, incised "Black Heart", signed on side by Anthony Dunlavy, 1901, impressed marks, 9"h, mint   1200-1700 June 12, 1995   Sold for $2000

Not Pictured:

4963. Weller Dickensware vase, incised and painted Native American in full headdress with feathers and clothing in orange, green and yellow on a green, blue to yellow ground, incised Hollow Horn Bear, artist's signature A. Dunlevy, impressed mark, 10.5"h, mint   800-1100 July 13, 1993   Sold for $1000

For more details please call:
(513) 321-6742

4964. Weller Louwelsa tankard, Indian in full headdress, impressed mark, 13"h, mint 600-900 July 15, 1992 Sold for $400

4965. Owens Utopian vase, portrait of male Indian with feathered headdress and braided hair, impressed JB Owens Utopian 12"h, mint 1000-1500 July 15, 1992 Sold for $1400

4966. Weller Louwelsa vase, portrait of Dickens, artist A. Dunlevy, 14"h, drill hole in bottom 700-900 July 15, 1992 Sold for $900

4967. Weller Louwelsa clock, yellow and orange nastutium decoration, impressed mark artist initial K, 11"w x 10"h, glass cover for clock repaired, pottery mint 600-700 July 15, 1992 Sold for $550

4968. Weller Louwelsa vase, portrait of Indian in full headdress, artist signed A.D., impressed Louwelsa, 12"h, mint 800-1100 July 15, 1992 Sold for $900

Not Pictured:

4969. Weller Louwelsa vase, silver overlay, orange rose, impressed Weller Louwelsa, silver marked, 10"h, mint 2000-3000 July 13, 1993 Sold for $1200

4970. Weller Dickensware vase, hi-glaze, incised scene from Bleak House, inscription on back, impressed mark, 10.5"h, mint 500-700 July 13, 1993 Sold for $450

4971. Weller Louwelsa clock, pansy decoration in yellow and orange on a dark brown to orange ground, impressed Weller mark, artist's initials on back, 11"w x 11"h, mint 800-1100 July 13, 1993 Sold for $800

4972. Weller Jap Birdimal vase, Geisha in colorful robes with red obi, squeezebag designs on robe of black and white, dark aquamarine ground, green grass from base, trees around top with white squeezebag outline, dark brown trunks, marked Weller Faience, signed Rhead on bottom, repaired chip at top 1500-2000 July 17, 1991 Sold for $1300

Not Pictured:

4973. Weller Jap Birdimal vase, 3 handles around neck, scenic of tall tress, hi-glaze, no squeezebag dec., 12", mint 500-750 June 15, 1990 Sold for $400

4974. Weller Art Nouveau vase, green bisque with peach, lady on side, 11"h, mint   150-250   July 18, 1990 Sold for $170

4975. Weller Matt Louwelsa with corn decoration, yellow and darker green against lighter green ground, A. Haubrich, 12.5"h, mint   300-400   July 18, 1990 Sold for $425

4976. Weller Xenia blue matt with red and white flowers, 11"h, mint   250-350   July 18, 1990 Sold for $280

4977. Weller Dickensware vase, men playing chess, light blue, peach and yellow body with hi-glaze, 5"h, mint 250-350   July 18, 1990 Sold for $240

4978. RV Azurean vase, white pinecones, signed W. Myers, 14"h, restored   600-800   July 18, 1990 Sold for $425

4979. Weller Dickensware jug, decoration of bridge over river, 6"h, mint   250-350   July 18, 1990 Sold for $375

4980. Weller Matt Louwelsa tankard, orange berries on light green, signed L.J.B., 17"h, mint   350-450 July 18, 1990 Sold for $225

4981. Weller Dickensware vase, Dombey and Son scene of men around a table, yellow, blue and green on peach ground, 8"h, mint   500-750   July 18, 1990 Sold for $600

4982. Owens pitcher, pansies, tan bisque with turquoise and white decoration, 12"h, mint   250-350   July 18, 1990 Sold for $175

4983. Weller Art Nouveau pitcher, woman amidst vines and fruits in greens and peach, 11"h, mint   150-250 July 18, 1990   Sold for $170

4984. Weller Louwelsa vase, brown glaze decorated with Indian & child, yellow & green, grown, black, artist signed, 15"h, mint   2000-3000   July 18, 1990   Sold for $1300

335

4985. Owens brown glaze pitcher #1015 with pansies in yellow/green & orange, simple floral dec., 13", hairline 100-200   July 18, 1990   Sold for $80

4986. Weller Louwelsa jug in unusual 4 sided shape with greenery and blueberries, 5"h, mint   200-300 July 18, 1990   Sold for $110

4987. Weller Louwelsa tankard with winged dragon having long curled tail, signed R.G. Turner, 17"h, mint 700-900   July 18, 1990   Sold for $300

4988. RV Rozane bud vase, dark brown with green cloverleaf dec., inscription Jamestown Exposition 1907, 5"h, mint 150-250   July 18, 1990   Sold for $165

4989. Weller Louwelsa pitcher, brown berries, green & brown leaves, signed A. Haubrich on side, 12"h, mint 200-300   July 18, 1990 Sold for $325

4990. Weller Louwelsa vase, brown glaze with palm fronds in orange & green, signed L. Mitchell, 11"h, repaired top 150-250   July 18, 1990   Sold for $110

4991. Weller Aurelian vase, orange & yellow ground with large dark orange poppy dec., signed Ferrell, 17"h, repaired top   400-600   July 18, 1990   Sold for $225

4992. Lonhuda planter, half moon shape loop handles each end, small yellow floral, partial paper label, 5" x 10", mint   450-550   July 18, 1990   Sold for $325

4993. Weller Aurelian pitcher with grapes, very dark brown ground with orange & yellow color behind dec. of grapes, orange & green leaves & stems, 12"h, mint 300-500   July 18, 1990   Sold for $200

4994. Weller Hudson blue **Delta** vase, white and blue irises, signed Pillsbury, 9"h, bottom drilled, chipped, otherwise mint   250-350   July 18, 1990   Sold for $250

4995. Weller Hudson blue **Delta** vase, white and blue irises, signed Pillsbury, bottom drilled, 9"h, otherwise mint   250-350   July 18, 1990   Sold for $375

4996. Weller Hudson Perfecto vase, pink to blue with pinecones and needles on brown branches, all outlined in black, signed Leffler, 10"h, mint   400-600 July 18, 1990   Sold for $600

4997. Weller Scenic Hudson vase, sailboat with yellow sail, dec. by Pillsbury, 8.5"h, crazed but mint   750-1000 July 18, 1990   Sold for $1100

4998. Weller White and Decorated Hudson, floral, 8", mint
150-200   July 18, 1990   Sold for $135

4999. Weller Hudson six sided vase, decorated with pink & white dogwood flowers on pale blue ground, 12", mint
200-250   July 18, 1990   Sold for $150

5000. Fulper goose figurine, marked, 9" long x 5" h, mint
100-200   July 18, 1990   Sold for $350

5001. Weller Bronzeware vase, thick metallic purple glaze speckled with light green, nice example, 12", mint
150-250   July 18, 1990   Sold for $160

5002. RV Futura vase, pink and green hi-glaze, 8", chip
250-350   July 18, 1990   Sold for $375

5003. RV Vista vase, landscape scene, two handled, 12", mint
150-250   July 18, 1990   Sold for $260

5004. Weller Glendale vase with bird among plants, 5", mint
100-200   July 18, 1990   Sold for $145

5005. RV Aztec vase, grey-blue with blue, orange, yellow & white decoration, 11 ", mint   250-350   July 18, 1990   Sold for $375

5006. RV Morning Glory two handled vase, lavender & light green on white, 10", minute flake on lip   100-200   July 18, 1990   Sold for $220

5007. RV Cremona vase, 2 handles, green, 8", mint   75-150   July 18, 1990   Sold for $100

5008. Owens Utopian Indian portrait on pillow vase, Big Tree, signed A. Burgess, well executed, 8"h, repaired
600-800   July 18, 1990   Sold for $350

5009. Weller Louwelsa pitcher with decoration of white horse head, signed M.T., 14"h, large crack at top   500-750
July 18, 1990   Sold for $275

5010. Weller Louwelsa pillow vase with cavalier portrait, 10"h, mint   900-1250   July 18, 1990   Sold for $500

5011. Weller Louwelsa pitcher with portrait of a monk, excellent artwork, 12", hairline at rim and glaze flakes, drilled for lamp   400-600   July 18, 1990   Sold for $220

337

5012. Weller Louwelsa pitcher, blackberries and leaves, 12"h, crazed and tiny glaze flake at lip   150-200
July 18, 1990   Sold for $50

5013. Weller Etna vase, grapes & vines, 15"h, mint   450-550
July 18, 1990   Sold for $400

5014. Weller Louwelsa vase decorated with purple & white violets, marked, 3.5"h, mint   100-150   July 18, 1990
Sold for $95

5015. Weller Aurelian vase, decorated with yellow irises, Hattie M. Ross, 11"h, mint   400-600   July 18, 1990
Sold for $850

5016. RV Rozane Royal vase, yellow roses, two handled, artist signed, 21"h, mint   1500-2500   July 18, 1990
Sold for $1100

5017. Weller Louwelsa ewer, brown glaze with yellow rose, 6"h, repair to top   100-150   July 18, 1990
Sold for $50

5018. Owens Utopian vase, decorated with orange trumpet flowers, marked, 15"h, mint   200-300   July 18, 1990
Sold for $275

5019. Weller Louwelsa lamp base, green & brown leaves, marked, artist signed, 10"h, mint   150-250
July 18, 1990   Sold for $200

Not Pictured:

5020. Weller Cretone vase, painted brown gazelles & flowers on tan ground, well decorated by H. Pillsbury, pictured in Huxford, p. 311, 8"h, mint   200-300   July 18, 1990
Sold for $325

5021. Weller Dickensware Chinaman tobacco jar, 6"d, small chip on lid   450-650   July 18, 1990   Sold for $325

5022. Weller Dickensware Turk tobacco jar, 7"h, small chip   450-650   July 18, 1990   Sold for $400

5023. Weller LaSa vase, golds & pink landscape, exceptional scene with clean glaze, no wear, 9"h, mint   450-650
July 18, 1990   Sold for $400

5024. Weller Louwelsa bud vase, orange floral decoration, impressed circular mark, 10"h, mint   150-250
July 13, 1993   Sold for $210

5025. Weller Louwelsa vase, standard glaze with white and orange poppies with long green stems, brown to green background, impressed Louwelsa Weller, signed Ferrel, 11.5"h, mint   300-500   July 13, 1993   Sold for $350

5026. Weller Aurelian footed vase, dark standard glaze with yellow lily decoration, artist signed F, 7.5"w x 6"h, mint
400-500   July 13, 1993   Sold for $300

5027. Weller Aurelian ewer, yellow and orange flowers in splashes of yellow, green, rust on brown ground, signed A.H., impressed mark, 6"dia. x 7.5"h, mint   150-250
July 13, 1993   Sold for $245

5028. RV Rozane Royal vase, standard glaze of brown shading to gold, yellow to gold daffodil, wafer mark, signed, 7"h, mint   150-250   July 13, 1993
Sold for $180

5029. Weller Etna vase, purple grapes, brown stems and green leaves on rose to gray to slate blue ground, impressed Weller Etna, 15"h, chip under foot
400-600   July 13, 1993   Sold for $325

5030. **Weller Sicard** vase, green clover decoration on iridescent green to red ground, signed Sicard on side, 8.25"h, mint 600-800 July 18, 1990 Sold for $850

5031. **Weller Sicard** vase, red and golden iridescent with blue highlights, signed Weller Sicard, 9.5", mint 700-900 July 18, 1990 Sold for $800

5032. **Swastika Keramos** vase, red and golden glaze with golden and red iris decoration, all outlined in purple, raised mark, 12", some scratches, mint 400-600 July 18, 1990 Sold for $450

5033. **Weller Sicard** vase, red with leaf decoration overall, golden and green drip from top highlighted with blue, signed on side, 7", mint 400-600 July 18, 1990 Sold for $425

5034. **Weller Sicard** vase, gold and purple, red and green ground with golden mum, highlights, with blue and green leaves from bottom, 19"h, not marked, pitting on side, hole in bottom 1000-1500 July 18, 1990 Sold for $2000

5035. **Weller LaSa** vase, golden and red, landscape with bamboo decoration in foreground, 6.5"h, wear and scratches, but mint 250-350 July 18, 1990 Sold for $150

5036. **Weller Sicard** vase, red, purple and gold with floral decoration in gold and green, highlighted with deep blue, purple, iridescent glaze, signed, 16"h, bottom repaired 750-1000 July 18, 1990 Sold for $850

5037. **Weller Sicard** vase, red, blue, green and gold iridescent glaze with crystals around bottom, circle design is predominantly gold, signed Weller Sicard, 5.25"h, mint 400-600 July 18, 1990 Sold for $400

5038. **Weller Sicard** vase, dark purple and green, dark green thistle decoration, signed, 8"h, mint 600-800 July 18, 1990 Sold for $800

Not Pictured:

5039. **Weller Sicard** jardinere, 11"h, cracked 400-600 July 18, 1990 Sold for $650

5040. **Weller Sicard** square vase, purple, gold, pink, green, and blue iridescent glaze, gold, green floral decoration, signed, 5", mint 400-600 June 15, 1991 Sold for $450

5041. **Weller Sicard** vase, dark purple, blues, green with silvery & gold highlights, 10.5"h, signed on side, repaired bottom 400-600 July 18, 1990 Sold for $550

5042. **Weller LaSa** vase, floral design, orange to red with gold highlights, 9"h, mint 500-750 July 18, 1990 Sold for $425

5043. **Weller Sicard** vase, red & purple with golden/green mum dec., 13"h, repaired bottom 400-600 July 18, 1990 Sold for $650

5044. **Weller Sicard** vase, light green, purples, blues, greens, 8.5"h, unsigned, scratches on bottom, mint 500-750 July 18, 1990 Sold for $325

5045. **Weller Sicard** plaque, woman's head in profile, iridescent glaze, predominately red with blues & gold, unsigned, 21"h x 16.5" at widest top, some chips around edges 2500-3500 July 18, 1990 Sold for $2500

5046. **Weller Sicard** vase, four-lobed with fluted top, signed on side and marked on base, 5"h, minute glaze flakes at base, mint 500-750 July 18, 1990 Sold for $650

5047. Weller Blue Ware vase, dancing lady, shrubs, fruit trees and small flying bird, 9"h, marked, mint 200-300   July 17, 1991   Sold for $115

5048. Weller Greora vase, bronze-like glaze with green scattered overall, marked Weller Pottery and also has the original paper label, 9.5"h, mint   200-300 July 17, 1991   Sold for $140

5049. Weller Chengtu vase, glossy red glaze, 16"h, mint 400-600   July 17, 1991   Sold for $325

5050. Owens Utopian mug, raspberry decoration, artist signed T.S., marked, 6", mint   100-200   July 17, 1991 Sold for $135

5051. Owens Utopian tankard, brown glaze with wheat decoration in reddish brown and green, 12", mint 200-300   July 17, 1991   Sold for $210

5052. Owens Utopian ewer, yellow roses and green foliage, artist Fanny Bell, 6"h, mint   150-250   July 17, 1991 Sold for $210

5053. Weller 2nd Line Dickens vase, portrait of a cavalier, shaded green to brown, marked, 12", professionally restored foot   300-500   July 17, 1991   Sold for $140

5054. Weller Modeled Etched Matt vase, with red grapes, green vines, and shaded orange to green leaves, 16"h, marked, restored hairline   200-300   July 17, 1991 Sold for $175

5055. Weller Bonita vase, floral decoration, artist initial on bottom, marked Weller Pottery, 10"h, mint   100-150 July 17, 1991   Sold for $170

Not Pictured:

5056. Weller Hudson vase, colorful pink, yellow, blue and green bird on black branches against a gray ground, band around top in same colors as birds, small black and gray bands below wider color band, impressed Weller, 14", mint   750-1000   July 17, 1991   Sold for $1200

5057. Weller Eocean Rose vase, gray-green to pale pink ground, decoration of lavender and white flowers with yellow centers, signed Leffler, 12", script Eocean Rose Weller mark, mint   200-250   July 17, 1991 Sold for $240

5058. Weller Dresden vase, windmill scene in blue and white on green to blue ground, 10", marked Matt Weller, LJB, small flake top edge   150-250   July 17, 1991 Sold for $250

5059. Weller Hudson vase, small berries and leaves in pink, black and yellow against pink to green ground, artist signed Hood, 7"h, mint   200-300   July 15, 1992 Sold for $300

5060. Weller Dickensware tankard, incised fruit and leaves, impressed signature, artist signed, 16.5"h, mint 400-600   July 13, 1993   Sold for $325

5061. Weller Dickensware vase, incised peacock on branch, green, yellow to blue ground, impressed mark, 14.5"h, minor glaze flakes   600-800   July 13, 1993 Sold for $425

5062. Weller Aurelian ewer, yellow, green and brown pansies, script signature, artist signed, 5.5"h, mint 150-200   July 13, 1993   Sold for $200

5063. Weller Hudson vase, pale lavender and yellow irises against a purple, yellow to green ground, impressed Weller, 11.5"h, mint   200-300   July 13, 1993 Sold for $375

5064. Weller Hudson vase, floral decoration in red, white, blue and yellow with green leaves and stems against a blue to light green ground, signed McLauglin, impressed Weller Pottery, 12"h, mint   500-750   July 13, 1993 Sold for $900

5065. Weller Faience mug, orange poppy and buds on an olive green ground, squeezebag outlined in white, designed by Rhead, 5"h, mint   150-250   July 13, 1993 Sold for $375

5066. Weller Dickensware vase, Indian portrait Lean Wolf, decorated by E.L. Pickens, 9", glaze flakes at rim 350-500   July 18, 1990   Sold for $325

5067. Weller Hudson vase, large white iris, signed LBM, 9.5"h, mint   400-500   July 18, 1990   Sold for $475

5068. Owens Matt vase, green with brown & white flowers, 10"h, glaze flakes at base   200-300   July 18, 1990 Sold for $325

5069. Weller Hudson vase, blue with pink & white dogwood decoration, by C. Leffler , 7"h, mint   200-250 July 18, 1990   Sold for $200

5070. Weller Cameo Jewel vase, purplish-blue matt with carved fish, bubbles raised in hi-glazed white, 10"h, mint 350-450   July 18, 1990   Sold for $375

5071. Weller Hudson vase, pink iris, by Hunter, 9", mint 350-450   July 18, 1990   Sold for $325

5072. Weller Dickensware jug, incised Indian portrait, bisque finish in orange, green to brown, enamel style dots of color over piece in blue, green, orange & cream, 6.5" x 5", mint   350-450   July 18, 1990   Sold for $300

5073. Weller Matt Louwelsa pitcher, iris decoration, peach and cream on a pale green ground, 12"h, mint   350-450 July 18, 1990   Sold for $200

5074. Weller Hudson vase, pink & white morning glories on blue to white ground, 9"h, mint   250-350   July 18, 1990 Sold for $300

5075. Weller Hudson vase, pink & white peonies on blue to pink ground, 11"h, mint   300-450   July 18, 1990 Sold for $425

5076. Weller Hudson vase, green trees frame lake with snow covered mountain behind, decorated by Pillsbury, 10"h, mint   900-1200   July 18, 1990   Sold for $950

Not Pictured:

5077. Weller Hudson vase, yellow and blue irises by Dorothy England, blue ground, 9"h, mint   250-350 June 15, 1991   Sold for $350

5078. Weller Hudson vase, blue, green to pink ground with yellow and blue daisy decoration, green leaves, black paper label, signed S. Timberlake, 9", mint   200-300 June 15, 1991   Sold for $275

5079. Weller Dresden vase, windmill decoration, blue and green, signed Matt Weller, 5", mint   200-300 June 15, 1991   Sold for $425

5080. Weller Dickensware tankard in brown, tan to green bisque, deeply incised portrait of monk by A. Dunlavy, #430, #12, 1901, initials K.B., 17"h, chip on base   400-600   July 18, 1990   Sold for $275

5081. Weller Eocean vase, purple to pink roses, pale green leaves, pink stems on a brown, green to almost white bottom, artist signed J.B., 10"h, mint   250-350 June 15, 1991   Sold for $450

5082. Weller Forest jardinere & pedestal, 29"h overall, mint 500-800   July 18, 1990   Sold for $550

5083. Weller Knifewood covered jar, berries, birds and leaves on a dark ground, excellent mold, 8"h, chip in rim 200-300   June 11, 1994   Sold for $350

5084. Weller Hudson vase, matt lilac and green decoration on cream ground, #488, 9"h, mint   300-500 July 10, 1994   Sold for $350

5085. Weller Hudson vase, white, blue and pink dogwood with green leaves, against rose to blue ground, Weller Pottery script signature, 8"h, mint   250-350   July 15, 1992 Sold for $375

5086. Weller Hudson vase, orange roses outlined in brown with green leaves against ivory ground, artist signed H.P., impressed Weller, 10"h, mint   300-500 July 15, 1992   Sold for $325

5087. Weller Hudson vase, blue and white roses on a blue to cream ground, signed McLaughlin, marked, 9"h, mint 200-300   July 13, 1993   Sold for $500

5088. Weller Hudson vase, beautiful deep blue with large white waterlilies and green lily pads, an outstanding and beautiful example, signed LBM, 8"dia. x 10", mint 650-850   July 18, 1990   Sold for $950

5089. Weller Blue & Decorated bud vase, green band of yellow and pink flowers, black branches on blue ground, 10", mint 150-200 July 17, 1991 Sold for $80

5090. Weller Modeled Etched Matt vase, incised orange and green daisies on bright yellow ground, 10"h, some bubbles around top in making, mint 300-400 July 17, 1991 Sold for $170

5091. Weller Pop Eye dog, black with cream spots, 4"h, mint 400-600 July 17, 1991 Sold for $475

5092. Weller Hudson vase, beautiful yellow, brown and blue Iris decoration on blue, pale green to pink ground, D. England, 8.5", mint 250-350 July 17, 1991 Sold for $375

5093. RV Rozane standard glaze ewer, orange and yellow pansy decoration, ruffled top, impressed Rozane, RPCo., numbered, incised Hero/JD and another initial, 11", mint 200-350 July 17, 1991 Sold for $250

5094. Weller Baldin vase, raised pink and yellow apple decoration on dark blue ground, 6", mint 100-200 July 17, 1991 Sold for $170

5095. Weller Hudson vase, pink, green, yellow and white flowers, green leaves, all outlined in black on pink to green ground, signed Pillsbury, 9", mint 150-250 July 17, 1991 Sold for $300

5096. RV Rozane Royal vase, pale yellow and darker green daffodil decoration on dark green ground shading to pale cream, Pillsbury, wafer mark, 9", mint 300-500 July 17, 1991 Sold for $550

5097. Owens Lightweight standard glaze vase, peach and white clover decoration with one four-leaf clover, artist signed, 6", mint 75-100 July 17, 1991 Sold for $195

5098. Weller Modeled Matt vase, raised pink and purple roses, purple stems on dark pink to yellow ground, impressed Weller block signature, 10", mint 300-500 July 17, 1991 Sold for $290

5099. Weller Modeled Etched Matt vase, incised red tulip, green leaves on bright yellow ground, 10", some roughness around top 300-500 July 17, 1991 Sold for $200

Not Pictured:

5100. Weller Louwelsa brown glaze vase, painted decoration of iris in yellow and dark green, incised M. Paine, impressed Weller, 7"h, mint 200-300 July 15, 1992 Sold for $350

5101. Weller Louwelsa vases, yellow and orange daffodil decoration, slender green leaves, artist signed M. Mitchell, impressed Louwelsa mark and numbered, 10"h, mint 250-325 July 15, 1992 Sold for $350

5102. Weller Louwelsa lamp base, one side with orange and yellow floral decoration with green leaves against a green to brown ground, opposite with solid orange floral design against orange to brown ground, signed by William H. Stemm, 13"w x 7"h, mint 300-500 July 15, 1992 Sold for $375

5103. Weller Louwelsa umbrella stand, orange grapes and leaves, artist Ferrell, 22"h, two small glaze flakes 300-500 July 15, 1992 Sold for $400

5104. Weller Louwelsa pitcher, Indian in full headdress, impressed Weller Louwelsa mark, 12.5"h, mint 800-1100 July 13, 1993 Sold for $800

5105. Weller Louwelsa vase, brown hi-glaze with hollyhocks, artist initials, impressed mark, 9.5"h, minor scratches 350-450 July 14, 1998 Sold for $325

5106. Weller Louwelsa lamp base, floral in brown, yellow and green, brass insert, impressed mark, 7"h, mint 200-300 July 16, 1996 Sold for $300

5107. Weller Louwelsa tankard, portrait of monk, signed, 12"h, mint 400-600 July 13, 1993 Sold for $425

5108. Weller Louwelsa standard glaze jardiniere and pedestal, large orange and yellow floral decoration on brown, green to orange ground, 24"h, 12"w top, mint 400-600 July 17, 1991 Sold for $375

5109. Weller Louwelsa vase, yellow and orange nasturtium, 10.5"h, mint 250-350 June 11, 1994 Sold for $275

5110. Weller Louwelsa ewer, silver overlay with floral painted design, impressed mark, 4.5"h, mint 1000-1500 July 16, 1997 Sold for $1600

5111. Weller Sicard vase, iridescent glaze with red, purple and green highlights, flower design, signed Weller Sicard, 5.5", restored top   150-250   July 17, 1991   Sold for $220

5112. Swastika Keramos vase, white and green applied coralene, 12", wafer mark, old paper label, some wear to coralene   250-350   July 17, 1991   Sold for $160

5113. Swastika Keramos vase, gold with red and dark green drip design over gold, 14", wafer mark, paper label, a few surface wear scratches, mint   250-350   July 17, 1991   Sold for $120

5114. Weller Eocean vase, white, green nasturtiums with black centers, green and gray leaves on a pale pink-gray to deep gray ground, Eocean Weller in script, artist initialed, 6.5", glaze miss in making, mint   150-200   July 17, 1991   Sold for $150

5115. Weller Hudson vase, white, pink and blue dogwood decoration on a blue to green ground, signed Axline, 10"h x 10", Weller pottery mark, mint   600-800   July 17, 1991   Sold for $600

5116. Weller Sicard vase, dark purple, blue and red iridescent glaze, gold highlights, floral design, signed Weller Sicard, 6", mint   400-600   July 17, 1991   Sold for $800

5117. Weller Louwelsa vase, orange cherry decoration on dark brown to orange ground, artist initialed, 6"h x 7", mint   100-200   July 17, 1991   Sold for $175

5118. Weller LaSa vase, green palm trees against golden ground with red sunset and mountain range in background, 8", mint   150-200   July 17, 1991   Sold for $170

5119. Weller LaSa vase, red, blue and yellow highlights, signed Weller LaSa on side, 9", no wear, good glaze, hairline   50-100   July 17, 1991   Sold for $215

5120. Weller Louwelsa ewer, yellow and brown floral decoration on dark brown, orange to green ground, impressed #74 and 2, 6", mint   100-200   July 17, 1991   Sold for $155

Not Pictured:

5121. Weller Hudson vase, four swallows around vase, light gray shading to pink, signed Pillsbury, 9", mint   900-1200   July 17, 1991   Sold for $1400

5122. Weller Cloud Burst vase, lavender, white and raspberry with metallic gloss, 7", mint   200-300   July 17, 1991   Sold for $220

5123. Weller Rosemont vase, three birds perched on branches, 10", mint   250-350   July 17, 1991   Sold for $450

5124. Weller Besline vase, vines, leaves and berries etched through orange glaze to white porcelain-like clay body, 8.5"h, glaze flake on rim   100-200   July 17, 1991   Sold for $260

5125. Weller Sicard vase, red and purple ground with golden floral decoration, signed, 8", mint   700-900   July 17, 1991   Sold for $600

5126. Weller Hudson vase, white and yellow flowers, pink and blue raspberries and green and gray foliage impressed Weller 11"h, mint   150-250   July 15, 1992   Sold for $220

5127. Weller Matt Louwelsa vase, harbor scene in shades of blue, impressed Weller Louwelsa 7"h, mint   200-300   July 15, 1992   Sold for $500

5128. Weller Glendale vase, two birds watching their nest, impressed Weller, 8"dia. x 9"h, mint   400-600   July 15, 1992   Sold for $550

5129. Weller Hudson vase, yellow daisies with black foliage against cream ground, impressed Weller, 11"h, mint   200-250   July 15, 1992   Sold for $240

5130. Weller jardiniere and pedestal, majolica type in shades of beige, brown and green, 27"h, mint   300-500   July 15, 1992   Sold for $550

5131. Weller Forest jardiniere, impressed Weller, 11"w x 10"h, mint 150-250   July 15, 1992   Sold for $500

5132. Weller Dickensware jug, scene of bridge, impressed mark, 6"h, glaze flakes around spout 150-250 July 15, 1992 Sold for $160

5133. Weller Dickensware vase, incised portrait of Dutch lady dressed in blue and white, impressed mark, 9"h, two tiny glaze flakes on top edge 250-350 July 15, 1992 Sold for $150

5134. Peters & Reed Chromal vase, snow covered mountain range with trees, 13"h, drill hole 150-250 July 15, 1992 Sold for $325

5135. Weller Modeled Etched Matt vase, incised yellow grapes, brown, yellow and green vines and leaves against orange ground, impressed mark, 9"h, mint 200-300 July 15, 1992 Sold for $240

5136. Weller Dickensware vase, incised portrait of Indian in full headdress, artist's initials, impressed mark, 13"h, mint 700-900 July 15, 1992 Sold for $650

5137. Weller Dickensware vase, incised woodpeckers on branch, green, peach to yellow ground, impressed mark, 9"h, glaze flakes around top edge 300-500 July 15, 1992 Sold for $290

5138. Weller Dickensware vase, street scene of several people, 13"h, mint 300-500 July 15, 1992 Sold for $375

5139. Weller Dickensware plaque, advertising Dickens Pottery, scene from Pickwick Papers and inscription around bottom about Sam Weller, 12"dia., tiny chip on edge 400-600 July 15, 1992 Sold for $3250

5140. Weller Sicard vase, iridescent glaze in pink, gold and green with deeper purple and blue highlights, mistletoe decoration in gold and green, signed Weller Sicard, 9"w x 5"h, mint 1000-1500 July 15, 1992 Sold for $1100

5141. Weller Sicard vase, metallic glaze of green, pink and gold with purple highlights, impressed Weller, 9"h, mint 500-700 July 15, 1992 Sold for $500

5142. Swastika Keramos vase, gold ground with white and green coralene surface, wafer mark, gold, 12"h, worn spot on side, otherwise mint 200-300 July 15, 1992 Sold for $130

5143. Weller Sicard vase, purple to green ground with floral decoration in pink and gold, golden dot design over body, signed Weller Sicard, 8"h, mint 1000-1500 July 15, 1992 Sold for $2000

5144. Weller Sicard bud vase, green to gold with pink highlights, floral decoration, signed, 6"h, mint 500-700 July 15, 1992 Sold for $475

5145. Weller Besline vase, orange mirror glaze with etched grapes and leaves in lighter orange matt, 11"h, mint 300-500 July 15, 1992 Sold for $550

5146. Weller Sicard round wall plaque, gold and green spider mum decoration with pink highlights on dark purple to blue ground, reverse signed Weller and initial J. Sicard, 10"dia., mint 1000-1500 July 15, 1992 Sold for $1200

5147. Arc-en-ciel vase, gold metallic glaze with purple and pink highlights, molded floral decoration, nice glaze, impressed mark, 10"h, mint 200-300 July 15, 1992 Sold for $350

5148. Weller Aurelian tankard, lion portrait, artist signed, 17"h, crazed but mint 800-1100 July 18, 1990 Sold for $1000

5149. Weller Louwelsa glaze ewer, green fish swimming down and around form from shell-shaped spout, handle in form of trident, artist signed, 11"h, slight wear 300-400 July 18, 1990 Sold for $650

5150. Weller Louwelsa tankard, brown to green with portrait of Indian brave in full headdress, artist signed, probably Dunlavy, 12.5"h, repaired top 500-750 July 18, 1990 Sold for $325

5151. Lonhuda pitcher, brown with orange rose decoration, yellow hi-glaze inside, artist signed, 13"h, hairlines 250-350 July 18, 1990 Sold for $500

5152. Weller Louwelsa tankard, Indian portrait by E. Sulfer, mint 1000-1500 July 18, 1990 Sold for $950

5153. Weller Sicard bowl, geometric design between four buttresses, 9"dia. x 4.5"h, mint 450-550 July 18, 1990 Sold for $450

5154. Weller Sicard vase, four buttresses extend to feet, floral dec. between buttresses, 4"h, mint 450-550 July 18, 1990 Sold for $800

5155. Weller Dickensware vase, Chief Hollowhorn Bear portrait on light blue to tan ground, signed A.D., 13"h, mint 1000-1500 July 18, 1990 Sold for $850

5156. Weller Dickensware mug, bisque finish, light blue, green, rusty orange, incised portrait of Indian in full headdress in blues, white & brown, 6"h, mint 400-600 July 18, 1990 Sold for $550

5157. Weller Dickensware tankard, Indian portrait of Chief Blackbear, artist signed A.D., 12", mint 1000-1500 July 18, 1990 Sold for $1100

345

5158. Weller Geode vase, white star design, marked, 7"h, mint 50-100   July 15, 1992   Sold for $600

5159. Weller Turk tobacco jar, 6"w x 7"h, chips at top, 12"h, three glaze imperfections, one in making 400-600   July 15, 1992   Sold for $400

5160. Owens Mission vase, dark blue and earth tones night scene of Spanish mission, artist C. Holy, 11"h, chipped   300-500   July 15, 1992   Sold for $200

5161. Weller pop-eye dog, black and white matt with pink highlights, 4"h, mint   300-400   July 15, 1992 Sold for $450

5162. Weller Hudson vase, pink roses with green and blue leaves on deep blue to green ground, artist signed J. Ronter, Weller stamp, 7"h, mint   200-300 July 15, 1992   Sold for $260

5163. Weller Hudson Perfecto vase, purple and pink rose decoration with green leaves outlined in black, pastel green to pink and lavender ground, 9"w x 10"h, mint 250-350   July 15, 1992   Sold for $750

5164. Weller Brighton pheasant, colorful figurine, 7"w x 5"h, unmarked, repaired tail 100-200   July 15, 1992 Sold for $135

5165. Owens Opalescent vase, nasturtiums on gold, green and white ground, impressed Owens, 6"h, mint   200-400 July 15, 1992   Sold for $290

5166. Weller Hudson vase, yellow, brown and white roses with blue and green leaves, artist signed, Weller Ware mark, 7"h, mint   200-300   July 15, 1992   Sold for $375

5167. Lonhuda Denver vase, peach and white carnations with green leaves and stems against orange, brown to green ground, artist signed, impressed mark, 9"h, mint 300-400   July 15, 1992   Sold for $450

5168. Weller Hudson vase, gray berries with brown, green and gray leaves on gray to cream ground, impressed Weller, 7"h, mint 100-200   July 15, 1992   Sold for $150

Not Pictured:

5169. Weller Coppertone bowl with frog on edge, good color, 5"h x 10", chip inside edge under frog   150-250 July 17, 1991   Sold for $200

5170. Weller Rosemont vase, black ground with decoration of purple and white cockatoos and bouquets of, roses, 9"h, mint   200-250   July 15, 1992   Sold for $425

5171. Weller Etna vase, brown to yellow daffodils, against dark gray, white to lavender ground, impressed Weller Etna, 11"h, mint   250-350   July 15, 1992 Sold for $300

5172. Weller Eocean Rose vase, white and red roses, green, cream and gray foliage, against dark gray, white to pale pink ground, artist signed McLaughlin, impressed Weller Eocean Rose on bottom, 13"h, mint   300-500 July 15, 1992   Sold for $550

5173. Weller Jap Birdimal vase, white and yellow bird in flight on green hi-glaze ground, unmarked, 8"h, mint 200-300   July 15, 1992   Sold for $325

5174. Weller Eocean vase, pink and gray mushrooms on green, white to pale pink ground, script signature, 6"w x 8"h, mint   400-500   July 15, 1992   Sold for $550

5175. Weller Dickensware vase, portrait of young lady playing a musical instrument while sitting on a crescent moon, tan to green ground, impressed mark, artist's initials M.C., 8.5"h, mint   500-700   July 13, 1993 Sold for $550

5176. Weller cat figurine, attribution, white matt glaze with black and orange eyes and black details, 14"l x 3.5"h, mint   1000-1500   July 13, 1993   Sold for $1600

5177. Weller Louwelsa vase, daffodil decoration, artist signed, impressed mark, 6"h, mint   2250-350 July 14, 1998   Sold for $400

5178. Weller Etched Matt vase, yellow with etched design in pale green, blue, and black outline, signed Ferrell, 8"h, cracked   100-200   July 15, 1992   Sold for $260

5179. Weller Matt vase, green matt with green leaves and red floral 12"h, mint   300-500   July 15, 1992 Sold for $375

5180. Weller Gnome garden ornament, figure peeking around green leaves and flowers, unmarked, 10"w at base x 16"h, several chips in making   1200-1700 July 15, 1992   Sold for $4750

5181. Weller Stellar vase, blue with white stars, Weller Pottery script signature, 6"h, mint   150-250   July 15, 1992 Sold for $500

5182. Weller Gnome garden ornament, gnome on boulder, unmarked, 11"w at base x 17"h, repaired foot 1000-1500   July 15, 1992   Sold for $5500

5183. Weller Velva covered vases, pair, orange to green with decoration of flowers and green leaves on panels and lids, artist signed H.P., Weller Pottery in script, 8"h, one lid has small chip inside, otherwise both mint   200-300   July 15, 1992 Sold for $185

Not Pictured:

5184. Weller Pan garden figure, Weller script signature, 10"w x 16.5"h, restored   2000-3000   July 13, 1993 Sold for $2100

5185. Weller Sicard vase, golds and greens on red, spider line type floral decoration, signed on side, 7.25", minute glaze flake on rim   350-450   June 15, 1990 Sold for $300

5186. Weller LaSa vase, landscape decoration, 9", mint 500-750   June 15, 1990   Sold for $450

5187. Weller Dickensware pillow vase, blue bisque with ducks flying over a seascape, 4 fish visible under the waves, artist signed, 9.5" x 9" w., mint   750-1000 June 15, 1990   Sold for $550

5188. Weller Dickensware mug, Dombey and Son with little girl and man sitting side by side, signed H.P., 3" x 5", mint   300-500   June 15, 1990 Sold for $300

5189. Weller Knifewood vase, peacock on fountain decoration, 11 1/4", mint   150-250   June 15, 1990 Sold for $325

5190. Weller Hudson vase, nasturtiums in pinks and yellow around top of pot, blue to pink ground, artist signed M. Laughlin, 9", mint   200-300   June 15, 1990 Sold for $300

5191. Weller Dickensware ewer, large ruffled top, blackberries in black and orange, yellow flowers and buds in yellow and orange, brown, yellow leaves, artist initials E.R. by decoration, 12", mint   250-350   June 15, 1990 Sold for $425

5192. Weller Dickensware jug, orange flower surrounded by small blue flowers, green leaves and stems on brown ground, signed C.L., impressed mark, 5"dia. x 6.5"h, mint   200-300   July 13, 1993   Sold for $325

5193. Weller Woodcraft candle lamps, pair, tree trunk in brown, green with red berry decoration, branch handles around top with leaves, original candle lamp holder and old bulbs, total height 17"h, one mint and one with tiny chip to leaf   500-700   July 14, 1998   Sold for $750

5194. Weller Woodcraft wallpocket, tree branch with owl looking out, 10.5"h, chip on back   150-250 July 14, 1998   Sold for $350

5195. Weller Baldin pedestal, brown, green with red apples and green leaves, curved branch handles and twisted base, 28.5"h, mint   400-600   July 14, 1998 Sold for $260

5196. Weller Louwelsa lamp base with wicker base and lamp fittings top, old wick and tassel shade, standard glaze with yellow and orange daffodil decoration, green leaves, 14"h, mint   300-400   July 14, 1998 Sold for $550

347

5197. Owens Utopian vase, brown glaze with orange and green leaf decoration, impressed mark, 5"h, mint 70-100 July 15, 1992 Sold for $95

5198. Weller Rochelle vase, hi-glaze pink and yellow flowers, no mark, 8"h, mint 150-200 July 15, 1992 Sold for $155

5199. Owens Utopian vase, lily of the valley decoration, initial T. Steele, 13"h, mint 200-300 July 15, 1992 Sold for $375

5200. Weller Sicard vase, red iridescent glaze with gold peacock feather decoration, blue and green highlights, signed around bottom, 5"h, tiny glaze flake 300-400 July 15, 1992 Sold for $340

5201. Owens vase, pastel pink and purple floral with green leaves on green to white ground, impressed Owens, 10"h, mint 150-250 July 15, 1992 Sold for $325

5202. Lonhuda ewer, orange and green leaves, blackber- ries and yellow flowers, Lonhuda signature, artist signed, 10"h, mint 200-300 July 15, 1992 Sold for $280

5203. Weller Sicard vase, red iridescent ground with gold and green clover decoration, signed Weller Sicard on side, 3"h, mint 250-350 July 15, 1992 Sold for $325

5204. Weller Eocean vase, purple and pink rose with blue and green leaves and stems, against gray to white ground, artist A. Haubrich, impressed Weller Eocean, 13"h, mint 400-600 July 15, 1992 Sold for $1200

5205. Weller Etna vase, red, yellow, gray and white daffodil decoration against gray, white to purple ground, impressed mark, 11"h, mint 200-300 July 15, 1992 Sold for $400

5206. Lonhuda vase, yellow floral with orange and green leaves by Albert Haubrich, impressed Lonhuda, 4"w x 4"h, mint 150-250 July 15, 1992 Sold for $130

5207. Weller Eocean vase, yellow and white daffodil decoration, 13"h, mint 200-300 July 15, 1992 Sold for $245

5208. Weller Sicard vase, red, purple and blue iridescent glaze with gold floral design, pink and purple highlights, signed on side, 9"h, mint 500-700 July 15, 1992 Sold for $850

5209. Weller Etna vase, red roses in relief, gray to white ground, Weller mark, 10"h, mint 100-200 July 15, 1992 Sold for $250

Not Pictured:

5210. Weller Aurelian vase, roses on yellow, orange and dark brown, signed M.L., 14"h, mint 500-700 June 11, 1994 Sold for $800

5211. Weller Warwick wallpocket, half kiln mark, 11.5"l, mint 200-300 July 15, 1998 Sold for $350

5212. Weller Warwick bowl with handles, 8.5"dia. x 3.5"h, mint 150-250 July 15, 1998 Sold for $370

5213. Weller Novelty vase, goose head handles, green and brown glaze, 4"h; with a **Weller Hobart** flower frog of two women, 7"h, mint 250-350 July 15, 1998 Sold for $325

5214. Weller Sicard vase, floral design in metallic glaze, not marked, 7"h, mint 800-1100 June 6, 1999 Sold for $650

5214. RV Rozane Woodland vase, orange and brown floral decoration, wafer mark, 10"h, restoration on bottom 600-800 July 13, 1993 Sold for $650

5215. Weller Forest jardinere and pedestal, earth tone forest scene, 32"h, mint 700-900 June 11, 1994 Sold for $1500

5216. Weller LaSa vase, iridescent scene with palm trees in foreground, unmarked, 11"h, repaired drill hole in bottom, with a **Weller LaSa** bud vase, reds and golds, signed on side, 6"h, mint   250-350   July 15, 1992 Sold for $450

5217. Weller Chengtu vase, marked Weller Pottery, 16"h, mint   400-600   July 15, 1992 Sold for $425

5218. Weller figurine, knight and his lady with dog at feet, Weller full kiln ink stamp mark c. mid-1920s, initialed DE, 9"h, mint   300-500   July 15, 1992   Sold for $1100

5219. Weller Etna vase, purple grape decoration with brown stems and green leaves on gray, white to pink ground, impressed Weller, 15"h, chip   300-400   July 15, 1992 Sold for $240

5220. Owens Utopian vase, yellow tulip decoration, artist's initials T. Steele, marked, 14"h, mint   200-300 July 15, 1992 Sold for $375

5221. Vance Avon vase, brown hi-glaze with yellow squeezebag line decoration circling vase, unmarked, 5"h, glaze flake on top edge 150-250   July 15, 1992 Sold for $265

5222. Weller Velva vase, tan, marked, 11"h, mint   100-200 July 15, 1992   Sold for $110

5223. Weller Etched Matt vase, orange sunflowers with green leaves and stem against yellow ground, 10"h, mint 250-350   July 15, 1992   Sold for $230

Not Pictured:

5224. Weller Eocean vase, red roses, incised mark, 12"h, mint 500-700   July 16, 1997   Sold for $800

5225. Weller Jap Birdimal pitcher, sailing ship decoration, impressed mark, 4.5"h, mint   200-300   July 16, 1997 Sold for $200

5226. Weller Rochelle candlesticks, pair, multicolored floral decoration, impressed mark, 10.5"h, minute nick at top 300-500   July 16, 1997   Sold for $250

5227. Weller Dickensware vase, three handles, hi-glaze with blue berries on green leaves and brown branches against a dark green ground, sterling overlay in cutout design, initialed M.S., impressed mark, #813, 8.5"h, restored, line to handle   800-1100   July 16, 1997   Sold for $1000

5228. Weller Forest floor vase, footed form in green, brown and light blue, 13"h, minute flakes to base   600-800 July 16, 1997   Sold for $500

5229. Weller Dresden vase, Dutch scene with woman and windmills in blue and green matt, impressed mark, 8.5"h, mint   600-800   July 16, 1997   Sold for $750

5230. Weller Oak Leaf vase, green and brown leaves on green ground, not marked, 16"h, mint   250-350 July 15, 1997   Sold for $250

5231. Weller Rosemont vase, birds and flowers on black ground, marked, 10"h, mint   200-300   June 8, 1997 Sold for $300

5232. Weller Hudson vase, light and dark pink grapes with green and pink leaves, ground shades from light to dark pink, impressed mark, 15"h, mint   1200-1700 June 8, 1997   Sold for $650

5233. Weller Rochelle vase, multicolored floral on colorful ground, signed E.P. on side, 8"h, mint   250-350 June 8, 1997   Sold for $325

5234. Weller Dickensware original oil lamp, brown and yellow owl portrait on brown ground with green and orange grass below, impressed mark, artist initials, 18.5"h, with painted glass globe, large glaze flakes 500-750   July 16, 1997   Sold for $325

5235. Weller Fleron vase, large hand-thrown piece with full ruffled top edge, green matt exterior with pink matt interior, script signature Weller Ware Hand Made, 9"dia. x 12"h, mint   200-400   July 10, 1994   Sold for $210

349

5236. Cowan lamp, blue lustre hi-glaze, ink mark, pottery 11.5"h, flakes to base in making, mint 150-250 July 16, 1997 Sold for $170

5237. Cowan lamp, plum hi-glaze, two sections, impressed mark, pottery 12"h, minute flake to corner 250-350 July 16, 1997 Sold for $250

5238. Cowan lamp, brown matt glaze with flower medallion, no marks, pottery 11"h, mint 350-550 July 16, 1997 Sold for $100

5239. Cowan lamp, blue lustre hi-glaze with metal base and top with stylized swirl design, raised mark on metal, pottery 7.5"w x 3.5"d x 7.5"h, mint 200-300 July 16, 1997 Sold for $110

5240. Cowan lamp, Chinese red matt glaze, impressed marks, pottery 9"h, finial missing, metal dented, pottery mint 350-550 July 16, 1997 Sold for $425

5241. Cowan lamp base, green matt glaze, impressed mark, 11.5"h, mint; with **Cowan** lamp, (not pictured), flattened form in green matt glaze, impressed marks, pottery 9.5"h, chips to base 350-550 July 16, 1997 Sold for $180

5242. Cowan lamp, green matt glaze, glass finial, impressed marks, pottery 11"h, minute flake to base; with **Cowan** lamp, (not pictured), green matt glaze with raised leaf design, impressed marks, 7.5"h, flakes to base 500-700 July 16, 1997 Sold for $200

5243. Cowan vase, orange and tan hi-glaze, raised leaf design, impressed marks, 8"h, crack and chips; with **L.D. Bloch** lamp, not shown, orange lustre hi-glaze, ink mark, pottery 9"h, mint 250-350 July 16, 1997 Sold for $70

5244. Cowan lamp, orange and tan hi-glaze, impressed marks, pottery 11"h, mint; with **Cowan** lamp, not shown, orange and tan hi-glaze, impressed marks, pottery 11"h, mint 600-800 July 16, 1997 Sold for $300

Not Pictured:

5245. Cowan lamp, molded design of squirrel and birds in brown and ivory, impressed mark, original fittings, later fabric shade, overall height 19", mint 500-700 July 15, 1998 Sold for $260

5246. Cowan vases with stands, pair, rounded swollen body, mottled green hi-glaze, stand in black matt glaze, impressed marks, both 8"h with stand, both mint 500-700 June 2, 1996 Sold for $650

5247. Aamco figurine, attribution, blue crackle glaze on female form with greyhound, faint markings, 15.5"h, mint 300-400 July 14, 1999 Sold for $450

5248. Red Wing vase, raised designs with golden drip, raised mark and 10"h, chips to design 250-350 July 14, 1999 Sold for $150

5249. Cowan console dish with flower frog, Art Deco design in black and silver with nude female figure pouring water; with matching pair of compotes and low candlesticks, all marked, six pieces, total frog and dish 10"h, mint 3500-4500 July 14, 1999 Sold for $3750

5250. Red Wing vase, stylized figures bordered by geometric lines and beads cover vase, green and yellow crystalline glaze, raised mark, 14.5"h, mint 500-700 July 14, 1999 Sold for $600

5251. Cowan bowl, yellow and pink matt glaze in swirl design, impressed mark, 14"w x 10.5"d x 2"h, line to rim, minute flakes   250-350   July 16, 1997   Sold for $60

5252. Cowan vase, orange lustre hi-glaze, ink mark, 12"h, mint   100-200   July 16, 1997   Sold for $60

5253. Cowan vase, green lustre hi-glaze, ink mark, 13"h, line to base, chip to rim, with **Cowan** compote, not shown, black matt and green hi-glaze, impressed mark, 7"w x 2.5"h, mint   150-250   July 16, 1997   Sold for $80

5254. Cowan lamp, figural design in white and tan hi-glaze, impressed mark, pottery 10"h, mint   600-800 July 16, 1997   Sold for $150

5255. Cowan lamp, flattened form with woman and ferns in tan and light blue matt glaze, impressed mark, pottery 12"h, mint   1000-1500   July 16, 1997   Sold for $650

5256. Cowan tobacco jar, mottled orange and brown hi-glaze, impressed marks, 6"h, lines and flakes   150-250 July 16, 1997   Sold for $190

5257. Cowan lamp, white hi-glaze with raised floral design, impressed mark, 10"h, mint   500-750   July 16, 1997 Sold for $150

5258. Cowan bowl, purple matt exterior, pink hi-glaze interior, ink mark, 11"dia. x 2.5"h, mint   200-300   July 16, 1997 Sold for $260

5259. Cowan lamp base, bird design in blue hi-glaze, impressed marks, 12"h, minute flakes   350-450 July 16, 1997   Sold for $290

5260. Cowan lamp bases, pair, orange lustre glaze, ink marks, 12.5"h, chip to one, flake to other   200-300 July 16, 1997   Sold for $60

5261. Cowan lamp, geometric design in green matt glaze, pottery finial, impressed mark, pottery 13"h, mint 500-700   July 16, 1997   Sold for $400

5262. Thelma Frazier Winter sculpture, brown bisque body with red hair covered in hi-gloss draping and wings in blue, white, pink and pale lime green on hi-glaze brown base, incised marks, 18"h, minor restoration 2500-3500   July 16, 1997   Sold for $2900

5263. Cowan bowl and flower frog figurine, orange/brown matt glaze, both pieces have impressed mark, figurine is 12"h, bowl is 15"dia, mint   400-600   July 16, 1997 Sold for $600

5264. Cowan vase, seahorse design in pink, impressed mark, 7"h, mint   100-150 July 16, 1997   Sold for $50

5265. Cowan vase, orange mat glaze, impressed Lakeware mark, 7.75"h, mint   250-350 July 16, 1997   Sold for $110

5266. Cowan figural, designed by A. Jacobson, bust of young man in black matt glaze, signed on back, original label, 14.5"h, mint   1000-1500   July 16, 1997 Sold for $4250

5267. Cowan figural decanter, king with scepter in black, pink and Chinese red matt glaze, impressed marks, 12"h, mint 700-900   July 16, 1997 Sold for $600

5268. Cowan bookends, pair, monk reads book in dark green matt glaze, no mark, 6.5"h, mint; with **Cowan** figural, girl in bonnet in cream hi-glaze, impressed mark, 7"h, repair to head   800-1100   July 16, 1997 Sold for $230

5269. Cowan figural flower frog, woman dances with scarf in cream hi-glaze, impressed mark, 6"h, chip to base 200-300   July 16, 1997 Sold for $120

5270. Cowan bowl, hi-glaze with green, yellow, brown and blue triangle design on cream ground, large foil label, impressed mark, 11.5"dia. x 3"h, minute flake to rim 600-800   July 16, 1997 Sold for $550

5271. Cowan figural, woman kneels in white hi-glaze, 6"h, line to face, chips to base   350-550   July 16, 1997 Sold for $180

5272. Cowan candlesticks, pair, angels and robed figure in yellow hi-glaze, impressed marks, 9"h, mint   450-650 July 16, 1997 Sold for $280

5273. Cowan figural decanter, king with scepter in white hi-glaze, no mark, 12"h, mint   500-700   July 16, 1997 Sold for $425

5274. Cowan figural, beaver with book and tree trunk in green matt, signed, 9.5"h, mint   700-900   July 16, 1997 Sold for $700

5275. Cowan figural, bust of young man in black matt glaze, original label, black, 14.5"h, mint   1000-1500 July 16, 1997 Sold for $5000

5276. Cowan charger, stylized birds in green hi-glaze, impressed mark, 15.5"dia., mint   400-600 July 16, 1997   Sold for $550

5277. Cowan centerpiece set, console bowl and two candlesticks, mottled blue and green hi-glaze, impressed marks, 15.5"w x 10"d x 6"h, all mint   400-600 July 16, 1997   Sold for $280

5278. Cowan centerpiece set, vase and candleholder, brown hi-glaze, impressed marks, 10"w x 7.5"h, mint   250-350 July 16, 1997   Sold for $90

5279. Cowan console bowl with flower frog, Chinese red matt glaze, impressed marks, 15"w x 7.5"d x 8"h, chip to base of frog, bowl mint   300-400   July 16, 1997 Sold for $160

5280. Cowan vase, dark green to cream iridescent glaze with pink, purple and gold highlights, 7"h, mint   300-400 July 16, 1997   Sold for $375

5281. Cowan charger, woman and dog dance in yellow hi-glaze, impressed mark, 15.5"dia., mint   400-600 July 16, 1997   Sold for $400

5282. **Waylande Gregory** figurals, pair, peacock in mottled purple and dark blue matt glaze with incised white decoration, ink mark, 18"w x 9"h, mint   500-700 July 17, 1996 Sold for $550

5283. **Cowan** bookends, pair, girl with full dress and bonnet in black matt, impressed mark, 7"h, mint   400-600 July 17, 1996 Sold for $550

5284. **Cowan** charger, hi-glaze with stylized birds in green, impressed mark, 15.5"dia., flakes to back in making, mint   300-400   July 17, 1996 Sold for $650

5285. **Cowan** bookends, attribution, pair, nude boy and girl in thick tan matt glaze, 6.5"h, mint   300-500 July 17, 1996 Sold for $150

5286. **Cowan** bookends, pair, bucking horses in blue hi-glaze, impressed mark, 9.5"h, mint   600-800   July 17, 1996 Sold for $1600

5287. **Cowan** golf plaque, Deco design painted with golfer and clubs in relief, hi-glaze, Victor Schreckenpost, 11.5"dia. 1250-1750   June 15, 1990 Sold for $1000

5288. **Cowan** tennis plaque, white bisque relief of tennis players and net, Victor Schreckenpost, 11.5"dia., mint 400-600   June 15, 1990 Sold for $500

5289. Cowan flower frog, nude woman poses with flowing scarf, white hi-glaze, impressed mark, 6.5"h, mint 150-250 July 17, 1996 Sold for $120

5290. Cowan flower frog, woman in flowing scarf poses atop flower form base, white hi-glaze, 9.5"h, mint 200-300 July 17, 1996 Sold for $450

5291. Cowan figural, elephant in cream matt glaze, impressed mark, 5"h, mint 200-300 July 17, 1996 Sold for $400

5292. Cowan flower frog, nude woman twirls with scarf, white hi-glaze, impressed mark, 10"h, mint 250-350 July 17, 1996 Sold for $850

5293. Cowan console bowl, condor head design in cream and blue hi-glaze, 15"w x 3"h; with a **Cowan** flower frog with candleholders, swirling vine design in cream hi-glaze, both with impressed mark, 10"w x 2.5"h, all mint 200-300 July 17, 1996 Sold for $150

5294. Cowan figural, dancing nude figure with flowing drape, nice pose, marked, 12"h, mint 500-700 July 17, 1996 Sold for $700

5295. Waylande Gregory figural, head of horse in white hi-glaze, incised mark, 6"h, mint 200-300 July 17, 1996 Sold for $210

5296. Cowan flower frog, woman with flowing skirts supports branches above flowered base, cream hi-glaze, 10"h, mint 250-350 July 17, 1996 Sold for $450

5297. Cowan flower frog, nude woman poses with flowing scarf, white hi-glaze, 6.5"h, mint 150-250 July 17, 1996 Sold for $160

Not Pictured:

5298. Cowan cups and saucers, set of four, with plate, fluted cup, 2.5"h, plate and saucer 4.5"dia., mint green hi-glaze, impressed marks, two saucers with chips, otherwise mint 200-300 June 2, 1996 Sold for $200

5299. Cowan strawberry jar, jar with four openings at shoulder, 7.5"h, with dish, 6"dia., mottled deep rose and yellow hi-glaze, impressed marks, mint 250-350 June 2, 1996 Sold for $450

5300. Cowan figural, elephant in blue hi-glaze with bright green highlights, impressed mark, 4.5"h, mint 250-350 July 17, 1996 Sold for $475

5301. Cowan figurals, woman with brown hair wearing long green dress holds light green basket, man with blue hair wearing flared green pants pulls yellow sword from pink and black sheath, both atop blue bases, all hi-glaze, impressed marks, 9"h, mint 1500-2000 July 17, 1996 Sold for $2100

5302. Cowan flower frog, nude woman poses with scarf atop ribbed base, white hi-glaze, 8"h, hidden chip to base 150-200   July 17, 1996   Sold for $290

5303. Cowan flower frog, faun sits atop large mushroom in cream matt glaze, impressed marks, 9"h, mint   300-400 July 17, 1996   Sold for $750

5304. Cowan flower frog, nude woman dances with flowing scarf atop flower form base, white hi-glaze, impressed mark, 7"h, mint   150-250   July 17, 1996   Sold for $375

5305. Amaco figural, bust of woman in white hi-glaze, ink mark, 6"h, mint   100-200   July 17, 1996 Sold for $140

5304. Cowan flower frog with candleholders, woman in flowing robes and headdress stands atop seashell base, flowers form cups, 10"w x 9.5"h, mint   300-400 July 17, 1996   Sold for $1600

5305. Cowan flower frog, nude woman poses with flowing scarf atop stylized water base, white hi-glaze, 6.5"h, mint   150-250   July 17, 1996   Sold for $140

5306. Cowan flower frog, two women with flowing skirts dance atop stylized water base, white hi-glaze, impressed mark, 8"h, mint   200-300   July 17, 1996 Sold for $475

5307. Cowan figural, woman with basket and long skirt in pale pink over cream glaze, 8.5"h, mint   250-350 July 17, 1996   Sold for $500

5308. Cowan flower frog, nude woman dances with scarf, cream hi-glaze, impressed mark, 7"h, mint   150-250 July 17, 1996   Sold for $475

Not Pictured:

5309. Cowan figural, elephant on block base, Chinese red glaze, impressed marks, 4.5"h, small chip to base 200-300   June 2, 1996   Sold for $210

5310. Cowan figural, elephant on block base, Chinese red glaze, impressed marks, 4.5"h, mint   300-400 June 2, 1996   Sold for $400

5311. Cowan vase, flared ribbed form in dark rust, rose, orange and gray hi-glaze, impressed mark, 9.5"h, mint 250-350   June 2, 1996   Sold for $325

5312. Owens vase, brown glaze with brown and caramel tulips on green stems and leaves, 10"dia. x 9"h, chip and line to rim   100-150   July 17, 1996   Sold for $230

5313. Cowan console set, centerpiece bowl with frog, two bud vases, four candlesticks, Art Deco style frog with figure of nude woman pouring water atop diamond-shaped bowl, all silver and gunmetal glaze, impressed marks, centerpiece 13"w x 9"w x 10.5"h, bud vase 6.5"h, candlestick 4.5"w x 1.5"h, all mint 1500-2000 July 17, 1996 Sold for $3500

355

5314. Cowan candlesticks, pair, seahorse design, pink hi-glaze, impressed mark, 4.5"h, mint 50-100 June 2, 1996 Sold for $40

5315. Cowan covered vases, pair, broad-shouldered form with open handles and floral design, blue iridescent hi-glaze with green, violet and gold highlights, inkmark, 9"h, mint 500-700 June 2, 1996 Sold for $1000

5316. Cowan console set, pair of candelabra with three cups each 10"w, flower frog in swirl design 7"w, bowl 12"w, all yellow hi-glaze, all impressed marks, repair to one cup, otherwise mint 200-300 June 2, 1996 Sold for $425

5317. Cowan lamps, pair, twisted stem on candlestick shape, orange lustre hi-glaze, original drilled holes, inkmark, 12"h, mint 250-300 June 2, 1996 Sold for $50

5318. Cowan vase, broad-shouldered form with star pattern, green over blue hi-glaze, impressed mark, 11"h, hairline 150-250 June 2, 1996 Sold for $350

5319. Cowan candlesticks, pair, asymmetrical swirl stem, mint green hi-glaze, impressed mark, 5.5"h, mint 100-150 June 2, 1996 Sold for $90

5320. Cowan charger, hi-glaze with scene of two polo players among flowers, all in vivid yellow, 11.5"h, hidden chips to back 400-600 July 17, 1996 Sold for $450

5321. Cowan charger, hi-glaze with horse and rider running with dogs among flowers in blue, brown, yellow, pink, green and black against a white ground, impressed mark, 11"dia., mint 800-1100 July 17, 1996 Sold for $1600

5322. Cowan plate, hi-glaze with fish, seaweed, bubbles and starfish in white against a light blue ground, impressed mark, 11.5"dia., mint 400-600 July 17, 1996 Sold for $750

Not Pictured:

5323. Cowan wallpocket, wide fluted form with roaring lion on back, blue lustre hi-glaze, inkmark, 10"w x 10"h, mint 200-300 June 2, 1996 Sold for $400

5324. **Cowan** decanter, ribbed design in blue hi-glaze with bright green highlights, impressed marks, 10.5"h, mint 350-450   July 17, 1996   Sold for $160

5325. **Cowan** vase, orange lustre, ink mark, 10.5"h, mint 150-250   July 17, 1996   Sold for $200

5326. **Cowan** flower frog, stylized deer and grass in cream hi-glaze, impressed mark, 8.5"h, mint   200-300 July 17, 1996   Sold for $425

5327. **Cowan** vase, flattened form with two handles in light and dark brown matt glaze, impressed mark, 8"h, mint 150-250   July 17, 1996   Sold for $120

5328. **Cowan** vase, light green and pink matt glaze, impressed marks, 4.5"h, mint   100-150   July 17, 1996 Sold for $70

5329. **Cowan** vase, flattened form, stylized bird with curling feathers, orange matt and brown hi-glaze, impressed mark, 11.5"h, mint   300-500   July 17, 1996 Sold for $500

5330. **Cowan** tray, Chinese red glaze with deer amid leaves, impressed marks, 3.5"w x 5.5"l, mint   100-200 July 17, 1996   Sold for $60

5331. **Cowan** vase, Chinese red glaze, impressed marks, 6.5"h, mint   100-200   July 17, 1996   Sold for $100

5332. **Lakeware** vase, blue hi-glaze, impressed mark, 7.5"h, mint   200-300   July 17, 1996   Sold for $100

5333. **Cowan** figural, woman in short skirt in pale pink over cream hi-glaze, impressed mark, 8"h, hidden chip to base   250-350   July 17, 1996   Sold for $400

5334. **Cowan** strawberry jar, with dish, Chinese red glaze, impressed mark, 7.5"h, mint   200-300   July 17, 1996 Sold for $300

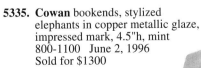

5335. **Cowan** bookends, stylized elephants in copper metallic glaze, impressed mark, 4.5"h, mint 800-1100   June 2, 1996 Sold for $1300

357

5336. Cowan compote, stylized seahorses in light blue, impressed mark, 3.5"h, chip to base   50-100   July 17, 1996 Sold for $20

5337. Cowan vase, flattened form in blue lustre, ink mark, 8.5"h, mint   150-200   July 17, 1996 Sold for $80

5338. Cowan vase, flattened form, stylized bird with curling feathers, impressed mark, 11.5"h, mint   250-350   July 17, 1996 Sold for $375

5339. Cowan candlesticks, pair, broad blossom forms cup in cream matt glaze, impressed mark, 4"h, mint   100-150   July 17, 1996 Sold for $50

5340. Cowan candlesticks, pair, seahorses in cream matt glaze, impressed marks, 4.5"h, mint   50-100   July 17, 1996 Sold for $50

5341. Cowan console set, bowl and candlesticks, two, mottled green hi-glaze, impressed marks, bowl 13"w x 9.5"d x 3.5"h, candlestick 5"w x 1.5"h, chip to rim of bowl in making, mint   150-250   July 17, 1996 Sold for $80

5342. Cowan figural, elephant in black matt glaze, impressed marks, 4.5"h, mint   250-350   July 17, 1996 Sold for $475

5343. Cowan covered vase, two-handled form with ram's head, in blue hi-glaze, impressed marks, 13"h, flake to base   200-300   July 17, 1996 Sold for $425

5344. Cowan vase, flattened form with seahorses in orange lustre glaze, ink mark, 8"h, mint   100-200   July 17, 1996 Sold for $70

5345. Cowan vase, ribbed form in purple and light green hi-glaze, impressed mark, 5"h, mint   150-250   July 17, 1996 Sold for $100

5346. Cowan lamp, stylized dog in black matt glaze, impressed mark, 9.5"h, hairlines to base in making, mint   400-600   July 17, 1996 Sold for $1600

5347. Cowan figural, gopher holds stump and book, raised letters read Light Seeking—Light Doth Light of—Light Beguile, green matt glaze, painted mark Rowfant Club 1925, signed R.C. Cowan, 9.5"h, mint   400-600   July 17, 1996 Sold for $1300

5348. Cowan vase, grape cluster design in blue lustre with green, gold and purple highlights, ink marks, 7.5"dia. x 5.5"h, mint   150-250   July 17, 1996 Sold for $100

5349. Cowan candlesticks, pair, nude woman leans against plant, flower forms cup, cream hi-glaze, impressed mark, 12.5"h, mint   600-800   July 17, 1996 Sold for $1700

5350. Cowan figurals, pair, large plumed bird perches on two stylized waves in blue hi-glaze, impressed marks, 12"h, mint   600-800   July 17, 1996 Sold for $1700

5351. Cowan goblets, four, ribbed design in blue hi-glaze with bright green highlights, impressed marks, 3"h, all mint   200-300   July 17, 1996   Sold for $150

5352. Cowan console bowl, Chinese red glaze, impressed marks, 9.5"w x 6"h, mint   300-400   July 17, 1996 Sold for $120

5353. Cowan candlesticks, two, Chinese red glaze, impressed marks, 5"h, mint   100-200   July 17, 1996 Sold for $40

5354. Cowan bud vase, light green hi-glaze, impressed marks, 6.5"h, mint   100-150   July 17, 1996 Sold for $40

5355. Cowan vase, blue and green hi-glaze, impressed marks, 6.5"h, mint   200-300   July 17, 1996 Sold for $190

5356. Cowan figural, bird in black matt glaze, impressed mark, 8"h, mint   800-1100   July 17, 1996 Sold for $2100

5357. Cowan figural, bust of woman in black matt glaze, impressed mark, 10"h, mint   900-1200   July 17, 1996 Sold for $3000

For more details please call:
(513) 321-6742

5358. Cowan vase, angular flattened form, black matt and silver metallic glaze, impressed mark, 8"h, mint 300-500   June 2, 1996 Sold for $500

5359. Cowan flower frog, two female figures dance on stylized ocean base, white hi-glaze, impressed mark, 8"h, mint   200-300   June 2, 1996 Sold for $600

5360. Cowan candelabra, woman with drape stands between two cups on leafy base, cream hi-glaze, impressed mark, 9.5"h, mint   300-400   June 2, 1996 Sold for $550

5361. Cowan console bowl, fluted oval form with two gryphon heads in cream, mint green and caramel hi-glaze, 14"w; with a flower frog in flower design, cream matt glaze, 5"dia., impressed marks, both mint   200-300 June 2, 1996 Sold for $190

5362. Cowan charger, designed by R.G. Cowan, large form with stylized birds, blue hi-glaze, impressed mark, 15.5"dia., mint   300-400   June 2, 1996 Sold for $550

5363. Waylande Gregory figural, chess horse head, gold metallic and cream hi-glaze, incised signature, 6"h, mint 200-300   June 2, 1996 Sold for $100

5364. Cowan vase, tapered cylindrical form in mottled deep rose and gray hi-glaze, impressed mark, 9"h, mint 200-300   June 2, 1996 Sold for $270

5365. Cowan flower frog, girl dancing with drape on flower-like base, cream hi-glaze, impressed mark, 7"h, mint 200-300   June 2, 1996 Sold for $210

5366. Cowan ashtray, ram spans a triangular base, blue hi-glaze, impressed marks, 5"h, mint   150-250 June 2, 1996 Sold for $300

5367. Cowan bud vase, slender broad-based form in deep rose metallic hi-glaze, ink mark, 7"h, tiny chip to base 50-100   June 2, 1996 Sold for $60

Not Pictured:

5368. Cowan dresser lamps, pair, fluted body with original blue shade, cream hi-glaze, impressed marks, 15.5"h with shade, mint   250-350   June 2, 1996 Sold for $210

5369. Cowan lamp base, light green and blue hi-glaze, squirrel and birds in forest scene, impressed marks, 10.5"h, mint 500-700   July 17, 1996 Sold for $375

5370. Cowan bookends, pair, toucan in copper, silver and black gunmetal glaze, impressed marks, 5.5"h, mint 1500-2500   July 17, 1996 Sold for $2800

5371. Clewell pitcher, copper-clad pottery, etched organic design, original patina, incised mark, 6"h, mint 350-400 July 16, 1997 Sold for $220

5372. Clewell vase, copper-clad pottery, flowers, brown patina, original paper label, 7"h, flaw to copper at rim 400-600 July 16, 1997 Sold for $230

5373. Clewell vase, copper-clad pottery, original brown and green patina, incised marks 390-2-9, 5.5"h, mint 300-400 July 16, 1997 Sold for $400

5374. Clewell vase, copper-clad pottery, original brown and green patina, incised mark 469, 8.5"h, mint 600-800 July 16, 1997 Sold for $800

5375. Clewell vase, copper-clad pottery, tri-corner form, original green patina, incised mark 31, 4"h, mint 250-350 July 16, 1997 Sold for $300

5376. Clewell vase, copper-clad pottery, incised design of irises and leaves, original patina, incised mark, impressed Owens, 13.5"h, mint 900-1200 July 16, 1997 Sold for $1000

5377. Clewell vase, copper-clad pottery, original brown and light green patina, incised marks, 4.5"h, small square of non-patinated area, mint 250-350 July 16, 1997 Sold for $400

5378. Clewell vase, copper-clad pottery, intricate raised swirl and line design, two handles, original brown and green patina, no mark, 10.5"h, mint 900-1200 July 16, 1997 Sold for $1600

5379. Clewell vase, copper-clad pottery, raised blossom design, original brown patina, no mark, 5.5"h, mint 350-450 July 16, 1997 Sold for $300

5380. Clewell vase, copper-clad pottery, original green and brown patina, incised marks, 5.5"h, stress lines 300-400 July 16, 1997 Sold for $400

5381. Clewell pitcher, copper-clad pottery, original brown patina, incised mark, 6"h, mint 350-550 July 16, 1997 Sold for $225

5382. Clewell vase, copper-clad pottery, original brown and green patina, incised marks, 5"h, dents 250-350 July 16, 1997 Sold for $375

5383. Clewell vase, copper-clad pottery, original patina, incised mark, 4.5"h, excellent condition 200-300 July 16, 1997 Sold for $210

Not Pictured:

5384. Clewell vase, copper-clad pottery on pedestal, incised Clewell, rusty brown and deep green patina, 6.5"h, two tiny lines in metal on pedestal, otherwise mint 250-350 June 15, 1990 Sold for $250

5385. Cowan figural, woman with flowing robe in muted orange hi-glaze, 14.5"w x 5"d x 10.5"h, minor chip and flakes to base 1000-1500 July 17, 1996 Sold for $4000

361

5386. Clewell vase, copper-clad pottery with original blue-green patina, 9"h, mint   750-1000   September 24, 1989 Sold for $950

5387. L.C. Tiffany vase, silver plating over relief decoration of flowers and stems, 8"h, mint   1000-1500 September 24, 1989   Sold for $900

5388. Clewell vase, copper-clad pottery, blue-green patina, 8"h, mint   400-500   September 24, 1989   Sold for $800

5389. Clewell vase, copper-clad pottery, original patina, 8"h, mint   400-500   September 24, 1989   Sold for $650

5390. Clewell vase, copper-clad pottery, original patina, sides decorated with raised sunflower, 8"h, mint   500-750 September 24, 1989   Sold for $750

5391. Clewell vase, copper-clad pottery with original patina, 9"h, mint   600-800   September 24, 1989 Sold for $600

5392. Clewell vase, copper-clad pottery, original patina, etched landscape of house and trees, 7"h, mint 600-800   September 24, 1989   Sold for $400

5393. Clewell bud vase, copper-clad pottery, original patina, incised Clewell 354, 6.5"h, mint   400-600 May 19, 1996   Sold for $260

5394. Clewell vase, copper-clad pottery, original patina, incised Clewell 466 147, 5"h, mint   400-600 May 19, 1996   Sold for $350

5395. Clewell vase, copper-clad pottery, original patina, incised Clewell 277-26, 16"h, mint   2500-3500 May 19, 1996   Sold for $2400

5396. Clewell vase, copper-clad pottery, original patina, incised Clewell 466, 5"h, mint   400-600 May 19, 1996   Sold for $375

5397. Clewell vase, copper-clad pottery, carved irises and leaves highlighted in a brushed gold patina against a dark copper patinated background, signed with paper label on bottom, 17"h, mint   2000-3000 November 17, 1991   Sold for $2600

Not Pictured:

5398. Clewell vase, copper-clad pottery, original patina, incised Clewell 364-6, 7"h, mint   600-800 May 19, 1996   Sold for $800

5399. Clewell candlesticks, pair, copper-clad pottery, original patina, incised Clewell 414-2-6, 9.5"h, mint   800-1100 February 12, 1995   Sold for $1200

5400. Clewell vase, copper-clad pottery, original patina, numerous incised vertical lines at top above prominent hammered marks, incised Clewell 4098-12, 20"h, mint 3500-4500   February 12, 1995   Sold for $3250

5401. Clewell vase, copper-clad pottery original green and blue patina, incised Clewell 412-6, 9"h, mint   700-900 February 12, 1995   Sold for $500

5402. Clewell vase, copper-clad pottery, original patina, incised Clewell 412-6, 9"h, mint   700-900 February 12, 1995   Sold for $475

Not Pictured:

5403. Clewell candlesticks, pair, copper-clad pottery, original patina, signed Clewell 415-3-6, 10"h, mint   800-1100 August 27, 1995   Sold for $1600

5404. Clewell vase, copper-clad pottery, original patina, signed Clewell 366-215, 15"h, mint 2000-3000 December 3, 1995   Sold for $1000

5405. Clewell vase, copper-clad pottery, floral design in etched brass over copper, original patina, impressed Weller, 4.5"h, excellent condition   500-750 November 24, 1996   Sold for $950

5406. Clewell vase, copper-clad pottery, original patina, obscured mark, 5"h, mint   400-600   May 21, 1995 Sold for $375

5407. Clewell vase, copper-clad pottery, original patina, marked Clewell #322-12, 8.5"h, mint   450-600 April 7, 1991   Sold for $375

5408. Clewell vase, copper-clad pottery, original patina, signed Clewell, 6"dia. x 3.5"h, mint   400-600 August 27, 1995   Sold for $400

5409. Clewell vase, copper-clad pottery, broad shoulder and tapered neck, original patina, signed Clewell 1005-24, 14.5"h, mint   3000-4000   October 23, 1994 Sold for $6000

Not Pictured:

5410. Clewell vase, copper-clad pottery, carved poppy buds stand up from top edge, reticulated openings around top running vertically, original patina, marked, 13"h, mint 1500-2500   October 4, 1987   Sold for $3300

5411. Clewell vase, copper-clad pottery, ribbed poppy pods at rim atop vertical stems, stems backed by a large poppy blossom, poppy pods atop vertical stems on reverse, original patina, paper label, 13.5"h, mint   2500-3500 May 21, 1995   Sold for $2600

5412. Clewell vase, copper-clad pottery, original patina, marked Clewell, #257-2, 15"h x 7"w, mint   700-900 April 7, 1991   Sold for $650

5413. Clewell vase, copper-clad pottery, original patina, signed Clewell 272-6, 11"h, mint   1500-2500 August 27, 1995   Sold for $1200

Index

Index

For more details please call:
(513) 321-6742

Index

Index

For more details please call:
(513) 321-6742

AUCTION AND BOOK CREDITS

Owners/Sale Managers-
Don Treadway
Jerri Durham
2029 Madison Road
Cincinnati, Ohio 45208
Voice: (513) 321-6742
Fax: (513) 871-7722

John Toomey
818 North Boulevard
Oak Park, IL 60301
Voice: (708) 383-5234
Fax: (708) 383-4828

Auctioneer/owner for Treadway Gallery • **Jerri Nelson Durham**

Auctioneers • **Michael DeFina, Christopher DeFina, Jennifur Condon**

Photographers • **Joseph Higgins, Mary Beck, Ross Van Pelt**

Computer Treatments • **Stephen Large, Dave Warren , Teresa Dorsey, Carrie White**

Treadway Internet: **check our site on the World Wide Web for the latest information: http://www.treadwaygallery.com**

<u>Staff:</u>
Cincinnati • **Thierry Lorthioir, Richard Meyer, Melissa Scheben, Matt Rainey, Stephen Large, Dave Warren , Teresa Dorsey, Ross Van Pelt, Carrie White** and **Jan Brown**

Chicago • **Anne Dickinson, Jane Browne, Lisann Dickson, Lucy Toomey, Kevin Mannella, Jason Lesner, Marty Uribe** and **Angela Whittaker**

Photos: **All Rights Reserved ©1999-2000 Treadway Gallery**